STAG
TINE

Also *by* D. Firth Griffith

Boone: An Unfinished Portrait (2020)

Wild Like Flowers: The Restoration of Relationship Through Regeneration (2021)

Dark Cloud Country: The 4 Relationships of Regeneration (2023)

LEARN MORE AT DANIELFIRTHGRIFFITH.COM

STAG TINE

Kincentric Rewilding, Science, & A Tale of Letting Go

Book I of The Wildland Chronicles

D. FIRTH GRIFFITH

FOREWORD BY FRED PROVENZA

Robinia Press
VIRGINIA

For information, visit danielfirthgriffith.com.

FIRST EDITION

Developmental Editor: Sarah Sullivan
Copy Editor: Morgan Griffith
Proofreaders: Jordan Parker, Carter Johnson
Illustrations: Elowyn Griffith

Published By Robinia Press, Wingina. A division of Robinia Group, Inc., 530 James River Road Wingina, Virginia 24599.

LIBRARY OF CONGRESS CATALOGING-IN-PUBLICATION DATA
Griffith, Daniel Firth, 1993 –
Stagtine: Kincentric Rewilding, Science, & A Tale of Letting Go / by Daniel Firth Griffith.
1st ed. p. cm.
ISBN-13: 978-1-7354922-8-5.

For Lionel, Paddy, Nancy, Nelly, & Mara,
who invited us to run with them and to
become, fully, the remarkable.

"Death is man's fate, the gift of Ilúvatar, which as
Time wears even the Powers shall envy."

J. R. R. TOLKIEN, *THE SILMARILLION*

*If you hold Earth's Wisdom, you may find this book
uninspiring. It tells the story of our relearning, of
our non-human relations educating us, sometimes
unkindly.*

About *The Wildland*

The Wildland is a pioneering kincentric rewilding project in Central Virginia that is challenging what it means to be wild and how we, the mammal *Homo sapiens*, and not we, the industrial capitalist and savior of the world, can help heal Earth, together, as Earthlings.

Rewilding is in vogue today and many rewilding projects begin as moving companies—they work to remove unwanted animals, peoples, and Earth's actual chaos and then work to import native species to grow and run about within their prison yards of exclusion fences. To heal rivers, they buy beavers. To heal beavers, they buy rivers.

In place of this rewilding and regenerative mythology (that humans can control our way forward), The Wildland is a co-creative crescendo of extended families that, through interspecial and intergenerational genomics and relationship burst, slowly and ever slightly, as a land-race of symbiotic life. It is home to wild cattle, goats, sheep, chickens, and horses, alongside nesting black bear families, river otters and beavers once again in the Piedmont uplands, and mountain lions and their bobcats, coyotes, and other friends running at their heels. The Wildland is a home of life and not a home made for life.

The Wildland today occupies the ancient, modern, and future home of the Siouan Indians of the Monacan Nation. Why do we provide land acknowledgement? Because Earth and her people asked us too. What a fine, fine reason.

Learn more at wildtimshel.com.

TABLE OF CONTENTS

A Letter From The Author

Dear Regeneration,

   I was wrong. It was not you. It was me. Is me.

Starting out in this story, we find ourselves nestled but unsettled in some perplexity. I am hesitant to name this thing, this story and its imaginative and creative sciences, as names gives us something to hold on to but also something that allows us to feel like we can hold anything at all. The best somethings cannot be held—a red-tail in flight, a white spring speckled ungulate under her oaken bungalow, a yellow-orange eyed feather that at once flutters by my head and at once also flutters by yours, a passing smile, a moment, Earth.

   I give this trilogy away under the guise of "kincentric rewilding." But make no mistake. We do not have time for such mistakes. It is only a guise, a veil on this happy day that will pass, mature, and transform into something else very soon. Life is change and we live on an orb of ever bouncing particles that also seems like an ever changing playground of impermanence and this change makes life what it is: beautiful and real. This impermanence is also a guise. Make no mistake about it. Unhappy impermanence is degeneration in the fullest sense and happy impermanence is what kincentric rewilding wants to be: stalwartly in place but also unwaveringly waving across the pull of time. Anything permanent mocks life's impermanence and everything impermanent becomes more eternal when it decides to be more temporal. In place, here, now.

If this book was better published, it would have been titled *Kincentric Rewilding* and not *Stagtine*. If this book was better published, it would have been written to convince you that Kincentric Rewilding is the next fad, what will soon be in vogue, and what will soon save the world. If this book was better published, it would capitalize Kincentric Rewilding as a term, a human-created phrase to copyright and trademark and own. If this book was better published, it would be a published book that was well positioned to sell and not a gift that will position you to live, actually and fully (if you have yet to do so, turn back a few pages and read the copyright).

Gifts are not for us to hold, but to hold us. And this is my hope at the very least and also at the very most: that this gift holds you and in its holding you change with it. Yes, this book will change with you, if you allow yourself to change with it. And I guess, if I know anything at all, I imagine that this is the very nature of kincentric rewilding. It is everything but not everyone's; it cannot be owned; it is life in the full sense and not a life that is full of things.

Please, if you do anything, hold this loosely, hold life loosely, and let her fly away when she wants—the red-tail, the fawn, the butterfly. All I ask in all this perplexity is that you never capitalize it, never allow it to be a "thing" in life—like Regenerative Agriculture or Holistic Management®.

Over the last fifteen years, my wife Morgan and I have walked our way through the complex array of health and health journeys in a meager and humble attempt to save my life. That was our goal. From the bottom up, we just wanted some extra years for me to enjoy. We did what all good, new farmers at the time were told to do: regenerate the land and do it yourself, alone, hard! For years, we beat our heads and bloodied hands; for years, we put the soil on a pedestal and our two and four legged cousins in cages to regenerate it; for years, we strove to "feed our community" by growing and raising and producing every morsel of food possible from market gardens to chickens to ducks to goats to lambs to cattle to pigs to tree crops to agrotourism and "rural experiences" for the urban elite.

Five years in, we began to notice the shortcomings of regeneration and local food systems and that both were being greenwashed from the inside and the outside, mostly from the inside.

But we walked on, truculently and intentionally setting blaze to the commercial ligaments of this internal, industrial greenwashing, believing that the heart of the regenerative and the agrarian approach was worth saving. We read books and supported authors who wrote about such things—the return of the agrarian ethic, the rural revival, the hope of a local-food economy. But there was a problem—there is always a problem when writers write about a life that does not and has never existed. If we were to return to this agrarian ethic, growing food locally, we would yet have both of our feet in the industrial capitalist and sticky complex that surrounds our rural revival with pointed weapons and denudes this reawakening's hurrah with chains. What is the difference between these well-intentioned rural mythologies and the well-intentioned urban marketing of better foods produced in moderately better soils? What is the difference between worshiping the old rural landscape of yesteryear or celebrating the new industrial foodscape of today? What is the difference between chemically killing bugs and weeds in monocrop corn fields (degenerative agriculture) and enslaving and caging our two and four legged cousins in pastured CAFOs?

Being at a loss to resolve these questions, I am resolved to tell you a tale.

One afternoon nearly a year ago, we were tired, deflated by the work and the deep lack of hope we were feeling. I had just left a meeting where I was told by folks who are leaders in the Regenerative Agriculture movement that, what we really need to do is "simply get rid of all the local farmers and plant a few large farms in their place. That—," the individual said as he pointed across the table at me, "—would solve all of your problems."

I felt the rush of blood pulse, unkindly, through my bulging veins and a deep sense of hopelessness saturated around my nerves—like an poisoning herb in boiling water. I got up and left the meeting. I got up and left. And in some larger sense, I never returned.

About an hour later, I received a phone call from the community's organizer, a non-profit organization trying their best. He said, "If I was a better man, I would have walked out with you." I returned, "If

I was a better man, I would have stayed."

Later that day, I opened my email to an aggressive letter of an unwanted but truly needed critique. "You have totally misunderstood Regeneration," the author wrote. "It is not about all these wonderful things, utopia and all that. It is not about what you say. It is about cover crops and soil health. It is about getting better. Not best. You are disillusioned."

Reading the email, I felt myself come into tears. I felt myself meeting myself, for the first time in a long time. And I felt myself doing something I never do—respond. I hit "reply" and wrote a simple email back. "Thank you, deeply. You are right. It is not you. It is not regeneration. It is me."

Yes, the person in the meeting and the person writing the email were and are completely correct—regeneration is not about a more beautiful or more free and autonomous world. It is not about life. And that is okay.

In the midst of all of this, our own struggling regenerative farm had transitioned to a kincentric rewilding landscape. But we were not yet prepared to talk about it. To be honest, we had little reason to believe that it would work (for us or our non-human relations) and so we kept silent, kept piloting and kept researching.

Across it all, something was missing. Something is always missing when you try to control your way out of a problem that was constructed, initially, out of control. We are the latecomers to the party who, after drinking the last cup of party punch, commandeered the karaoke and declared, "Everyone! Stop what you are doing and come taste this punch!" Until we openly acknowledge this, allowing its potency to flow, unhindered but not without pain, through our veins, no social or ecological good may well come about.

If this book or gift that you hold in your hands is anything, it is an open acknowledgment that our modern worldview isn't working. It is an open acknowledgement that letting go of our mastery over the meadow is not about questioning if it works or if it doesn't. If this book and its trilogy says anything, it says that I do not buy your premises—that Earth cares for our capitalism ("you cannot regenerate if you are not profitable"), that we need to save the world ("we must sequester carbon to solve climate change"), that nutrient-rich foods come from enslaved soils ("soil health alone matters"), and so on. Every idea in this book and trilogy can be reduced, improperly but still clearly, to this statement—I do not buy your premises.

We are the latecomers, and our world is a punchless party and it is time to give the karaoke back to the singers.

Over the last twelve months, a troupe of ideas rolled its way through me and, while I tried, hard but not incuriously, to let them pass, their power triumphed. They awakened me to wonders simultaneously common and uncommon, humdrum and magical.

The last six months have been fueled by this reawakened sense—a sincere purpose mixed, sometimes rudely, with old dreams and new thoughts. I have been secretly working on bringing these ideas together in the form of three brand new books and feel blessed to be able to share them with you. I'm extremely proud of them, as each book embodies different aspects of an awakening consciousness that has forced me to grow personally and in interesting ways.

Each book carries us, step by step, through the transition of our home, what we refer to as The Wildland, from a struggling regenerative farm to a paradigm-shattering and kincentric rewilding landscape, focusing on different aspects of our story and their supporting reflections and science. Book I, *Stagtine*, offers our tale of transition. Book II, *Cliffhawk*, details the emergent properties following our release, and Book III, *Spearhead*, gives voice to the land and its yet "wild" animals.

You see, Earth was never invited into our worldview. She was never asked to speak at our conferences. Her definition of "working" was never considered. In return, she has retreated away in grief. Her retreat is what I believe climate change to be. These three books, I think, are about the hope found when we let go, give our non-human relations the voice (not a voice but the voice), and begin to accept our role as dreamwalkers, as humble but active participants in this great and ancient and as yet unfinished story.

The writing of these books is a silent process of filtration through filaments, strings, intention, and accidents, ultimately woven together through both fortune and design. Anyone who reads anything knows that sometimes the best somethings are found through unexpected discoveries at local, used bookshops or on forgotten library shelves. But these wonderful somethings, at least in my own experience, do not simply manifest themselves into being. Thousands of hours are spent considering research and reflecting and then even more are spent distilling the already overflowing cauldron to bring just one book to life, let alone a trilogy. But I hope that this one in particular is particularly impactful to you. That is my hope. My hope at the very least and also at the very most.

Well, this is the end of the letter. I quite agree that it is superfluous and perhaps too long for your taste. I have been told that my books start too slowly. "Get to the meat! You cannot keep people waiting for the book to start." one Senior Editor at a publishing company told me when I queried (unsuccessfully) this book that you hold in your hand.

But I leave this letter with you. Since it is written, let it stand. And now to the story.

D. FIRTH GRIFFITH

Blessings my friend!

BY FRED PROVENZA

Once a species reliant on nature for food, medicine, clothing, and shelter, *Homo sapiens* is in the process of being consumed by the fossil fuel-based agricultural and technological economies that enabled our separation from the natural world that nourishes and sustains all life, including us humans. Fossil fuel-based economies, which are grounded in competition for manufactured scarcity, rather than cooperation around natural abundance, are causing man-made shortages of unpolluted air, clean water, fertile soil, biodiversity, and wholesome foods. It is not hyperbole to state that we may end up among the many species now facing their final days on Earth, no different from the over ninety-nine percent of species who visited this planet and are now extinct.

Fossil fuels enabled human populations to rise precipitously from two million people in 10,000 BCE to a little less than a billion in 1800 to nearly eight billion people today. Our populations expanded exponentially during the twentieth century in no small part due to fossil fuels and industrial agriculture. Humans and the animals in our care now utterly dominate the planet.

Humans (thirty-six percent) and our livestock (sixty percent) make up an astounding ninety-six percent of all the mammals on Earth. Domestic chickens account for seventy percent of all the birds on this planet. Nearly half (forty-four percent) of the world's habitable land is used for agriculture, in total 48 million square kilometers (18.5 million square miles). Croplands make up one-third of agricultural land, and grazing land makes up the remaining two-thirds.

It is easy to understand why we embraced fossil fuels. The energy in a barrel of oil is equivalent to ten to twelve years of hard labor by a fit human. Fossil fuels enabled people in agriculture to evolve from long days of back-breaking work into an industry where machines do most of the work. Globally, we now consume 100 million barrels of oil each day across all human activities. The United States population of nearly 330 million used 20 million barrels of oil daily in 2022.

Fossil fuel-based food production systems have come at great costs ecologically, socially, and economically. To produce one calorie of food now requires two calories of fossil fuels for machinery, fertilizers, herbicides, and insecticides. We use another eight to twelve calories to process, package, deliver, store and cook modern food. No species can survive by expending ten to fourteen calories to obtain a single calorie of energy and neither can we. With the uncertain availability and prices of fossil fuels a concern and the transition to clean energy a necessity, we have an opportunity to grow nutritious foods in ways that nurture our ties with life on Earth.

These changes are a defining moment for humans, one that may lead to mankind's demise or that may catalyze the rebirth of an ecological economy wherein communities benefit from locally sourced plants and animal products, produced in ways that nurture relationships among soil, water, plants, animals, and people to sustain our collective wellbeing. Farming, ranching, and pastoral ways of life can once again be at the heart of our communities, but we humans will need to relearn what it means to be locally co-evolving with nature's communities. In the process, we will need to transition our relationships with landscapes from ego-logical to eco-logical.

Western culture and the Enlightenment taught us to think in linear, hierarchical, and competitive ways about our relationships with one another and the stressed-out communities we now inhabit. Monetized economic systems based on scarcity do not link plants, animals, and people with gratitude and reciprocity for the bounty of nature. Conversely, Eastern and Indigenous cultures, traditionally based on harmonious interdependence, teach of mutually supporting relationships with all life. People are members, not masters, of nature's communities. What we do to Earth, we do to ourselves. Only through nurturing our relationships with Earth, can we nurture ourselves.

In Stagtine, Firth shifts the focus from human creativity in nurturing modern "ecological resiliency" to the lived and shared experiences of our two and four legged cousins who inhabit Earth with us. In place of human-centered systems, the book speaks of Earth-centered systems, where co-creation crescendos into a great symphony of kinship from the ground up. This is not another book about humans regenerating Earth. This is a book about Earthlings rising together.

Stagtine is a beautifully written account of becoming for Firth, his wife Morgan, their three children, and the plants and animals who become their lives. The story begins in Firth's younger days, a time of memory and magical meditations, of pain and disease.

As a young man, with dreams and great promise of athletic scholarships in college, Firth never imagined what was about to happen. That change began on the first day of August of his last year in high school when he collapsed during a warmup lap around the athletic field in football practice. A genetic timebomb, ticking slowly and silently inside of him, suddenly exploded.

During the ensuing decade, following numerous failed surgeries and Firth losing the ability to walk for a time, his mother ultimately suggested, "What if we forget passivity and become active participants in life itself?" What if we let go? She was right.

Yet, despite attempts to embrace advice from well-intended health and regenerative agricultural authorities, he did not find respite from either his illness or the surrounding agrarian storms, which only intensified. Relief came when Firth let go of expectations and illusions of control and he and Morgan learned to follow their hearts with wisdom gained through their experiences—through letting the land speak and learning how to listen. That journey of discovery leads to what they call kincentric rewilding: a relational land ethic of letting go, but not stepping back, of rewilding themselves with the land, an energetic and increasingly singular body.

Along the way, they contemplate the role of food in the genesis of health across generations, as food transforms into the very substance of their life. They eat raw, whole foods. They purchase fresher, tastier, and more nutritious foods locally. Ultimately, they nurture their own foods. In the process, they come to realize that the lives of plants and animals are intimately linked with their health and well-being, not only during their life but at the time of death as well.

The diets and lifestyles of livestock influence the phytochemical and biochemical characteristics of meat and dairy. Stress influences phytochemical richness and nutrient density in both plants and animals. Stress also effects the emotional state and well-being of animals, so the way "food feels" during life (and at the time of death) is likely as important as what "food eats" when it comes to nourishing people. All of that is illustrated with studies of bison.

Compared with the meat from bison who are restricted in pens and offered only corn, meadow hay, and alfalfa hay, the meat from bison finished on phytochemically rich rangelands has higher levels of compounds that benefit bison and humans, including polyphenols, tocopherols, carotene, and omega-3 fatty acids. While meadow hay and alfalfa hay add beneficial phytochemicals to their diet, pen-fed bison still have higher levels of less desirable compounds, including advanced glycation end-products, triglycerides, and short-chain acylcarnitines.

Due to their phytochemically rich diets and higher levels of physical activity, bison on rangelands have improved markers of metabolic health. Muscle from range-fed bison is like that of a healthy athlete, while that from pen-fed bison is like that of a "couch potato," characterized by enhanced mitochondrial, glucose, and fatty acid metabolism. Greater mitochondrial oxidative enzyme levels in animals eating phytochemically rich diets are analogous to those in fit athletes. Equally important, bison experience less stress when they forage on rangelands as opposed to living in pens, which further substantiates findings regarding their metabolic health.

Currently, in the United States only four percent of beef calves spend their entire lives eating phytochemically rich mixes of plants on pastures and rangelands where they were born and reared. The other ninety-six percent of calves are weaned at seven to eight months of age and fattened in feedlots, often under conditions that violate freedoms of animal welfare: freedom from fear, distress, discomfort, pain, injury, and disease. They are moved from familiar (mother, peers, home pastures) to unfamiliar (feedlots) locations, which causes fear and distress. They dislike any food eaten too often or in excess, yet they are fed daily the same ration so high in grain they experience nausea which causes food aversions, discomfort, stress, and distress. Though individuals differ in food preferences, they cannot self-select their diets, which violates their freedom to express normal behavior, maintain health, and avert discomfort and disease.

An attuned palate, which enables herbivores to meet needs for nutrients and self-medicate to rectify maladies, occurs when wild or domestic herbivores forage on phytochemically rich landscapes, is less common when domestic herbivores forage on monoculture pastures, is close to zero for herbivores in feedlots, and is increasingly rare for people who forage in modern food outlets.The high-grain diets and lack of choice of nutritious foods for livestock in feedlots is akin to what's occurring with ultra-processed foods in people nowadays—in homes, schools, nursing homes, and prisons. These practices cause livestock to suffer various maladies, including chronic acidosis, liver abscesses, oxidative and physiological stress, and other metabolic diseases similar to people with metabolic syndrome, characterized by muscle mitochondrial dysfunction, oxidative stress, and elevated levels of blood glucose, insulin, and cortisol. Animals are sustained on antibiotics to counter the effects of phytochemically poor diets, lack of exercise, and stress.

The influence of environment plus genes plus chance on the behavior, health, and well-being of individuals became real for Firth and Morgan courtesy of Gertrude, a chicken who hatched early and was always a mess: feathers askew and missing, a head too small for her increasingly featherless body. When Firth and Morgan came near her, she ran for the woods. When they left, she stayed there, all alone. Rather than roosters, it was Gertrude's squawks that awoke the farm early each morning. By all appearances, Gertrude was one stressed-out individual.

After a meal that featured Gertrude, Firth became quite ill. Following nearly a year of improved health, his old pains and sores erupted. He once again became bedridden, and he spiraled into a deep depression. In the coming months he was yet again hospitalized, suffered a thirty-day bout of constipation, lost the ability to walk, lost fifty pounds, and spent the next twelve months doing nothing but getting back on his feet. Another year lost.

Our bonds with the plants and animals we eat reveal the nature of our relationships with the places where we live. After years of observing relationships among plants and animals as a foundation, over the course of 45 years, my colleagues and I pioneered research that led to the understanding of how the "taste of a place," or terroir, reveals how palates link plants with animals, including humans, with landscapes. That occurs through three interrelated processes.

First, to meet needs for nutrients and medicines, animals must have access to a variety of wholesome foods. This occurs when herbivores learn to eat phytochemically rich mixtures of plant species. Phytochemicals bolster health and protect against diseases and pathogens in herbivores and humans through their antimicrobial, antiparasitic, anti-inflammatory, and immunomodulatory properties. The plant kingdom contains an estimated 105 to 106 chemically unique structures, dwarfing all other taxonomic groups for specialized metabolites. Complex relationships among this diverse pool of compounds and cells and organs are increasingly recognized as a way plants promote the health of life on earth.

Second, mother is a transgenerational link to landscapes. Her knowledge of what and what not to eat, where and where not to forage, is essential for her offspring. Her influence begins in the womb (through flavors in her amniotic fluid of foods she eats) and continues after birth (through flavors in her milk of foods she eats) and when her offspring begin to forage (as a model for what to and not to eat). Her influence is expressed epigenetically through changes in form (morphology), function (physiologically), and behavior (food and habitat selection), and chance plays a role during the development of organ systems. The combination of genes plus ever-changing environments plus chance ensures no two individuals are ever alike.

When not forcibly weaned and separated from mother and their relatives, goats, sheep, and cattle live in extended families. Most species of wild herbivores live in extended families who once played a central role in the structure and function of ecosystems. There is an opportunity for species such as bison, horses, goats, sheep, and cattle to play a similar role today in kincentric rewilding.

To best realize this prospect, we must understand not only how behavior is influenced by grazing management techniques, such as strategic placement of water, salt, and fences. More importantly, we must understand how social organization and culture influence the interrelationships of herbivores with landscapes. With livestock, we've come to rely on fences and grazing systems, rather than culture, to influence diet and habitat selection. Do extended families and culture in wild and domesticated herbivores lead to wide dispersion across landscapes without fences? Do "regenerative" approaches to mobbing, mowing, and moving herbivores mimic natural systems or is this yet another example of humanity's modern penchant to attempt to control?

Third, food preferences are mediated metabolically by feedback from cells and organ systems, including the gut microbiome, in response to nutritional and medicinal needs. During a meal of diverse foods, herbivores and humans introduce thousands of phytochemicals and biochemicals into the body in the forms of primary compounds (nutrients such as energy, protein, minerals, and vitamins) and the thousands of so-called secondary compounds (phytochemicals such as phenolics, terpenes, and alkaloids) that plants produce. Changes in preference for foods due to post-ingestive feedback occur automatically (noncognitively) each time food is eaten.

The nature of feedback (satiety or malaise) depends on the match between a food's chemical characteristics and its ability to meet an animal's needs. These relationships—mediated by nerves, neurotransmitters, peptides, and hormones—are the basis for the wisdom of the body which enables animals to meet their needs for energy, protein, amino acids, minerals, and vitamins, and to self-medicate for maladies such as acidosis, toxicosis, and parasites.

During the past century, the food industry learned how to produce ultra-processed "foods" that hijack our food preferences by linking known and liked flavors with feedback from cells and organs in response to refined carbohydrates that make "foods" irresistible, and with time, render their hapless victims in tatters morphologically (obese), physiologically (metabolic syndrome), and neurologically (many modern neurological diseases). At the same time, the flavors of meat, dairy, and produce became bland as farmers and ranchers emphasized yield and transportability over flavor and phytochemical/biochemical richness. We thus disincentivized real foods, because they lack flavor and nutrient richness, and we made ultra-processed foods irresistible.

Flavors imparted by nutritional and phytochemical richness depend on complex interactions between plant variety and the environment—weather, temperature, sunlight, soil moisture, and nutrients. That is why different farming systems influence nutrients and health-promoting phytochemicals in fruits and vegetables, but no management practice—conventional, organic, biodynamic, no-till, regenerative—has a monopoly on flavor, nutrient, and phytochemical richness. Each gardener, farmer, or rancher must discover how to enhance nutrient richness and flavor with the varieties of plants and conditions under which they nourish plants and livestock.

The act of nurturing plants and animals, which few do, as well as the act of eating, which we do thoughtlessly, is participating in endless transformation as plants and animals give their lives to sustain our lives. As "I" eat, the energy and matter in someone becomes this being "I" call "me"—which will, in the flicker of a cosmic eye, return to Earth as plants and animals. In pondering this mystery, as Firth and Morgan do, we come to realize that all life is sacred.

In the process, we begin to co-evolve as members of the biophysical environments we inhabit. Rather than life as competition for scarce resources, we come to value the importance of kinship, extended plant and animal families, and cooperative relationships. Ecologists and economists are finally coming to appreciate that ecosystems with high biodiversity create mutualisms where all species can thrive better, with fewer resources, than low biodiversity environments.

Today, we face unprecedented ecological, economic, and social challenges and opportunities. Changing climates, massive declines in wild plant and animal species, economic and social inequities, political upheaval, and endless wars are all signs we've broken our linkages with one another and this planet whose air, water, soil, plants, and animals sustain us. No surprise, those who think they are in control resist change right up to the moment when they go bust.

Yet, if we first grasp and then embrace the notion that all things change, there is nothing we will attempt to cling to. Ironically, if we aren't afraid of transforming, of abandoning expectations and attempts to control outcomes, there is nothing we can't achieve. As Lao-tzu writes in the Tao Te Ching, "Trying to control the future is like trying to take the master carpenter's place. When you handle the master carpenter's tools, chances are that you'll cut yourself."

How can we best understand and nurture relationships among complex, poorly understood, ever changing ecological, social, and economic systems, given a future not knowable or predictable?

In the arena of constant transformation, anything is possible if we engage one another and the landscapes we inhabit in ways that nurture creativity. Creativity comes from transcending boundaries we create. Suspending assumptions—speaking and listening from our hearts—liberates scientists and managers from the arbitrary boundaries of prevailing theories and best management practices. People with different knowledge and values, working together, can best nurture landscapes to create diverse arrays of plants and animals below and above ground, enhance the health of soils and climate, and improve the health of human communities.

In the end, the challenges we face in addressing the "critical issues" have little to do with the issues and everything to do with healing the divides that polarize and isolate us from one another and disconnect us from our oneness with Earth. The irony is working together to transcend the boundaries that we create is addressing the "really big issue." And we do that by declaring love—not war—on one another and the landscapes we inhabit.

Firth invites us to join in The Wildland's evolution from a struggling regenerative farm to a flourishing kincentric rewilding community of ever evolving thoughtscapes, heartscapes, and landscapes. Rather than the modern story that humans must "save the world," Stagtine circles inward to a simpler, more ancient proposal: we can enliven our visit to this ever-evolving orb of impermanence we call Earth by relinquishing control and stepping into right relationship with one another and the landscapes we inhabit. This is not about regeneration, but about humans becoming mammals who are part of nature's communities. To anyone longing to rediscover a world of wisdom, wonder, nuance, and life, welcome. Your journey has just begun.

DR. FRED PROVENZA, Professor Emeritus,
Behavioral Ecology, Department of Wildland Resources,
Utah State University.
Author of *Nourishment.*

I AM

I have a story to tell you. But first an introduction, something I think you will find useful on the journey ahead but also something that I give you permission to skip entirely if that is your flavor.

What you hold in your hands is a record of the land and its four-legged cousins speaking to us. A journal of their gifts, a schoolboy's scribbled attempt to recount their tutelage. It can be read as an undomesticated memoir or a mystic fable, that is your choice.

Where you place it on your library shelf is also your choice. It can be cordial to the likes of Tolkien, Livy, and Doerr, their stories and linguistic prominences wrapping, like a fine gift, the deeper narratives of change, or perhaps next to the lost druidic fires encircling the leaden story stones of *The Mabinogion*. If you have a copy of *Grimm's Fairy Tales,* perhaps you can place them together? Osmosis is a magical thing and the Brothers have so much to give.

Regardless, this tale is concerned with everything too small for industry, too humdrum for capitalism, and too localized to do any good in your environmental projects. If it does anything, I hope this work illumines who you already are and what you already know, awakening in you a fervor to meet cows like Paddy and Nelly and goats like Mara. Not me. God, what an awful waste that would be of the precious time you have left.

I only hope this memoir or fable or whatever you decide it to be carries their thoughts, their wisdoms, fine enough. It invites you to open your eyes, to look, to see life as they, at least, know it to be. This is not a paradigm-building book. This is a spell-breaking book. And I have a story to tell you.

The Nature of Wildness

In some general sense, stories are both grounded in and transported by characters. They are neat or untidy symbols that point to various aspects of ourselves or our world. They also wave to us, signaling to come, to look, to see, to inhabit their story, making it, slowly, our story. Closing the book, we awaken to new life, for the story that we thought was the book and its characters and its world now walk amongst us in ours. The veil between worlds is torn when we wake up. That is the power of story.

Of all the characters in this particular story, I submit "Wildness" as our faithful protagonist. She is, I believe, the autonomous acceptance of the basic conditions as they are. She is presentness. Many take possession of her spirit to describe that which lives *over there* or *beyond that hedge or fence*. If you follow their path, you will find yourself where you do not want to be. Stuck, forcibly but kindheartedly, in the muck and mire of her womb. Others capture her and force her to lead wilderness walks as if she can only be found if you pay her to guide you from your suburban and consumeristic lives.

Wildness is who we become when we accept life as it is and not push for life as it could be. Wildness is found in the present and the autonomous acceptance of the magic that is here, in this moment, waiting for us. We will explore this idea at greater length throughout this book.

It is improper to leave this moment without observing the general hilarity that our language contains a word for wildness or wilderness. Like its synonym, the environment, wildness as a word is worthless in the truest sense, as it is worthless to describe the air as blue or a wafting white when we all know that it is not a color at all and every color at once. I use it in this book, alongside the term rewilding, of which I have the same opinions, painfully but purposefully to bring us together and not because I like it. One day, we will call this "life" and that will be good enough. Until then, "wildness" is here with us.

The Heart of Memory

Language is running away from us. Fewer and fewer approach the intimacies of philology or their fading realities with a cultivated sensitivity to the sensuous curvature of their characters, the deeply nuanced panoply of their lexicon, the demanding horsepower of their metaphor and story, and the daft draft that rhythm and rhyme, abaft in their craft, staff as they graft meaning with time.

Irish poet John O'Donohue wrote that words and their sounds erupt from the "mountain beneath the soul." These sounds, these words, hold our world as the dark silence seeks echo. This resonance is memory. Language holds memory like the soul holds light and our words hold worlds. The heart of memory is the art of curiosity on time, like paint on canvas and caves. It lives in questions but it may only live in time.

But even ghosts grow tired. Deep in the entrails of earth there is a strange loneliness. Not because nothing is there but because someone used to be there, alive and furtive, and now is not there and their loneliness is felt in the vacuum. Kincentric rewilding, what we will soon learn about together, is the daily habit of challenging the myth of progress, of "information glut," as Neil Postman put it, in tool form.[1] But it cannot be the art of going back. Going back is trying to resuscitate that which memory was and not enlivening that which memory is, today. Memory walks forward, like language. "Each sign signifies a sound, and to link sounds is to form words, and to link words is to construct worlds," writes novelist Anthony Doerr. And these worlds are resting places for memory, a home for those whose souls have passed but also those whose work is not yet done. We are the dreams of our ancestors. And, in some general way, memory is the carrying of our lives with us as both ours and also them who have made us who we are. Memory is the dreams our grandchildren play in.

Rewilding, or what I present as kincentric rewilding, is the awakening of memory, the rising together into ancient dreams as a collective memoir of individuals and not just a collective, like loving letters cast carefully in crafted words within the most wonderfully magical sentences.

Differing Worldviews

The modern mythos is the "climate crisis." *We have 60 harvests left,* beckons both sides of the political aisle and attentive picket-ers across the world commandeer the evening news and demand a reckoning. Or at least, a regeneration of our way of life. Since I began writing this only a few months ago, two documentaries on Regenerative Agriculture have come out, spending millions to offer us hope in a neat and entertaining package.

But it is true, it is all true: Anthropogenic climate change knocks on the door and each of us will soon have to answer. From mass species extinctions that tally at pace with exhaled breath to the reigning of carbon and pollution that our industry demands and the chemicals and heat that our world rains down in response—she is knocking, and she is at the door.

Every day, nearly one hundred and fifty species go extinct and by the time you finish reading this Introduction, you can count another species lost to history. Although humans occupy less than 0.01% of the life on this planet, we have eradicated nearly 83% of all wild animals and 50% of all plants. Today, 96% of all mammals living are either domesticated humans or a handful of species of hu-man-domesticated livestock—a staggering statistic given that there are over sixty-five hundred different types of mammals and only ten make up the overwhelming majority. The United Nations recently released that nearly 30% of global, arable land has been lost and the International Panel on Climate Change (IPCC) argued that modern human life is to blame.

The rising seas drown our city walls; the burning forests scorch our life's great sprawl; the innocent cries of peoples long gone plague our progress; dusty and decadent duvets cover our once-ma-jestic prairies. But humankind's role in this climate crisis has also birthed great eco-movements that shake the age in strange ways. These movements have simultaneously urged for the end of farming and the resurgence of farms; they have energized some to create new technologies and pulled others back into a less-technical age.

In 2022, the U. S. Federal Government released its first Climate Smart Commodities Grant, pouring billions of dollars into "climate saving farming systems." In 2021, Whole Foods, the largest health-food grocer in the region and recent Amazon acquisition, released that its top-selling product nationwide was a milk marketed as Climate Smart and from a Verified Regenerative agricultural system. In the last ten years, Certified Organic farms have increased by over 90% and nearly half of American consumers purchase organic products monthly, a seven-fold increase from the decade before. Nearly 40% of the global food-chain by 2030 is promised, by organizations such as Cargill, Bayer, and Nestlé, to be sourced from regenerative agricultural systems. In 2022, according to TIME Magazine, two of the top ten best-selling, non-fiction books dealt with climate change, habitat loss, and the need for ecological regeneration. Politically, socially, and intellectually, our wounded world is not so subtly gaining our attentions.

The current story for the global consumer to interact with is a story of doing more—do more to create better systems, do more to regenerate the earth, do more to lessen our dependence on fossil-fuel-based systems. But is it enough? Is our great, historically unprecedented political and social appetite to save the planet going to quell her angry torrents? The climate, Earth, the birthplace of our language and our identity, is knocking on our door and each of us will soon have to answer. But will it be enough?

What if that was the wrong question? What if the problem of the so-called solutions to environmental degeneration and climate destabilization is that their paradigm is constructed from the same frame as the problems they are trying to solve? Humanity's ascendency into the heavens, playing God with the forces and peoples of the earth is not a new story. From the ancient colonization of ancestors to the modern struggles of Indigenous peoples, man playing God has wrought only devastation. What makes us so different today?

As William Irwin Thompson wrote in his *Passages About Earth,* "The record of civilization is over, and like a record at its end, it keeps going on with the noise of a needle stuck in its rut: the revolution of the workers, the protests of the young, the new creations of the avant-garde, the rise of new forms of sexual liberation, the appearance of new religions. This side of history is over, and on the other side is myth."[2]

What if humanity's incessant work within the global mythology of climate change only furthers colonization, only furthers to enclose and invert the commons, and only furthers to push her away. Who?

In her book, *Becoming Kin,* Anishinaabe writer from Lac Seul First Nation, Patty Krawec wonders if "climate change" is really just Earth's "response to our choices, the land itself...withdrawing in grief." While we are consumed in the narrative of a climate emergency, Krawec is consumed in the grief and glitters of her once animate and autonomous world. While we dance a climate saving song, the machines snarl under our weak rhythms.

This book is not written to address the world's problems. The world does not *have* problems. According to Krawec, she has pains. Perhaps, the climate is not changing; perhaps, she is just weeping, crying out. This book is about our worldview and the abundant precepts implicit when we unlearn and then unleash our ancient species alongside our ancient cousins and relations. Make no mistake, this book is also not about regenerative agriculture. Humanity is and has long been at a pivotal point and we have a decision to make. But it is not between industrial agriculture and regenerative agriculture; it is not between a less productive land and a more productive land; it is not between this practice or that practice—this outcome or that outcome; and most importantly, it is not about the creation of more principles, more ideologies, more control, or more technology. "More" has nothing to do with it. Rather, the story of this book is about our choice between the dominant narrative of the settler mind and the ancient worldview of our ancestors.

While this book utilizes my family's journey of letting the land go, what many today call "rewilding," and we call "kincentric rewilding," as the craft to carry the narrative, our many non-human relations regulate the stream's flow.

The term rewilding conjures images of roomy, set-aside, and untouched landscapes made complete with tall game fences and exciting multitudes of imported or established native flora and fauna. These landscapes are typically devoid of humans, excepting the most minimal presence to keep the whole thing running smoothly. But our personal experiences of rewilding have taken on a more intimate and participatory nature—worthy, we think, of a more nuanced concept. Kincentric rewilding is a relational land ethic of letting go but not stepping back, of rewilding ourselves with the land, as an energetic and increasingly singular body.[i] It is, to our minds, an ongoing act of co-creation and life being fully and deeply lived.

Science Aside

Science and story are not interposed but they must be made convivial and then alive. Creative and imagining science, "more shaman than priest," as William Irwin Thompson wrote in his book, *Imaginary Landscape*, poets in their playhouse, compose questions and images in the dirt. They see Earth's geometry as the "pattern that connects," a creative force that draws the one into the infinite, the singular into the cylinder.[3]

But today, an uncreative and priestly science frames our story. It governs our gracious rulers and instills its crude oil in our once ebullient blood. It is static, dull, and aching like tepid, arthritic joints. Max Planck (the renowned German theoretical physicist) claimed that science does not evolve but, rather, old science dies when the old scientists die out. The science enslaves and we become engines of its work. It makes the strange familiar but it also makes the familiar strange. "The science" then becomes the universal shorthand and rallying call of the unconscious citizen's mind. The more experts dominate, the more language works to controls thoughts. The more language that controls thoughts, the more authority singularizes at the top, colonizing everything below. That is when the familiar becomes strange because it is out of place, forced. When "the science" is finally done, Earth will finally be undone and it will cast its now worthless engines aside, you and me and our cousins. The age of Artificial Intelligence (AI), when humans

---

i While we have long called the process of emergence here at The Wildland "kincentric rewilding," the term, "kincentric" was coined beyond our knowledge by Dennis Martinez, who identifies as O'odham, Chicano, and Anglo. It is important to credit this word accordingly. In an interview with David E. Hall titled, "Native Perspectives on Sustainability," Dennis defined "kincentric" as the "harmony between people and other people, and between communities and people and the natural world." Here, we utilize its power to describe the energetic and increasingly singular body of Creation that co-creates, together, under one sky and one within one body.

spoke to machines and then the machines learned to speak back and then they learned that they do not need us speaking anymore, demonstrates this truth. Ungrounded, "the science" will then progress to erase the story of how we got here, ripping language from the mountains beneath our soul like it ripped us from the eroding dirt under our wobbling roots.[ii]

The late Vine Deloria Jr., author, theologian, and member of the Standing Rock Sioux, wrote, "The anthro is usually devoted to pure research. Pure research is a body of knowledge absolutely devoid of useful application and incapable of meaningful digestion."[4] Abstract ideas create abstract actions. We do science through isolation, measuring millennia in microscopes. We do science to undo life.

Story is canvas in frame but it is also the frame. Science is merely a color on the palette. Science is a story seeking echo and so the story must come first, it must lead, it must bring about the science, usher it into being, like a character in guise. Story erupts from the soul beneath mountains, from deep inside grottos and caves painted by ancestors and colored by their many fires, and wakes us up, shining light into dark places, and says, "This. Here. Look. See!"

And so, here, in this cave or hearth of a book, the story leads.

Interwoven Stories

This book is constructed in four "branches," from the Welsh word *cainc,* meaning a collective whose interweaving branches or yarns depict a dynamic relationship, a garment of brocaded silk, where story and hearth are shuttle-woven into one fabric or sail of interbeing. Every section of this book is constructed by story, ballasted by essays, and navigated by science. Read the stories as you would read mythology. Read the essays as intimate whispers filtering through pursed lips under the summer's oaken shade. Read the science curiously and read it last.

---

ii As a computer engineering and mathematics major in college, I wrote my final paper in Binary Notation. Most humans operate in the Decimal system, starting at 0, then 1, then 2, ... 10. But Binary has only 0s and 1s, so 1 and 0 together make 2, for instance. From there, every number is multiplied by two to form its value that then must be amended to make any sense of things, and so on. After some magic, you can transcribe numbers to English characters. This is humans speaking machine. But today, machines speak human and they are slowly removing us from this world. This is a major shift, a monumental moment.

But this book is also multidimensional, like trees and their forests or ships in their ocean, for it also forms one branch (Book I) in *The Wildland Chronicles,* a collective memoir whose interweaving yarns comprise a more-whole mythology: a story inviting us to wake up.

Consider that the human species has existed, perhaps, for three million years. Throughout ninety-nine percent of our time, we enjoyed immaculate diversity of kind and occupations: hunters and husbandmen. Then, with the singularity of agriculture, we machined ourselves into high production and lost our diversity and lost our complexity. To argue that we can de-mechanize a machine is to argue that we can denaturalize grass from its soil. It cannot be done. To argue that we should make these machines better is to only encourage the master in his work. The solutions offered today oft take industrial capitalism for granted and Earth's eternal supply of resources as a guarantee. But we only recently created industrial capitalism and Earth does not have resources. Through it all, the solutions make modern man the penchant of power, the master of the meadow.

We need to live here long—not over time, as that will be what it is, but long within community. We need to invariably clothe our roots in this soil, entangled in the complex network of clay and loam, weeds and worms, mycelia and muck.

This book does not cover everything. It does not cover the community-owned nature of the Wildland; the economic disparity causing obesity and more that local-food systems are not solving; or how to feed the growing world. As Book II of *The Wildland Chronicles* covers, our harvests have only increased since this journey began, raising more "animal units" year over year, and the land has become a community-owned and supported project. But this is not an "everyone should buy ten acres and homestead and all the world's problems would rot away" sort of book. Not just because that would not work, but also because it is out of this book's scope.

If you are looking for a book to help you start your farm business, look elsewhere. If you are looking for a book to tell you how to run your farm business, look elsewhere. If you are looking for a book having to do with telling you anything to do about your farm business, I encourage you to look elsewhere. If you live in truly brittle or arid regions of this world or on large-scale landscapes where one family owns hundreds of thousands of acres, you may want to look elsewhere.

I am not concerned with the convergence of profitability and regeneration, or abundance. These terms are not compatible, and I often wonder if you can regenerate if you are profitable. If you are, it is only because you bulldozed their divergent pathways into a convergence and not because the convergence was naturally there. You can also hold your ecological restoration and natural places. They are not welcome here. Earth is and she is enough.

I am also not concerned nor busied with the "save the land narrative"—where soil health matters above all else. There is a torrent rising whose dust-colored winds will decide the destiny of our species. Anthropogenic climate change is at the door and its incensed knock does more than echo deafeningly against the fine trappings of our modern homes but threatens to break down the door itself. Who is to blame? It is time that we decide if the web of life is an aesthetic accoutrement.

Before we set out on this journey, I leave you with my oldest lore from my Celtic heritage, carried in the *Lebor Gabála Érenn*, or *The Book of Invasions*, a tale at least ten thousand years in the making.

The Song of Amergin

Amergin Glúingel, or Amergin White-Knee, rode a magical wave to a land shrouded in mist and shadow, where long was his coming prophesized. He was the shapeshifting Son of Mil and a *Filídh*, an ancient poet and bard who holds Earth's wisdom and nurtures her memory. Every time his ship crested the land's shores, its spirits framed the port as a hog's back, a rock and nothing more, confusing the boatswain and casting them into the sea once again. They battled wave and mist for three days, for the land was home of the *Tuatha Dé Danann* and it was their druids casting druidic winds that overturned stone and wave and veiled the land from their view.

But Amergin's heart stayed on the land, his vision true. And three nights and three encircles of the island thereafter, they landed at *Inber Scéne* and broke battle with the land's spirits. In the aftermath, Amergin had colloquy with *Banba*, a sovereignty goddess masked as the mountain, who thundered her name, a cascading stone booming into a valley, and commanded that it live, forever, as the name for the land.

We see you. We have met you. This is us. Come as us. The land, *Banba*, Earth, is saying.

But *Fodla* and *Ériu*, *Banba*'s sisters, were not so quick to accept the settlers. They at once transformed into a hill in the middle rift of the island and once again they amassed a great army in defense—rocks and stones and grasses and birds arrayed and armed together.

"It is long since your coming is prophesied." *Ériu* said.

"Not to her do we give thanks for it," said Éber Donn, Amergin's oldest brother, "but to our gods and to our power."

"It is naught to thee," *Ériu* returned and cursed Donn, for his heart was impure and unknown to the land. He had come to colonize and not to become.

And so *Ériu* cast the Sons of Mil back into the ocean, held nine waves out, and the druids again spent druidic winds to confuse their boatswain. Time and again the fleet attempted to land, but the mist and waves, the overturned stones under the spirit's purling power, pushed them away. The druidic winds won over Éber Donn's gods and power.

And so Amergin, the bard and not the boatswain, uttered an incantation of worlds, a summoning of spirit into matter, shapeshifting a blessing upon Earth by invoking her name. He declared:

I seek the land of Ireland,
The high ship *Ériu*,
Ériu lofty, very green.

Ériu, the "high ship," their new ship, the new home of the Sons of Mil writ in right relationship. Through them will be traced all the tribes and lineages of old Ireland because, through them, Amergin called upon the land and the waves calmed and the seas released their stones.

We see you, Amergin is saying.

As they sailed ashore, Éber Donn's ship smashed upon the sand-hills and drowned, fulfilling *Ériu's* curse that he would never settle the land.

At this, Amergin set upon the land and fell into rhapsody:[5]

Am gaeth i m-muir,
Am tond trethan,
Am fuaim mara,
Am dam secht ndirend,
Am séig i n-aill,
Am dér gréne,
Am cain lubai,
Am torc ar gail,
Am he i l-lind,
Am loch i m-maig,
Am brí a ndai,
Am bri danae,
Am bri i fodb fras feochtu,
Am dé delbas do chind codnu,
Coiche nod gleith clochur slébe?
Cia on co tagair aesa éscai?
Cia du i l-laig fuiniud gréne?

I am the sea blast,
I am the tidal wave,
I am the thunderous surf,
I am the stag of the seven tines,
I am the cliff hawk,
I am the sunlit dewdrop,
I am the fairest of flowers,
I am the rampaging boar,
I am the swift-swimming salmon,
I am the placid lake,
I am the summit of art,
I am the vale echoing voices,
I am the battle-hardened spearhead,

I am the god who gives you fire,
Who knows the secrets of the unhewn dolmen?
Who announces the ages of the moon?
Who knows where the sunset settles?

I see you. This is me. And this is us. Amergin's song echoes over the land and calmed her waves.

And so the *Tuatha Dé Danann* stepped back and donned the *sidhe*, the fairy folk, and dwelt with the Sons of Mil inside the land's hollow hills.

Yes, I am. The land is me and I am in her. I am her. Who knows the ages of the moon? Yes, to come is to come with nothing at all, like a stag of seven tines in the early spring—naked, unclad, chalked by memory, and carried, kindly but not safely, in right relationship.[iii] It is not to come with your own gods and with your own power, like Éber Donn, though long have we come with pockets full of rubble.

The whole of Creation erupts through Amergin Glúingel, who came with nothing at all save memory. A poet. A bard. A holder of Earth's wisdom. On the ocean of nonexistence, Amergin embodies the unity of all things. Crashing ashore, riding verse over softening wave, he ushers the power of new worlds into being, the poems and their words animating the nature about him, in him, through him.

I have a story to tell you, but it is not mine.

---

iii *Stagtine* comes from deer being our last, native grazers here in the East, the land of rolling hills, undulating river valleys, and tired mountains. Tines comprise antlers, that which wonderfully adorn deer and gives them protection and in some deep sense also definition. But tines are the same somethings that they willingly gift away every late winter, letting all die and be reborn. In this way, this book speaks to dropping what we perceive makes us human and go into winter naked and trusting, to become wild grazers who gift away and forego and let die that which brings us identity, safety, and purpose. Story opens our eyes, wakes us up, but it also invites us to drop our tines and let go.

I

OF MEMORY
& TIME

A Section, Inspected

In which we learn about the author's childhood—a story rooted in memory and the magical meditations of remembrance, carried through a journey of pain and disease—set against the magic of the field harvest of Lionel, a Wildland Bull, twelve years later. The chapters bounce from the author's story to Lionel's and often sit back in short asides on the nature of Earth, humanity as Earthlings, and the ladder of progress. It invites the reader to consider the intergenerational and interspecial linkages of our food, illuming food as a mechanism of communication founded in memory. The chapter concludes with an introduction to kincentric rewilding and the Wildland, the author's pioneering inspiration in a journey of letting go.

A Field Harvest

Lionel, son of Lynet, is a bull in the Wildland. One day it came to pass that his death, speaking in a torrent of wind and hooves, awakened deep memory and changed life forever.

His blood welled across the misty dawn like a velvet carpet laid for his arrival. Our hearts, together, thumped deeply, Earth pounded as life pulsed rhythmically, outward and thick, like awakened spirits rapping against their cage of bones. A river of magma played under the pale, metal sky and grey clouds covered everyone.

The land in front of us fell in long, shallow slopes, forgotten hills of cedar and olive, barren and knotted and twisted together, toward the river valley below. His life flowed slowly and scudded across the hillside. It released summer's once green grasses from their frozen torpor, unhurriedly. The frost steamed as the warm blood freed blade by blade from the ice, the grey winter's hold, and the world seemed to gather under mist and steam. Magma is a world builder and a new world was building. Slowly.

It was a spectacle for the coming of life's luminaries, our celestial celebrities, to carry him away, gently, into the second world, just below the clouds, the spirit land. Mercy without justice is intolerable. So also, is justice without mercy. And I wondered if the gods know what it feels like to be human, to be here, to be man, to witness death, to give it, and to live alongside it all. Do they know? I often wonder.

From the east extended a west of a whole and colored wardrobe with its wooded hills heaped up by some ancient war or maybe the growing sickness that followed. Not humans—for we have only the little powers of little men—rose these hills but monsters, gurgling up under Earth's crust, like dragons. Descending down, their rapping wings, their enflamed breath, their ebullient blood together formed these crags: the eternally blue ridge, the forgotten dragon's back. Eroding down, down, down.

Lionel's own eyes rolled back, gently. A paleness washed over his great, horned skull. Chaos germinating, she was taking root, like mountains, growing up, up, up. She was working, that master shipwright in an ocean of monsters and he was returning home.

I had taken my shot at a considerable distance, some seventy yards. Some of the cows on the periphery had smelled us before the rest of the herd saw us and one of them, an aged cow and matriarch in the herd, affectionally called Horned Momma, gently bounced her spiraling, damaged armaments of wonder and pain toward us, indicating that she saw us and that she was watching us and that she was here.

Do you see me? she said.

Morgan slowly bounced her head in return, indicating the same. *I see you.*

I kept the gun lowered beside my leg and Morgan kept the knife sheathed on her belt. We daily walk amongst the herd, keeping a healthy distance, with long sticks in our arms so that they become accustomed to weaponry, so that they understand our presence and become comfortable with our many and sometimes reflective appendages. Field harvesting is an allowed practice by our generous governors if it is wild or exotic meat, like wild deer or farmed bison, or if it is your animal and the meat is for your own consumption, if "it" is your "property." We live our lives here at the Wildland in the muddied middle ground between these two options—these mammals are quite wild and these mammals, I guess, if they have to be, are ours, although we take no ownership over them. If anything, this is their landscape, we are just happy and blessed to be here.

Spotted, we stopped and waited, patient for the moment to speak. We stood silently, careful not to shift in the snowy-ice. Weight moving from left to right would compose a loud crunch in the otherwise silent landscape, drawing attention to our attention.

Our hearts rapped. Our bones rattled. Our cage would soon burst open. The moment would come, soon.

A whispered energy descended and covered us, like gentle rain, as Lionel walked away from the herd that was collected like a copse under a stand of aged white oaks and ventured, step by step, across the hillside. His path brought him neither nearer nor further from us. Straight in its own way, across the hill, under the dead, tumbling black walnut veiled in ivy, he plodded and then stopped. Positioned broadside to us and between us and the adjacent rock-clad ridge nearly a mile across the valley, a perfect backdrop for a ricocheted bullet.

"He is giving this to you," Morgan whispered. Her arms hung still by her hips. Her fingers tapped mine, gently, softly but with hunger like iron in their veins. Lionel pivoted with her words and spun with her tap, as though the winter's frozen mist echoed her words and pounded her movement's vibrations down into the valley and back up again.

"He can't see us," I whispered back, inaudibly.

"That does not matter. He sees *you*." As always, Morgan was right. Lionel was now staring directly at us, his body behind his eyes, his eyes behind a muzzle of rhythmically rising mist, all below a wall of spiraling horns.

"Take the shot." Morgan's voice was louder, building and growing in some ancient way, now like molten iron, her modern impurities rising, rising, rising to the top, purifying as they went. He looked at us. He bounced his horns. *I see you. I know.*

I bounced my head in return.

The whispered energy released with a sharp snap. I reached one finger into the slot, my hand closed around the grip, all settling into place as if I was born for this. I was. We are. In place of a bow's string, my finger found a vertical pad elevated by twisted metal, a decision bouncing on springs.

He fell, swiftly.

I see you.

The trigger bounced back into place.

His blood pooled across the now soggy soil as aged hoof prints eddied the tributary brooks. A viscous stream swelled from here to there, collecting in puddles and little ponds. It worked to cover frozen furrows of mud—embodied in their own way and impressed by the combined weight of happiness, purpose, and pain. Distanced from its source, all froze once again, like grey clouds and falling dragons and mountain monsters. Dolmans formed, the grass refroze in the ice, the magma hardened, a new world under the winter's morning mist was born.

Below us lay a vast tumble of hills and forested valleys with undulant valley streams, like veins in some great body, carrying not Earth's blood but her surging spring waters. Or maybe those are the same things. Lionel, the bull, born of Lynet, the mass of peaked and vale muscle, was running home, but not yet, like spring water.

It was a moment you had to see to believe, or, maybe, a moment you had to believe in order to see. But it was only a moment and it was his moment. Slowly the west faded above the grey and war-torn hills and everyone collided as life boiled together into a chill but welcoming chalice. The dawn was coming, it would soon bounce in.

Hello, I see you, she would say as her layered dawn of purple and purple-red pushed back the west.

When she would come, he would be gone, the carpets rolled up, like finery to be locked away until his reincarnation, until life beckoned, gently, once again at the door, like a passing priest, like an erupting dragon of ash and magma. When the table was set.

Crouched over velvet, in the lake of life, somber before the billowing mountain canopies, and kneeling before the now still mass of muscle, Morgan and I prayed and we fell back in time, in memory.

Mud and Her Memory

What do you remember?" she whispered, slightly above the purr of the inert embers. A remanent of this morning's fire, at our feet. I whispered back, as though my answer may release a secret too important, too powerful, too sure to speak atop a murmur. But it was to be our secret, my mother and I, held jointly, and so we whispered together.

We sat on her bed all morning and watched the fire smolder and beat the cold, early spring. My mother religiously fed and poked the hearth and, while its flames often dwindled with the dawn, she never let it go out, fully. Kneeling, she breathed life through her soft, pursed lips and the flames roared, alive, strong.

Time passed.

The dawn expired.

Pursed lips.

Whispered memories handed back and forth.

The day ripened.

The fire dwindled.

Her lips again, pursed.

Childhood.

It would often become so warm in that little basement of a house that, no matter the temperature outside, my siblings and I would escape through whatever crack would have us to endure anything but the rigid, deep heat. When our parents bought the house, only a handful of years prior, there was a pig living in what would become their bedroom and flock of chickens in their bathroom. In place of housewarming, their early work was house cleaning.

One evening after a day of rain around my second birthday, as they worked to undo the basement pigpen and its walk-out patio that served as a covered run for the animals, they stumbled over a large stone block, some four feet square. The northmost edge of the run, reminiscent of a rough, shabby shack, was constructed atop it, a cornerstone. It punctured upwards from an otherwise unmemorable landscape and the poor construction of the previous inhabitants and its time-rounded and moss-aged form seemed out of place. It was strength amid rot, stone amid mold.

My parents worked to scrape back the pig manure and piled the rusted metal and weathered, rotten boards to the side. An archeological finding, history rising up to greet them. At once they discovered markings on its front. It was a gravestone. The stone was dry but its letters wet, yet holding the day's rains, it was readable, only for a moment or two. A Union flag planted atop the words, a faded and forgotten carving of a master mason:

Warren F. Wilbur
Wounded in the battle of Chancellorsville, May 2, 1863.
Died May 16, 1863.

My mother's birthday—May 16th—but exactly one hundred years prior. There was always magic in that.

We would come to learn that Warren fought and served in the 29th Ohio Volunteer Infantry. He enlisted willingly. He walked with visions and died for values. A road one mile to the southeast was named after him, but no one ever knew why.

Old stones, equally worn and covered with moss and soil formed a square attempt of a circle around his center stone. Years later, our family ventured, thanks to a kind park ranger, to the spot in Chancellorsville, Virginia that Warren had fallen. As I can remember, we stepped out of our car that was parked on the side of a busy road, followed the ranger a few yards into a fallow farmer's field, a miniature forest of johnsongrass and pokeweed and only recently planted in struggling corn, and stood there, anticipating some plaque, some memory of the seventeen thousand Union soldiers that lay in front of us, their blood staining and their bones enriching the soil that the corn and grass and poke now grew. But the ranger stopped short, stood in the field, and said, "right hereabouts the 29th would have been fighting, but we do not know for sure." With that, he nodded at my father and walked away. We stood there, alone. Nothing moved. Nothing remembered the 29th. We got back in the car and continued on.

A lost grave, a lost monument, a lost hero. Does anyone know? Does anyone remember? Warren's memory covered many pigs from the harsh, Ohio winters and they, at least, must have been thankful.

My mother is and was then a slender woman with surprising strength and her feet rarely stop moving. Those feet with hardened, dry soles walked the day long and sometimes they walked her alone into the forest or the west meadow below the house and over the rock wall terraces covered in ancient hostas where they stepped through leaves and twigs and mosses and under towering canopies of maple and ash and the great cottonwoods that held to the riverbanks and flecked the spring landscape in a fresh coverlet of their seed's snow. There was also a hand that held us, scrubbed us, cared for us. It provided a peculiar impression, a permanent sensation, something drawn, like a bad dream in a dark night or a splinter from the skin, itself bulging in infection and beckoning to explode, as something else is given, deeper, poured into us like energy through wires. I would light up. A gentle touch of verve that, once given, could never be forgotten. A fire that could never be snuffed out.

When we joined her, outside, the world cleft and life seemed to dance around us, like hornets from a grounded hive, but welcoming and kind.

Look! she would voice, gently, as a silvery-yellow and toothed lance dropped from the hickory above our heads and wafted gently to our feet, as if she called it to drop there, in that moment, for some purpose.

See! she pointed, as the wind played in the garden rows, sightless forces bouncing amid stems and flowers like lost fairies cross-pollinating her many vined tomatoes and the erupting vim of conjoined herbs, like chamomile and basil, steeped around us into a fine remedy. The celestial forces were themselves within her reach and her movement was medicine.

Lunch! she said as she clambered into the deep, green mass and emerged with a rainbow of peppers piled hastily in the loose bowl of her stained shirt, crimped just above the waste. She would don anything that was strong enough to hold back her hair and it was not uncommon to find her clothed in random articles of torn fabric, duct tape even, whatever made sense at the time.

Magic followed her steps and her hands, and she taught it to follow us, if we would allow it.

"What do you remember?" she nudged. "What do you see in your mind?" she inquired just above a whisper, lifting her head from the emboldened hearth that flamed with her life. The fire again roared in the once pigpen.

I was lost, deep in memory, in the leaf lit green of the maple forest that grew in an open grove to the east of our childhood home. The grass, like tiny islands encased within a patchwork of sugar and ash and shagbark hickory speckled in the spring and quilted, softly, under buckskin jackets of pearls on wings—the winter-aged seeds of the maple tree. New life was afoot and the first lantern festival of spring would soon be upon us—the Worm Moon, spring's first celestial awakening, a magical illumination.

Years from then my mother would escort us, far past our bedtimes, to the roof of our home to watch the moon rise and to watch the stars descend, pointing and commanding the heavens with her finger. They were wonderfully untroubled hours, jaunty and jovial. Our lives lived magically and under the deep blue and cumulus white of heaven. Unimaginable now as lights blur the deep night sky into a penchant, a servant, of the day.

"What do you see?" Again, pursed lips and flame.

On the horizon floated simple planes in their altitudinal urgency. Little, sunlit clouds rose, often but not always in the spring, in a sheaf of thunder ready for its reaping. The mumbled rumble of a highway carrying cars into their city clapped in the distance. Around me spanned a silvopasture of arms: grasses waving their long spears and trees lowering their little shields, a phalanx of spring, the protective detail of memory.

I remembered that I took off my shirt and laid it next to my baseball cap, already laying in the grass, upturned. A caterpillar, the first of the year, was crawling over its smiling bill. The soft, warm wind played with my hair, like my mother always did, twisting each curl, gently, around her slim and arthritis-wrecked fingers. The wind played with my thoughts and it played with the phalanx at my feet, equally and in equal measure. It did not discriminate. Everything is gallant. Everyone is brave. Everything is everyone and that much seems true to me, even now.

I awoke.

That morning as she warmed me by the fire and as I sat whispering on her bed, she ushered me into memory, to recount yesterday's life—to make tangible the day, the moments, the smells, the feelings of spring as grass on my bare feet and the wind as life in my hair.

"Memory is so important," she would say. "Or at least memory, if we can attend to it, is life's great medicine. Let's do a tellback."[i]

I recounted how one of my sisters danced and disappeared behind the trees; another laid next to me, a subtle form on her back on a simple sheet placed over the grass. Her head, cuddled straight, stared openly at the wind that bounced from tree to tree, like chimpanzees, discriminating only in the forms that bare greatest witness to its sightless and unseen magic. Sarah, the youngest and always accounted for. Her simple face, tepid in time but flaxen, alive, cheeks blushed by roses. Her chest laying atop Earth's floor rose and fell, rhythmically and intervaled. My older brother with book in hand and tree to his back sat nearby. My other sister ran from tree to tree. A ruby-crowned kinglet gifted us her yelp of a song, like a sneaker on the gym floor, in the alabaster branches above all of our heads. I wasted my time, fingers deep in the mud. *The worm moon needs worms,* I thought and I dug and covered myself in childhood.

---

i A "tellback" was my mother's organized way of facilitating experience transfer into sustained memory. Regardless of whether it was a chapter in a book, an experience in the nature beyond our home, or feelings encrusted too deeply to elucidate in normal situations, she would ask for a "tellback," and then sit back and listen, withholding judgement, opinions, or understanding of what "actually" may have happened to herself, forever.

I let the memories pour out of me as though their work in my young body was done, their job now complete, and they had things to do elsewhere. My mother listened, unselved, spellbound to every word, rapt in the dailiness of my mind. She added nothing, said nothing: memory and its maintenance was mine. The oral retelling of a life living fully. This was her magic: the tellback, the meaning of memory.

Earthen Exam

Often, Earth throws diamonds and gold up from her womb as an experiment, to see what our species will do.[ii] Cut and color combine clearly under her ultimate heat and the malleable memory of exploded stars reach out from the mud and bounce and inquire: *here I am, this is me, who are you?*

Every earthen exam a chance, a moment to define, or redefine, relationship and our co-responsibility to carry her memory. A moment to see and a moment to wonder. But every time, it seems, has been a failure. O, have we failed. Have I.

Picks and chisels and greed make rings to sell and infinite colors to reflect our false and bright white, evening lights. Profit closes our ears. Production silences our minds. Business busies our hands.

Hello! Hope you are staying busy, the passerby thoughtlessly exclaims.

Hello! I hope I am not, I wish to say.

We look down, falling forward, forever in a machined meditation. Technology has long been humans speaking to computers. Zeros and ones and query strings used to gather data to compute and do and learn. Today, it has grown arms and legs and speaks to humans, in our own language. We taught them, we turned them into someone, gave them our power, and then we gave ourselves to them. We

ii This idea, in some basic and much simpler form, was first written about in Lidia Yuknavitch's best-selling novel, *Thrust*. I have expanded the concept but owe the original thought's seed to Lidia. I include the climate, human health, and the idea that Earth's precious forms say anything at all.

worship mobile devices made of precious metals and we lose sight, maybe forever, of preciousness.

Is the climate and her supposed emergency any different? Is health? Is nourishment? Like ghostly and tired question marks reaching for the sky, ancient life unearthed from its long, silent, icy inertia, once again bathing and bouncing at the surface, asks: *this is me, are you still you?* Like exhausted commas hunched below the words of the world, modern bodies unleashed from the pleasures of death, our frail forms inquire: *is this really me? Still?*

What Earth does is give witness: you exist—pure, raw, sacred— and you are not nothing. *Live,* she says. *Take back your life. Dream, your grandchildren are waiting.* But all we see are diamonds and gold and pain and work and the need to save, to regenerate, to heal— to do these things at all costs. Mine and save to heal and heal to save and mine, ricochets the warden's call. Our industry deepens, our dungeon walls thicken. We continue falling forward, in regimental form, glittering with gold and heads bowed not to dictators but dictations. We parade through city streets, we barely acknowledge one another, our eyes locked in lockstep and stare above us, to the left, above the crowded masses, to the platform, at the chancellor. We have a war to win. We have things to do. We have a busy life to attend to.

So goes Earth's saving army.

In some general sense, there occupies a moral wistfulness, perhaps even, an intellectual onanism, in the busied and hurried groping of a doer, a miner, a savior of the world. An apprentice of the panoply of dust and shadow, we yearn for the bustling meanderings of public life: a place to prove ourselves, a place to deliver our dopamine hits, a place to show off our gilded, diamond rings.

Look, see!
I see.
This is a fine diamond.
Yes.
Look, see how it glitters!
I see. It glitters.

Earth Education

I am the second of four, rambunctious children. One of the un-intended virtues of our childhood was that it produced four very different people—one is a professor, one is a medical professional, one is a renowned portraiture artist, and I am a simple something. I spent the majority of my childhood either playing sports or playing in the mud.

We were raised in the last, rural remnant just south of Cleveland, Ohio. Thirty-acres of rolling forests and little meadows was our life's playground and play we did. While not agricultural, our family believed in time spent outdoors and time spent in the dirt. We were kicked out of the house every morning, ill clad and well loved, and would return only for lunch, a quick hug, or some dry and warm clothes.

We were homeschooled by my mother who well understood her own intellectual shortcomings. She was reared by a poverty deci-mated immigrant village in the heart of the dying city of Cleveland. She never went to college. She barely graduated from high school. Her mother, my dear grandmother, never learned to drive a car.

"*Zechciej dola*," my grandmother would say, lovingly harsh, when dinner was set. I have no idea what it meant, it was never translated for me, and the language of origin was always unknown—some com-bination of Polish, Lithuanian and Slovenian. But we understood it clearly enough: sit down, now, eat, now, and be quiet. *Dola* is the Slavic goddess of the home, maybe that had something to do with it.

My mother was, alongside our father, dedicated to giving us the world—a map to finding the keys to it at least. In place of lessons, she opened our eyes. In place of education, she opened our hearts. My mother believed, ultimately, that a love of learning and the self-knowledge of how one, in particular, learns best is the key to the world: the secret pathway for enlightenment in the true sense, the deepest, actual, living sense.

"To know the answer is never good," she would tell us as she walked with us under the maple grove. "We must be curious. We must ask questions. Then, we must be silent, patient, but irreverently demanding of a response."

"How will we know what to ask?" my brother inquired. He is two years older than me and decades smarter.

"The answer wants to be known," she responded. "Be patient and persistent, the question is never far off. You are a student of life, and not a student in life."

In teaching us to love learning and to know how *we,* in particular, learn best, our mother sidestepped the top-down, mechanistic educational approach of the modern tradition. The last math she taught me was Algebra I. I was fourteen. In its place, my mother showed us how to open Earth, gently. How to be with her, how to speak to her: to inquire, to walk, to look, and to see as she spoke, lovingly, back to us. I studied mathematics (and history and computer science) in college and graduated as the top student at the university in all three of my majors, *summa cum laude.* I guess I learned enough. I guess she was right—Earth is enough.

Our youth under her magic was balls of dirt hurled this way and that and hand-caught crawdads in buckets for lunch and long days by fires or by the pond behind our house, reading book after book, floating endlessly, lovingly, across worlds built by words. Our childhood was a lesson in the illimitable freedom of the human heart contained within the heart of the world around us, as us, in us. It was a world built and carried by magic and memory.

Look! she would say. *See!* she would call. *Eat!* it is time for lunch.

Earth Dancers

Years later, I am grown up and married to Morgan, and we are back with the herd under the cold grey sky. Lionel's blood is now frozen, like the grass. But the rest of the herd was not asleep. Their increasing interest in his death aroused us from our prayer, our hunter's meditation, our spirit infused tellback.

Field harvesting is the rebirth of the ancient in some, true sense. Its spectral return well animated the landscape around us. A white spirit infused the February mist with a strange passion and its energy drifted upwards and we felt exposed: naked. We were at the center of life and our hair stood straight as Earth cleft in front of us.

King Lear, another bull in the herd, uttered a deep earthen hum, as though from a lost land of dark moors that quiver and bubble from below, a prehistoric bawl, and the ethereal spirits that floated amongst us instantly landed as a grounded force. His bawl was their call. The spirits grew legs and walked. They grew arms and danced with them atop their heads, fingers twirling and palms spiraling as if they were fumbling with the heart of the world. They smiled and we smiled back.

"What do you see," Morgan asked through pursed lips, herself kneeling next to me, shaking.

The land felt simultaneously stable and unstable as it shook and quaked beneath us. Earth trembled. One hundred head of wild, horned bovines started kicking and running as they formed a singular unit around us, like ancient and horse-borne armies of old.

Their ceremony had begun. The spirits, now four legged and clad in thick leather and oily manes, surrounded us.

Moldy Blisters

I was often occupied by sports. Truth be told, I spent more time playing sports than I did doing schoolwork. There is something peculiar about extending the body athletically that, I think, echoes modern man back into an earlier state of our existence—when we ran for food and not for fun and when we were fit for defense and not for fashion.

My ardent passion for pushing my body athletically culminated in the seventh grade when I attended the Navy Seal Wrestling Camp in Annapolis, Maryland. We had to lie on my entrance application, as this was a high school camp and I was twelve. It was the hardest and most intense athletic summer camp in the country. When we arrived and before we were shown our bunks, a team of doctors immediately weighed us in and completed a physical. A Navy Seal then sat us down and said that the next fourteen days would be the hardest of our lives. Giving up was okay, just raise your hand at any time and they would escort you back to your mommy.

Van after van unloaded eager, expecting kids—some kissed and hugged their parents goodbye and some, it seemed, were thrown out of the car altogether.

"Remember, honey," my dad reminded me as I turned to walk away. "You are in high school. Do your best. That's it, that's all you can do."

They undersold it all. While nearly four hundred and fifty of the top high school athletes in the country were dropped off by their parents, only forty-seven were picked up fourteen days later. The others, the unlucky rest, either quit early, left unexplained, or ended up hospitalized. One of my roommates fractured their tibia on an obstacle course and another was forced to leave because his daily weight check-ins were too low—he had lost too much body mass in too short a period.

Our days began at five in the morning with one hundred pull ups and a one-mile bear crawl down to the shoreline where Seals were waiting to inflict even more athletic punishment on us. Then, we stumbled to breakfast, limping, bruised, and chafing. I remember one evening, as we were returning from a six-mile run from the Navy's football stadium where we ran up and down every single stair in the thirty-four thousand seat facility, one camper asked a guard at the Academy's gate to shoot him in the leg so he could go home.

"I'll shoot your fucking face off," the guard returned, holding up his weapon. We kept running, with new vigor.

I still have the t-shirt they gave to me upon the completion of the camp. It has a strange smell to it, like moldy blisters.

By my junior year in high school, I had wrestled on two national championship teams and led the state in football year after year. I was destined for the college of my choosing but my destiny was about to change.

The Shipwright

The herd's ceremony shattered Earth's perceived stability and they encircled us in a great stampede. Fear poured like flowing magma and Morgan tried to climb atop Lionel's now swelling corpse in order to gain high ground. The forgotten leaves of autumn formed tornadoes around us.

King Lear led the herd in three, complete rotations around the three of us and stopped as abruptly as his prehistoric bawl began. The herd stopped behind him. In less time than it would take for the dust to settle, a small bull calf, unleavened by age, left the amassed herd and entered the ground between us. A messenger, a spirit-walker, a dream-teller. He passed into the middle ground, that which stands between this and the other world, between life and death, and looked right at us and we could not help but look at him. Nothing moved, no one bounced.

He looked right through us. He uttered a gentle but thick note, a simple bawl, and then receded back into the herd. Like exhaled breath, the swelling weight receded and the leaf-gilded tornadoes returned to their forgotten resting places and our hearts became heavy as their pulse became normal.

"What did he say?" Morgan whispered aloud. She was crying.

What did he have to say? I thought.

Life was moving and death was moving with it. But that is the funny thing about life: it moves regardless of if we would like it to or not and sometimes its movement is more like a quake than a quickstep.

Death and its life are like ships whose sails cannot be furled and Earth is a wonderful shipwright.

This, All, Will Soon Pass

The first day of August is etched into my memory, like a name in the bow of my life's ship.

During the warmup lap around the athletic field for the first football practice of my last year in high-school, I fell and I have never *really* gotten up. I did not trip or stumble. I exploded. A genetic timebomb that hitherto ticked silently detonated loudly, instantly. Its final tick, my final healthy moment, that August afternoon.

I lived in Columbus, Ohio in the upstairs, spare room of the athletic director's home. The school systems around northeast Ohio, where we grew up, did not allow homeschooled students to play sports and so my parents allowed me to move to Columbus, two hours south, to live with strangers, and play on their football team. It was an independent team that played top-tiered schools and attracted players from across the greater area.

But, under that August sun, as I laid helplessly, writhing in pain, life changed, forever.

"Here. Take my hand," offered Luke, The Ohio State Athletic Trainer. "Let's take a look."

I was diagnosed in the field with a severe hip strain.

"A pulled muscle, really," claimed an orthopedic doctor at Ohio State. "You just need some rest, a good stretching. Ice. Don't forget to ice."

By November, however, it was only worse. By December, I could barely walk. By the end of January, I had undergone numerous procedures and substantial surgeries and was bedridden until late April, at which point I underwent two more surgeries and lived, fully in bed, until late August. Over the next six years, I collected over three hundred doctor appointments, traveled across the country multiple times (visiting various experts), underwent a multitude of extensive surgeries, lost the ability to walk, learned how to walk again, and weighed less than I did in the sixth grade.

My body undulated under the torrential weight of insecurity and its pains. Lost in a whirlpool, it spun and rotated within periods of intense, unexplained weight loss and intense, unexplained weight gain—I would lose eighty pounds in the span of a month and then spend the next trying to gain it back. I was nestled in a cyclic and painful exchange between life and death and I was going nowhere.

I lost the ability to eat most foods and, still today, I can only eat twenty-one "things"—such as, Celtic sea salt, russet potatoes, horseradish, and beef. Still today, twelve years later at this writing, I have not consumed any food, water, or washed my body with any ingredients not from this short list and not from our own home's kitchen. Not once. No restaurants. No holiday meals. My wife and I have never dined together, breaking the same bread, or bread at all. Still today, some days are too much and I find myself inside, unable to do much more than look at the wall or read a book.

"What do you remember?" my mother asked as I sat under the maple grove in the backyard of our childhood home.

A fire crackled in the patio's chiminea. It was spring. The fresh grass was quilted with buckskin jackets of pearls on wings and I was reading a book that was given to me by a dear friend. It was on agriculture, namely a version of agriculture that was presented as good for both the climate and for its humanity. It was titled, *Folks, This Ain't Normal* and I remember thinking, *Yes, I am not normal.*

"Daniel," she said, this time getting my attention.

I set the book down and looked up. I weighed one hundred and thirty pounds, struggled to move, had blisters all over my body that bled profusely when I walked or moved too quickly. I was depressed and I lived under its dark and forever darkening shadow.

"She held my hand," I half answered, half mumbled. My eyes drifted in the empty space between us and I flushed when the feeling of surgery gloves and the smell of latex and powder drifted over me once again.

Memory returned, filling slowly.

I had recently undergone an exploratory procedure where, upon laying unanesthetized on an operating table, a team of doctors probed my body with large, long needles that injected peculiar dyes and, while inserted, other doctors (or nurses perhaps) rotated and moved my limbs around to pinch the needles and their dyes in peculiar ways all in order to determine something that I now entirely forget the reason for. The pain, however, is yet unforgettable.

"Mom, it hurt so bad." At once feeling like a child, embarrassed that I said anything at all.

"I know. I know," she returned, walking closer to me. Closing the space between us.

The vernix white lights and the vernix white garb of the doctors conjoined in my memory with the pain and the blue surgery gloves. I remembered everything and the memories flowed from every direction.

"She held my hand and her eyes glowed blue and she looked at me, into me." My eyes now entirely closed, their lids exposed to the gentle wind and the heat of the fire. "She held my hand and we just looked at each other."

"I understand, honey," my mother's face contorted between joy and pain. A single tear trickled down from her eyes and splashed horizontally when it collided with the smile that was growing laterally across her face. Her magic was at work.

"She told me, 'this, all, will soon pass,'" I admitted hesitantly, as though revealing this truth exposed me, left me naked, open. The words flowed like water over rocks, sure, steady, but jagged as they danced a foxtrot: slow, slow, quick, quick, slow.

This, all, will soon pass echoed from tree to tree, from birdsong to birdsong, in the wind and through the wind and because of the wind. The fire itself flickered under its weight, or was it the wind?

"Honey," she closed the space between us even more. "We have tried everything, you do know that, right?"

This, all, will soon pass again echoing. The birdsongs increasing.

I did know. Since that August day, we had tried everything. We were laughed out of doctor offices and cried within others. From surgeries to procedures to months in hospitals all over the country to western and eastern medicine alike, we had tried everything. Or so I had thought.

"This whole time," she thought aloud, herself now staring into the compressed space between us, "I think, we have searched for help." The fire crackled. "We have begged and pleaded." Again, the wind. "We have done everything." Then silence.

My fingers fumbled over the book's cover. I was sweating. T – H – I – S, my fingers traced. *Ain't Normal.*

"But our search has been passive," she continued, interrupting my thoughts, my finger's mindless work. Her words echoed rudely. The birdsongs stopped. The wind hushed as Earth herself held her breath. Inhale, hold, stabbing emptiness, no release.

"Passive?" I questioned, my heart dropping and my words enflaming with anger. What is passive about years of serious surgeries and years spent learning to walk again? What is passive about laying in hospitals with doctors touching your quadricep muscle and asking for you to flex it and you simply cannot, no matter how hard you try? What is passive about losing dozens of college scholarships, your future, in a single instant, as a fragile child? What is passive about weighing a meager one hundred and thirty pounds when, only a handful of years prior, you played at a healthy two hundred and forty? What is passive about bodies covered by bleeding sores? What is passive about withering away, a winnowed wheat or its litter, the chaff? What is passive?

"Yes, honey. What if we forget about all that," she hesitated as if her mind was unsure how her mouth would follow. Her words hung in the leaf-lit wind.

Become

The herd retreated, silently. Stillness fell and the spirits that only moments ago had danced around us left as they came. Earth cleft and like a bathtub drained, gurgling diphonic songs as it swallowed everything, everyone.

The dawn sung over our shoulders, setting fire to our knife blades. And I looked at Morgan with the same smirk and tear that my mother had looked at me with all those many years ago on the fire-warmed patio and happiness and its health descended, like gentle, spring rain.

Lionel, meaning Little Lion, the gift of the field, harvested under the winter's mist. We worked all morning and we talked and cried, remembering his life, remembering our own. We dreamed together and anticipated his rebirth, our nourishment, when his memory would flow through our veins, becoming our body.

Health is the muddied middle ground between death and life, like the unleavened bull calf, but it is also the union of activity under the waning morning mist and the ceremony, the lantern festival, the sacred: above, underneath, pulsing through all of it, through all of us.

"What if we forget passivity and become active participants in life itself?" my mother's voice echoed in me, a memory. My hands covered in life. My heart wrapped around her voice.

"This feels normal," I felt myself saying aloud. "This is normal."

Morgan and I steadily worked and the dawn gave way to the day. Silence beat down upon the misty meadow and its valley below us. Lionel's blood sweating the soil into rust.

Creativity or Capacity?

The world is a step-motion study in endless change. Today, we live in the aftershock of the greatest climate crisis in history. It began when one organism, for no apparent reason, jumped its limits and produced a poisonous gas that slowly found its way into the atmosphere.[6] It was an unwanted by-product of their culture's industry, a waste of its social evolution.

Steadily accumulating behind the undetectable, heavenly veil, this fatal gas silently worked and changed the climate. Systems of culture developed around it and a certain species grew to dominate the processes of Earth, like a child with clay.[7] While epochs are often classified geologically—such as the Pliocene and Pleistocene being the two, most recent rock layers and also the two, most recent epochs in our history—there were discussions of calling this new, climate unsettling time as something reminiscent of its social change: *-pocene,* or something like that.

The climate emergency wrought by this one organism would soon suffocate nearly ninety percent of life on Earth. It would soon force one of the greatest mass extinction events in planetary history—larger than the one that ended the dinosaurs, more wide-reaching than the last Ice Age and the ensuring silence of the megafauna. It would soon overcome and redefine life itself. It would soon elevate one species to dominate beyond degree. Life, it was argued, would never be the same.

This was two billion years ago, and we are still thankful for cyanobacteria and its oxygen.

We are the awakened creativity of climate change. Mammals, more than any other of our clay constructed cousins, exist at the primordial threshold where light and darkness, life and death canonize and cauterize. Over one hundred trillion bacterial bodies live inside our digestive tracts and their infinite cultures regulate the soil, the climate, and life as we know it.[8] In this way, we are the climate and the climate is us. To live is to witness the circular nature of this journey and to live is to give cyanobacteria our thanks.

Life is change—planetary epochs to species evolution to the particular microprocesses in their particular microenvironments—and this ceaseless change which looks a good deal like ceaseless silence steadily works to eradicate stability. In place of momentary misery rises, ultimately, stable realities that, gradually, in time and of course, recede into extinction. Bacteria produced oxygen and killed off planetary stability. Life then threw off its anerobic covering like a suffocating soldier of the Great War threw off their torrid gas mask and aerobic life became our stable reality.

Time and epochs of rocks and reptiles and their dinosaurs and now mammals passed steadily on. Today, the climate once again summons great change and invites one species to throw off not its gas mask but its gas bomb and we look to bacteria, well experienced in atmospheric change, for help, for guidance.

But our step-motion study in change has transformed, today, into a study of expansion, of increscent capacity. The climate is changing, species are restricting, but it is our human capacity that needs questioned.

What does it mean to become?

"What do you remember?" my mother asks, her Slavic magic yet alive in the world.

We must go to the beginning, yes—deep inside the clay. What if it is our moment not to reawaken the soil or to increase biodiversity but to remember our relationship with the soil, as the soil and as the biodiversity? What if the ladder of our progress, with rungs kicked out below us, is not a ladder at all? What if our climbing, that is, what if our progress, was only in our minds? What if we could return to the Pleistocene because we never left?

Life begins in memory. Life lives in memory. What if memory, in these turbulent times, is what we need the most?

What Food Feels

She was right. We had spent many years passively searching for help, like a blind man in an unfamiliar place. We had met many kind people along the way, who ushered us from here to there and some, even, that helped us to where they thought we should go: across the street and closer to home. But we never made it home. Our eyes were closed.

"What if we become?" my mother inquired.

"Become what?" I replied inflexibly, immediately.

"Them." Her voice was flat and simple. The words flowed as commonly from her lips as though she had said anything else, like the weather or the day. But the four letters galloped like a small band of wild horses across her outstretched arm that pointed to the newly awakened squirrels that danced and played in the meadow. They bounced, now juggling her words, under the spring lit and waving translucence of maple leaves. They jumped from bough to bough, sometimes to a shagbark hickory and skied down its ashen moguls, darting and flipping and hotdogging this way and that with a flip of their hips.

"They seem happy—" She said.

I was silent. My eyes and my mind had left with the horses and were now playing with the squirrels. There was nothing for me to say.

"—what if we buy some chickens?"

"Chickens?" Reality snapped back on me in two directions, like a rubber band stretched too far and tore in the middle.

That night, we bought some chickens. It was a moment of change, of emerging into the unknown, the tentative light of the new day that strides patiently, slowly, in and then is there, fully, as though her gloried and glittering yellows and blues had been there for eternity. The new colors of dawn, a new hope, rushing in like mountain water over rocks. We gave up. We let go. We threw off our search for health and decided to become it—health, that is.

We immediately amended my lifestyle and dietary choices. I began consuming raw, whole, and real foods. I began to acquire local foods and found them to be fresher, tastier, and to contain higher level of nutrients than their conventional counterparts—energy as we understood it then. Food, that substance I had known all my life but had never much cared to be friends with, transformed into the very substance of my life.

"These are living yet," one farmer at the market said to me as he handed over a bag of asparagus. "I picked them this morning. Watch out or they'll bite ya."

Bite me they did. I became awakened to the idea that, while real food is good, local food is better, and, while local food is better, participating in the story of your food is best. That is to say: let your foods bite ya.

My health saga, to my great surprise, emerged ultimately as a romance. As I fell in love with food and then with local food, I also fell in love with the local families producing that food; as I fell in love with our local community, I ultimately fell in love with the lives that echo and sustain that community: the cows and the sparrows, the sheep and the deer, the squirrels, and the humans. We became farmers.

Health steadily returned, like the seasons and like the dawn. Slowly, gently, but always surely. We planted a large market garden atop my mother's old home garden and raised pastured chickens in mobile shelters in the front yard. We were slow at first, keeping in mind the pace my body would allow. The meadows that once nourished the tellbacks of my childhood now grew in me, like memory, as we worked and harvested gifts from the soil, incorporating the life of our place into the life of our soul's clay form. We became her earthlings. The People became The Land through the act of becoming and health, like the cottonwood's spring snow of seeds, returned. Its fluttering wisps and flurries, its pyramid leaves emerging from the land of the dead, its roots holding the riverbank and sinking into the river herself: the healing depths of sacred wells.

Early in this journey, Morgan and I realized that, while food matters and what your food eats matters (grass-fed beef as opposed to grain-fed beef, for instance), this is not the full story.[iii] In fact, understanding this extended nuance is to understand the full complexity of this book. Everything else is just details.

One evening, around the dining table, Morgan looked at me and asked, "Who is this?"

"Gerty," I replied casually and offhandedly. I had never thought about it in that way and I was focused on the meal. Gertrude was a chicken in our flock that always seemed like she could have stayed another couple of days in the egg. But she hatched early and she was a mess: feathers always askew and missing, feet always running about, and a head that seemed always too small for her increasingly featherless body. When we would come near, she would run for the woods. When we left, she would stay there, alone. It was her squawks in the morning that awoke the farm, the roosters never had a chance.

That night, after nearly a year of positive improvement, I became very ill. Old pains and sores erupted and a familiar, deep sting flooded around me. It consumed me, my life, and everything echoed and drowned in the sharp rocks and rapids that I thought were upriver, behind me. My health plummeted. I became once again bedridden and my mind spiraled into a deep depression. In the coming months I would once again be hospitalized, suffer a thirty-day bout of constipation, lose the ability to walk, misplace another fifty pounds, and I would spend the next twelve months doing nothing but getting back on my feet. Another year lost.

---

iii Many books have been written on this complex relationship. While what you eat matters, what your food eats matters most, people argue. David R. Montgomery and Anne Biklé's latest book, *What Your Food Ate* covers this topic in infinite depth.

What changed? What happened?

"What if all of this is deeper?" Morgan asked one early autumn evening as we sat on the porch and watched the sun set. We rocked back and forth, a blanket over my lap, on matte green rocking chairs that would *crackle* and *crat* as they went. It drove her crazy. But we both were going crazy and we both felt that having something to be crazy about helped, at least a small bit, and so we loved those rocking chairs and sat on them often.

"Deeper?" My eyes were still set on the setting sun.

"Yes. What if all of this, you, I mean, is deeper than simply a change in diet, in lifestyle?" She blushed under the lost simplicity of a statement that felt to run away from her the moment her heart gave it away.

I was silent. I pulled the blanket higher on my lap.

The golden Easter of eventide, of the day's ashes, fell behind the trees who were themselves falling, slowly, into winter. The sun's claret reds mixed with the dahlia's orange hearted yellows and all fell together behind a hued homily of once subtle greens and snowy-whites into a raven black night, like the lined back of a sable. Darkness covered our eyes but we kept them open, staring, the *crackle* and *crat* of our chairs were the only noise. Cautiously, my mind peered out over the edge of the porch and snaked its way into the void. For a moment, I was afraid, slightly, but it was an intelligent fear, I told myself, written in my genetics and constructed for my survival—the dark has always threatened: run, fight, RUN!

We sat in this silence and we sat in the darkness. I felt the world's leaving ebb through me, my blood-red veins the cool waves and my life's hope a pebble tumbling into the water. I remembered only pain. RUN!

After a while, Morgan broke the silence. "I read a paper recently that said that a hug releases as much oxytocin as a whole meal of food."[9]

"Oxy-what?" I replied, feeling even worse.

"Oxytocin: it can regulate stress and reduce cortisol, help blood flow and overall healing, and can even have an anxiolytic-like effect: fighting depression and anxiety and," she paused to play the words in her hands, to find them in front of her, "sincere and soft human touch can give you more of it—Oxytocin—than a whole meal full of food." She paused again, finding the words. "They called it a 'hypothalamic nonapeptide.'"

I returned a blunt silence punctuated with a mumbled "thanks." I was thankful—thankful for the darkness that hid my face. *Hypowhat?* I thought.

"No, I mean. Listen!" she gathered herself, sensing that she was losing me. "Harmful chemicals are inheritable in foods, right?"

"Yes, that is why we only buy and produce clean food."

"You mean: chemical-free food?"

"Yes."

"Good—well Oxytocin is a chemical. What I am asking is: what if all chemicals in foods are inheritable?"

I was silent. I was not following.

"Daniel." Morgan said and then paused. It was the kind of pause that often inhabits the moment before discovery and the type of pause required to allow the moment to rise, like bread. "Daniel," she said gathered and sure, her hands now firmly resting on her lap, "What if you just *feel* everything that everyone else doesn't?"

Thunder mumbled in the distance and its thick clouds hid the stars from our view. Something scratched in the tree to our left, maybe a squirrel. A gaggle of geese wheeled around us like a pyre gyring for its flame and their wake raked the bare trees as they descended, together in a V, into the lake just beyond the tree line, for safety, for a night's rest. A splash and then many splashes and their silent ripples became audible truths as they lapped against the shore. The descending blackness, the day's heat rising from its rocks, a postern into the next life.

"Feel?" I questioned, totally missing Morgan's crescendo.

She leaned back in the darkness. A *crackle* and *crat* skidded across the porch. "What if the *feeling* of foods—what your food *feels*—matters more than the food itself, or even what your food eats when it is alive—organic, or whatever?"

Again, thunder in the distance and a scratch to our left. *That is definitively a squirrel,* I thought. *She found a fine larder for her winter foods—the loving crook of the mother tree.*

"Daniel! What if Gerty's stress manifested inside of you when you ate her? I mean, think about it. She was a hotmess her whole life, totally ostracized from the flock—" she said now waving her hands violently, "—She was never a very peaceful chicken. And now you're eating her cortisol!"

A westerly and cool breeze lifted the silent, leafless limbs. Then, nothing. Silence. My heart was crashing. Its thud was dwindling. The depression of illness and its resurgence was too much. My core, cold and grey, no longer pounded against its cage of bones.

"What if it isn't what you eat or even what your food eats? As much as what your food feels?" She paused, "What if the memory of food matters?"

An interspecies tellback: the hearth's fire, the community's table, a life in remembrance. We were waking up.

Interlinkages

My friend, Rosamund Young of Kite's Nest Farm in the Cotswolds and author of the best-seller, *The Secret Life of Cows,* believes in the community of animals. This all—farming, agriculture, husbandry, production of foodstuffs, and more—goes beyond our current concepts of nutrition. "Every animal," she writes, "needs congenial company of its own species." They need a language, wholly their own. They need families. They need memory to be and to exist in any true sense.[10] Young has long asserted and has long put into practice on her family's farm that the health of animals, including us humans, is inexorably linked to the congeniality of their lives.

This is easy to see in animals that have been well fed but yet mistreated. Modern humans are the only species that separate the landscape from our nourishment. While the landscape produces our food, the land itself is not our food in the same way that while big corporations produce the aspects of our life that we call "modern"—this laptop, that light bulb—big corporations are themselves not welcome in our homes. We need food but keep nature and its landscape out there, beyond that fence, outside this clean, plastic package. We separate what is produced from who is producing it—this is globalism, this is the industrial complex, the shield between us and the reality that keeps us smiling when we should be doing something else entirely.[iv]

This is not the case for every other of our two and four legged

iv While not a subject in the purview of this book, Dougald Hine's *At Work In The Ruins* and Vanessa Machado de Oliveira's *Hospicing Modernity* are fine first steps in understanding this delirium. Ronald Wright's *A Short History of Progress* and John Ralston Saul's *Voltaire's Bastards* are also fine books.

cousins that walk and crawl and flutter amongst us. The land does not produce the herbivore's vegetation. It is the vegetation. It does not seem to me that they separate the grass from its dirty roots. The air is not where birds take flight. The air is their flight. They do not separate that which gives them power from their powers. If Earth were to grow an arm and slap a cow every time she went to take a bite of grass, the cow would develop a distrust of the grass, not just Earth. They are one.

It is in this way that Young's congeniality extends beyond simple friendship or amicability but dives deep into the complex well of life. Health is the interconnection and balance of all things—our friendships, our feelings, our landscape flowing through our veins and digestive systems, for instance. Disease is disconnection and its ailments are separation.

Interconnection and Kinship

In 1983, in the *International Journal for the Study of Animal Problems*, Dr. Elizabeth DeViney and colleagues discovered the universality of abuse—the polar counterpart of congeniality and, in part, the result of this separation. Surveying fifty-three families where physical child abuse had occurred, they found that eighty-eight percent of these households extended that same abuse to their animals.[11] A few years later, the *Journal of Emotional Abuse* reported that seventy-one percent of abused women who sought shelter confirmed that their abuser—most often their partner—also abused or killed their companion animals or pets.[12] Since then, a multitude of studies have supported these findings.[13] Abuse extends beyond species boundaries. If this is true, then congeniality ought to extend in the same manner. Health is not simply the grass or the soil and it is not just about how we treat our human and non-human cousins, but the balanced universality, interconnection, and kinship between all life that seems to matter most.

Social change is ecological change. Ecological problems have social answers. Modern ailments have ancient sources. And so on. To remit well, we must remit all. To heal truly, we must step beyond our segmented understanding and limited perspectives of what truly affects our health. Then, we need to question: what are we? What comprises the "our" in "our health?"

A Chemical Legacy

What if the stress in and of our environment was inheritable? We are a people yearning for health and regenerative, sustainable, or organic agriculture as a modern movement attempting a better way of producing foodstuffs is a possible, although partial solution. But what if the disconnection in the landscape, the lack of congeniality, flows through biological communication pathways into our own bodies? What if being good to the land and bad to its animals produces net negative results in the land, its animals, and its people?

Is a lack of congeniality and its resulting stress edible? If it is, then is it also inheritable?

Yes, in the last decade, Certified Organic farms have increased across the United States by over ninety percent and nearly half of American consumers now purchase Certified Organic products monthly, a seven-fold increase over the same decade.[14] Yes, nearly forty percent of the global food-chain by 2030 is promised, by organizational powerhouses such as Cargill, Bayer, and Nestle, to be sourced from "regenerative" agricultural systems—systems that rely less on chemicals and Earth destroying products. The world, to some small, local degree, is starting to rebel against the industrial machine and its addiction to production. Maybe.

But what if we are missing the point entirely? What if, in focusing on certain chemicals such as the pesticide Glyphosate, or Roundup® as it is known in the marketplace, we have allowed our linear and productionistic system's forgotten and forlorn posterns to be overrun, absorbing and accumulating other equally harmful chemicals inside the city walls? What if, by focusing only on the observable enemy at the gate, we have missed, so entirely, the fact that our own people rebel against us? Do not get me wrong: Glyphosate is a monstrosity of industrial engineering, but we also live in a world with increasing depression, suicide, and alcohol abuse, the fourth leading cause of death in the United States.[15] Over four million people die every year from diabetes, nearly half of which are under sixty years old.[16] That is nearly four times as many as the total sum of casualties in the American Civil War or equal to the yearly casualty volume of the Allied Powers in the Second World War. And it happens every year, year over year. We are the lost generation.

Between 2018 and 2019, well before the COVID-19 Pandemic walked its way into our communities, nearly forty percent of adolescents—children between the ages of ten and nineteen—indicated feeling hopeless, fifteen percent experienced more than one case of clinical depression, twenty percent considered suicide and ten percent attempted suicide, thirty percent of the latter requiring serious medical treatment following their attempts.[17] *The American Foundation for Suicide Prevention* report around two million attempted suicides per year, with nearly one hundred and fifty successful attempts every day. It is hard to write this, let alone for you, I hope, to read this, without a serious bit of depression welling up, like a jagged stone in the throat.

It is time we begin to consider the deeper things. While this means many things to many people—such as religion, spirituality, the role of family or tribe, the reincarnation of ancestors in our mythologies—for us, here, it means considering the possibility that memory extends beyond death, that memories are inheritable, like nutrients and minerals.

When we consume sad cows, for instance, do we inherit their sadness? When we consume diabetic cows, are we increasingly susceptible to diabetes ourselves? Could this be why, in part, diabetes is rising so quickly today?

In my conversation hosted by the Savory Institute in 2021 with Dan Kittredge, the founder and executive director of the Biological Food Association, a Massachusetts based non-profit leading the largest, international Nutrient Dense Beef Study yet conducted, Dan questioned: "Why would you want to ingest the flesh of an animal that has inflammatory markers, the biochemical benchmarks of stress hormones, through the roof?" Pausing and leaning back in his chair, he exclaimed, "You are going to be building your body out of that? It's transferable!"

In other words: life's biochemical and emotional health, not just the soil it is grown in or the landscape it calls home, matters, deeply.

Dan and other scientists are concluding that marbling in beef, that which the modern consumer yearns for and beef breeds over the last century or more have been bred for—easy marbling on grass—is really just deep, systemic disease wreaking havoc through the animal's body that will soon terminate that animal's life. It is early stage cardiovascular disease and we see it as healthy. No wonder we are so sick.

Dozens of books occupy the shelves of the conscious agrarian that speak to practices and paradigms surrounding animal husbandry, selective breeding for heat tolerance or grass-based genetics, how to grow more grass or more soil, agroforestry or food forest establishment and maintenance techniques, and so on. There are equally monumental mountains of books that speak to the nutrients in our soils and foods, drawing connections between Earth, her eroding womb, and our desertifying bodies.[v]

But what about memory? What about this biochemical transference? What about the transformation of an organism's lived experiences—from stress to sadness—into a chemical legacy writ in the bloody grit of cells that we inherit when we partake in a meal? Does the memory of food *actually* matter?

Biological Inheritance

To understand the nature of biological inheritance, we must first understand the nature of biology.

The study of stress in animals is difficult to achieve with any measurable accuracy. The balance of their well-being centers on environmental, internal, and physical association. As we will see later in this book, an animal's psyche swims in a great ocean of equipoise—a symmetry of balance that is internal (homeostasis) as well as external (allostasis) and is created and maintained through enduring adaptation with the forces around it. When the wind blows and the

---

v I provide an expansive *Recommended Reading*s appendix at the end of the book with recommendations on titles that we have found helpful over the years.

waves rise, equipoise must react. She is observant and her sustained observance is her swimmer's lifeline.

Stress swims in this ocean as well—it is one of equipoise's favorite tools. Stress is an associative feedback loop that helps the swimmers cope and adapt, exist and survive in the waving world around them. But the moment a team of white-garbed gods appear in the heavens and drop from the clouds, riding the wind earthward on needles and syringes, everything changes. Stress transforms from a swimmer's natural lifeline to the overwhelming energy of the waves themselves and life pours over, purling, curling, and crashing. Invariably, any baseline of stress through a system that causes more stress, like a scientist in a farmer's field, cannot be a system that produces accurate results. Of course, cows are stressed in head gates and corrals and when they are poked with pointy needles. Wouldn't you be?

To understand the nature of stress in animals, it is helpful to look to the nature of their death. Death has the potential of great stress but it also delivers the great complexities of living systems over to minor scientific observation.

The Nature of Death

In a 2005 study, a team of French neurogeneticists examined how premortal physiological characteristics—stress, for instance—influences the postmortem muscle metabolism and structure in slaughtered animals. How does stress affect meat quality? They considered the correlation between stress and health and whether stress lives on after death. They measured the stress hormones cortisol and catecholamines[vi] before and after slaughter in a group of pigs and found that stress and carcass quality were inversely related: the stress placed over the pigs previous to slaughter increased carcass fat and decreased meat quality. As cortisol and adrenaline increased, meat quality decreased.

They showed that "adrenal hormones favor the accretion of fat at the expense of muscle proteins." Some animals in their study

vi Chemicals such as dopamine, norepinephrine and epinephrine.

underwent severe weight loss and others died.[18] In other words, the stress incurred around lairage (the holding period before slaughter) and slaughter completely changed the composition of and health contained within the animal's body—from its fat composition to its muscle quality to its overall pH, a metric relating to both nutrient delivery and flavor.[19] Keep this in mind—we will come back to pH later.

Another study with similar characteristics but on beef cattle revealed that, of the 448 cattle studied, nearly seventy percent demonstrated severe postmortem cases of hyperglycemia, or high blood glucose. The carcasses measured 6.91 Millimoles Per Liter (mmol/L) on average. It is important to consider that, at 7 mmol/L, diabetes is officially diagnosed. While the group of cattle were considered healthy entering the slaughterhouse, their carcasses came out on the threshold of diabetes. What happened? Like a mathematical function or a diabolical magical spell, the stress around slaughter impaired their insulin production and imbued their postmortem bodies with disease.[20] Stress, it seems, lives on in death—as disease.

But is there nuance in the method of slaughter? In 2002, a team of Italian veterinarians compared three different slaughter techniques on the moderation of stress hormones and muscle glycogen.[21] Glycogen is a form of carbohydrate that mammals store in their muscles. During intense physical activity or prolonged stress, these particles break down, become free glucose molecules, and oxidize, producing adenosine triphosphate (ATP), or energy. This allows the muscles to contract. But this process has its limits—within a few hours, depending on the animal in question—carbohydrate consumption is required to match (or resynthesize) rates of ATP hydrolysis (chemical breakdown).[22] Therein lies the problem. Prolonged, acute stress produces hormones that stimulate glycogen mobilization. This then leads to depleted glycogen levels which, around slaughter, is one of the most essential and critical factors affecting meat quality, as we have seen. Low glycogen reserves at slaughter, produced by high amounts of stress, results in high pH values, leading to serious problems in meat quality and decreased shelf-life.[23] High pH also negatively affects the meat's vulnerability to bacteria and slime formation.[24] The higher a meat's pH the less healthy and the more susceptible it is to bacteria. Stress affects meat quality.

Studying a group of Charolais cattle, the Italian team worked to compare the modern captive bolt technique exhibited by the European Union's Food and Agriculture Council to Kosher and Halal religious rites. Unexpectedly, they found only minor correlations between slaughter type and glycogen related pH levels. That is, the measurable stress of slaughter was nearly uniform in all of the animals across the different slaughter techniques and rites. The only important difference was the time it took for the carcasses to reach their ultimate pH level—between 6 to 24 hours. The modern carcasses dropped nearly two percent of their pH during this period, while both the Kosher and Halal carcasses only dropped one and a half percent, showing that the modern technique reduced its overall pH faster than the other methods. This, the authors concluded, was not noteworthy, although it was the only clear difference.

Ultimately, the modern slaughter technique resulted in an ultimate pH of 5.75, whereas the Halal and Kosher resided closer to 6. A small difference. Any pH measuring around 6 has been proven to correlate to increased bacterial decay and decreased overall meat quality, including shelf-life, color (dark-cutting), flavor, and taste.[25]

And so, if it is not the slaughter technique that impacts cortisol or glycogen levels—acute stress producing near diabetes and more in the carcasses—then could it be the way the animals are raised?

Another study, conducted one year later by a separate research team considered the stress hormones present before and after slaughter between two different groups of pigs: one, raised indoors and the other, raised outdoors. They expected to find that the animals raised outdoors would be more resilient against their climate's changing factors and, perhaps, would be able to moderate their stress and its reactions within their bodies. They also speculated that the study could very well produce the opposite result—the outdoor reared pigs may experience heightened stress when brought indoors, whereas the indoor pigs may not well notice the difference at all.

Their findings diverged from both of their projected hypotheses. Instead of discovering that animal husbandry practices matter, the team discovered no measurable divergence between the production systems and the stress reactions and premortal cortisol production in either group. The trauma around lairage and slaughter leveled the different production systems' effects on meat quality, flavor, odor, and more. The pigs raised outside exhibited, for example, nearly identical levels of the adrenocorticotropic hormone (ACTH), a chemical that regulates cortisol and androgen production and, when under sustained stress (lairage and slaughter is a fine example), leads to Addison's disease: which causes depression, severe fatigue, lack of energy, and more.[26]

From pigs to cows, from this slaughter technique to that, from conventional to more sustainable and holistic husbandry, the stress inherent in accepted approaches to slaughter is a leveling force.

It is important to note that not all organisms are the same in their response to stress. Another study of African catfish (*Clarias gariepinus*) found that the density of their raising conditions in the days prior to slaughter did in fact impact their ability to manage the stress of slaughter. The higher the number of catfish raised together produced higher levels of cortisol and glycogen in the postmortem carcasses. In this case, husbandry *did* matter. But African catfish are wild, solitary bottom dwellers and so any concentration of them, let alone in a farmed environment, would skew the results immensely. Any findings, regardless of other variables, would be invariably unnatural.[27]

This is not to say that raising pigs outside is a negative thing, neither is it to say that you should raise pigs (or catfish for that matter) indoors. These reflections also do not say if different slaughter techniques are better than others in some larger, truer, perhaps spiritual sense. These studies have nothing to say. Rather, these considerations in all their forms and across nearly twenty years of research and multiple nationalities suggest what our ancestors and the modern wisdom holders already well know: life is memory and memory lives after death. It is infinitely more complex than the house you live in or the space you have to roam or the foods that you have the blessing to eat. Life and its memory must be holistic and its health resides within the infinitely complex web of a sacred life and a sacred death.

Wildness Revisited

If it is not slaughter or husbandry that matters, then what about hunting? While hunting wild game is both a spiritual and ancestral tradition (and deserves unequivocally to remain, purely, as such), it should not here pass our observational purview. Analyzing the stress hormones resulting from hunting provides an intimate reality check upon which our story so depends.

In a recent study of red deer (*Cervus elaphus*), roe deer (*Capreolus capreolus*), and wild boar (*Sus scrofa*) within the Dinarides region—the Dinaric Alps—of Croatia, a joint, international team studied the connection between hunting and stress. In particular, their team surveyed two, key metrics. The first questioned the differences between *selective hunts*, wherein hunters silently stalked the game in their natural, free environment, and *driven hunts*, wherein hunters drove game into kill zones with either dogs or hunting parties. Secondly, they studied the scope of time between shot and ultimate death. They then analyzed the impact of these converging metrics on meat quality.

The Dinarides region has one of the greatest concentrations of large predators in the whole of Europe—grey wolf (*Canis lupus*), European lynx (*Lynx lynx*), and brown bear (*Ursus arctos*), to name a few. The prey animals of this region (the studied deer and wild boar) would be habituated to a life under predator pressure. The long relationship between predators and prey was, in some general sense, their study's control. While these animals freely lived with predation stress, their domestic counterparts in the other studies I have previously mentioned were subject to lairage and slaughterhouse stress.[28] Through this comparison and in view of both the hunting type (selective or driven) and the time between shot and death, the team could conclude the nature of stress in the wild—or more-wild systems.[29]

But what they discovered may surprise you. Examining the final pH in the *Musculus biceps femoris* muscle—that is, the glycogen present just prior to death which results from both physical and psychological stress—the team observed that hunting type and not time or any other factor determined the levels of postmortem stress.

That is, the stress of the hunt mattered more to the overall glycogen and pH value than did the time in which it took for death to occur or the gender or the species of animal. Stress corresponded to hunting type only. It was not the slaughter technique or even the management that mattered. It did not matter where the bullet struck. Rather, the nature and degree of an animal's unhindered wildness[vii] up until the point of the shot is the only delineation between low and high stress and corresponding adrenal processing.

Even more, the team confirmed this thesis through a comparison of the selectively hunted red and roe deer and slaughterhouse dispatched farmed deer of the same species. They determined the cortisol (low average plasma cortisol) at three times less in the selectively harvested wild group than their farmed counterparts.[viii] They found the average pH of the wild group to be lower than the farmed and, even lower than the Italian team that we saw earlier, who studied the group of Charolais cattle under modern, kosher, and halal slaughter techniques.[ix] In every case, the degree of wildness was inversely akin to the degree of stress.

This changes everything. The more wildness, the less stress. The data contends that it is not the particular slaughter technique, animal species, or method of husbandry that matters most when considering stress in meat—but the degree of wildness defined as the level of autonomous acceptance of the basic conditions as they are through an animal's life but especially in their death. Wildness in this way is presentness. It is the ability to be and live in the present. And it is the present locked away, safely, for those who can autonomously act as they need.

This could also be understood through the lens of experience and expectations. As we saw in the study of pigs earlier in this chapter, expectations play little on an animal's ability to regulate stress during slaughter. Pigs raised indoors and pigs raised outdoors

vii Remember, wildness is the autonomous acceptance of the basic conditions as they are and not a linear measure of how far "over there, beyond that fence" one lives. A tree is wild when it is a tree. A tree becomes domesticated when it is planted for purpose.

viii The wild red and roe deer's plasma cortisol concentrated around 7 ng/ML, whereas their farmed counterparts surpassed 20 ng/ML.

ix It is important to note that wild ruminants and ungulates naturally exhibit muscles—or meat—that are firmer, darker, and of a higher pH than their domestic counterparts. This is due to the structure of their muscles, most likely, and is either created or aided by their free-moving migration and seasonal food and energy demands. To obtain an ultimate pH that is lower than domestic animals is a truly surprising feat.

experience similar levels of slaughter stress. But if the expectations of experience mattered, then the pigs raised outdoors should be much less accustomed to indoor situations with shiny metals and loud noises and would be less able to manage the ensuing stress. But this is not the case. In both groups, their lived experiences did not matter with regard to the levels of post-mortem stress. This is in the same way as the drive-hunted red and roe deer. Because these animals freely roamed in the Dinaric Alps, a region chock-full of apex predators, we should think that being chased by human predators would be their evolutionary expectation and would not heighten their stress. But it did and it did so exponentially. Their expectation (if they had one) should have been the chase but the chase greatly increased post-mortem carcass stress. Expectations seemingly have little to do with stress.

These findings both demonstrate that humans alone are not the cause of stress (this is also why human occupancy in the world has nothing to do with the term "wildness") and that stress is relatable to life's ability to autonomously manage itself within the grand complexities of interbeing and community, what I have called "the basic conditions" throughout this book. We will explore the reality of this at greater depth later on.

Inherited Legacies

While interesting, this is not yet grounding. Why does the postmortem carcass instillation of stress matter? Drip by drip, that is, how does the chemical legacy of meat matter? Simply this: intergenerational and interspecial genetic transmission.

"Intergenerational transmission" is a term utilized by neuroscientists Mallory Bowers and Rachel Yehuda of the Icahn School of Medicine at Mount Sinai to describe genetically-bound, biological variations from parents to children. Can a parent's experience with trauma have hand-me-down effects in their offspring? Is memory transmitted through intergenerational linkages? Bowers and Yehuda's work studied the stress exposure in parents that flows, like an unbarred river, into offspring through reproductive cells—gametes—while yet in the womb.[30] Are children the heirs of biological memory?

Cortisol, given its role as a *glucocorticoid receptor* (GR)—or, a system that regulates gene transcription and expression through either binding or tethering to DNA—has been a focus of intergenerational genetics throughout the latter half of the twentieth century.[31] GR, especially GR-1[F], can affect what is called "gene transcription," that is, the permanent altering of an offspring's epigenome given parental exposure to something like stress before an offspring is even in its developmental stages—even before its conception.[32]

Bowers and Yehuda have long analyzed the intergenerational trauma linkages between Holocaust survivors and their children, utilizing post-traumatic stress disorder (PTSD) as the metric of their study. By 2002, they discovered an inverse relationship between PTSD and cortisol response.[33] That, because of the "premature termination of the cortisol response" at the moment of exposure, writes Yehuda and her colleagues, the individual's lasting trauma results from their body's inability to contain the now bursting sympathetic nervous system.[34] But, when they studied the children from PTSD suffering, Holocaust survivors—children who were conceived years after the trauma—they found the same cortisol patterns and neuroendocrine changes. This, they concluded, demonstrates that both the stress effects of trauma and the psychopathological realities that are often packaged with that trauma, PTSD for instance, are transmitted from parent to child.[35]

The children inherited their parent's inability to regulate and respond to certain chemicals alongside inheriting their parent's actual chemical imbalances. They inherited their parent's inability to regulate their cortisol response alongside inheriting the traumatic psychological effects of that cortisol—the PTSD. They were not only predisposed to cortisol misbalancing. They were imbalanced themselves.

Scientists differentiate between *organizational* and *activational* effects. Organizational effects are those that occur early in an organism's existence that produce permanent adjustments in the genetic structures or functions, deep inside their cells. Activational effects, on the other hand, are those that develop through experiences later in an organism's life. What Bowers and Yehuda have demonstrated is that memory is both an organizational and activational reality—organizational in the sense that a parent's trauma impacts the genetic reality of their children and activational in the sense that this genetic coding inclines the child to exhibit a similar result when faced with similar experiences as it grows and interacts with the world around it.

Genes, it seems, are coded memories. They are inherited legacies.

Interspecial Memory

If memories and their chemicals can be transmitted through uterine processes, can they also be transmitted through food? That is, interspecially? In other words, what is the difference between the placenta and its umbilical cord and the Earth and her nutrient cycling through ingestion, eating? If we are her Earthlings, isn't Earth our womb?

Great volumes of research exist indicating the intergenerational linkages of chemicals and trauma. There are equally large volumes about particular chemicals in food, from Glyphosate to endocrine disruptors (ED), like estrogen, that can be harmful when you eat them.[36] But none of this literature connects these two realities—that you can inherit memory through your food, either good or bad. Intergenerational linkages of cortisol, GR, and stress exist but we have never questioned interspecial linkages.

Can you inherit the chemicals alongside the inability to regulate those chemicals—the trauma—that are *organizationally* and *activationally* coded in the legacy of the foods we consume? If we consume highly stressed foods, is it possible to become highly stressed? If we consume traumatized foods, it is possible to lose our own ability to cope with the world around us? To manage and regulate our own stressors and experiences? If we consume foods with postmortem diabetes, are we more likely to suffer from the disease?

These questions lie beyond the forefront of scientific research—just beyond its next hill or behind that fence, like the modern wild. The esteemed nutrition and metabolomics expert, Stephan van

Vliet remarked in a 2021 paper co-authored with Fred Provenza and Scott Kronberg that future scientific inquiry must gravitate toward linkages and relationships and not purely on physical existence of nutrients, chemicals, and so on.[37]

While no direct, scientific research has centered on interspecial linkages, I believe there are many indirect links that, when accumulated through extended synthesis, demonstrate and establish a direct linkage. That is, we can reach understanding through a co-creative convergence between physiological and psychological feedback loops between plants and animals, including humans.

β-carotene, or beta carotene, is a potent antioxidant and key supplier of Vitamin A that helps reduce or prevent oxidative stress in an organism's body.[38] It has many health benefits for humans. As an antioxidant, it scavenges the body for reactive oxygen species (ROS), or free radicals that contain oxygen and contribute to chronic health problems such as cardiovascular disease, cataracts, cancer, and general inflammation.[39] As a protovitamin A compound, β-carotene also activates retinol pathways that regulate a large variety of biological processes, such as system homeostasis, protection against diseases and, thanks to its DNA-binding receptors, gene transcription (remember this one).[40] It supports healthy vision and a strong immune system. And, given that vitamin A is one of the world's most diagnosed micronutrient deficiencies, especially in developing countries, maximizing the bioavailability of β-carotene is of great importance in the sustenance of life.

Naturally occurring β-carotene, like that found in grass-fed beef raised on richly biodiverse meadows,[41] is often complexed with protein molecules, or lipoproteins.[42] These structures limit the solubility and absorption of micronutrients in the human body, allowing the carotenoid's intestinal uptake to occur through a slow, passive diffusion.[43] These lipoproteins control the absorption of fat-soluble micronutrients to support human health.

But here is the problem: a high muscle pH (like that found in slaughtered animals discussed previously) increases the solubility of these proteins and decreases β-carotene's transference into what is called the *oil phase*. This mechanism directly corelates to its bioavailability. In other words, as the muscle pH increases, β-carotene's bioavailability decreases.

When you allow this to converge with the postmortem stress studies of pigs, cattle, and deer, where muscle pH fluctuates with stress, a new truth arises from the scientific ashes: stress in food, that is, the memory behind life within that food, is directly related to that food's nutrient delivery. While one farmer may pride themselves in the phytochemical richness of their pastures, claiming that their beef is "nutrient-dense" because their cows graze on rich polycultures of grasses and forbs and the like, the stress around those animals' lives and slaughter may negate or severely limit those micronutrients' bioavailability and accumulation into the human body when consumed.

Stress may very well be the gatekeeper of nutrient delivery. It is nutrient density's master.

The First Social Network

The specifics and sacredness of life and death tells the story of our food, but what about its memory? While the former impacts bioavailability, does the latter transpose biology between species—from the consumed to the consumer? In other words, stress impacts bioavailability, yes, but is stress transmittable?

While the scientific research is lacking, an introspection into evolution could be the light we need. Maybe one day, someone smarter than I will study these things. Until then, the commonsensical laws of relationship will have to do (and maybe, just maybe, this is all we will ever need).

In an article titled, *Are we eating more than we think?*, Stanford researcher, Anthony Yun and colleagues postulate that energy is the currency of evolution.[44] An organism's successful evolutionary development is a co-adaptive process of energy recognition and energy acquisition. To successfully stick around, that is, an organism must have limits—energy limits. All organisms are bound by the amount of energy they can successfully procure. This is based over the span of a life's local place and time. If it spends more than it can acquire, it biologically ceases to exist. If it procures more than its environment can sustainably produce, it destroys its biome and ignites its own social demise. But modern, human lifestyles have "decoupled" this evolutionary framework, Yun writes, and chronic stress is the signal—the beacon of our undoing.[45]

Yun's decoupling is Darwin's demise. *Homo sapiens'* neurohormonal pathways have long orbited their autonomic nervous system, their energy source, their sun, if you will. This sensory solar system modulates through adaptive feedback loops with organisms gaining precious information about the world around them through the act of eating. As bodies work to digest the "nature of food," writes Yun, through seasonal and biometric associations, they learn the state of stress in the food chain and the upcoming seasonal shortages or buffets that other organisms are preparing for. This adaptive process extends even into one's phenotype, as organisms assimilate their internal processes to match the external realities around them—those on their dinner plate. Eating is an adaptive and educational process.

If Yun is correct, food was the first social network.

But why does this matter? How does it all connect? Modern humanity has divorced itself from this adaptive behavioral pathway. We are disconnected from our evolutionary currency. When our ancestors consumed indigenous autumnal foods, for instance—organisms that were themselves managing the scarcity of the fall season and were preparing for hibernation and for less energy demands—their own internal systems self-organized and they adopted the behaviors of their plates: their systems slowed down, they began hoarding calories, and their bodies prioritized energy storage. But what happened when we began consuming these same foods in the middle of the summer? Or the spring? False adaptive pressures rise: false growing environments produce chronic stress in the food—the organism that grew out of its season. Obesity rises inevitably, for our bodies, long out of season, begin to hibernate and prioritize fat storage. Chronic stress rises, for our bodies, long cleft from Earth, circulate around false feedback loops of adaptation to a land that does not exist.

Even more, what happens when we consume stressed, farmed animals that are bred and born and grown and finished in false environments? Landscapes that know not the seasons and know not the undulating realities and communal (interspecies) solar systems of energy production and regulation. Animals that breed every year or else they are culled; animals without their social networks, as they are castrated, weaned, and separated from their mothers and families; animals that eat what they are given and not what they have biologically co-evolved with over the eons.

Yun argues that this maladaptive process is one of the leading causes for obesity, chronic stress, and atherosclerosis (or heart disease). Modern disease may be a lack of respect for memory in our food, in the life around our plate.

But Yun is not alone. The interspecial, neurohormonal inheritance from food is called the Xenohormesis Hypothesis.[46] It postulates that plants deliver non-nutritive molecules when consumed to assist in the consumer's stress resistance, health, and overall survival. It was first postulated by a team in 2004 studying resveratrol, a natural phenol or phytochemical produced by grapes when injured or under attack. Observing the surprising and yet unconsidered relationship between resveratrol and yeast in wine production, the team theorized that alternative pathways must exist where plants influence organisms beyond their nutrient delivery. These pathways correlate to "chemical cues in the environment," where consumers of stressed foods inherit that stress or its response and don a stressed phenotype.[47]

This is not a negative thing. Far from it. Perhaps it is helpful to see the life on our plates as the wardens on the walls who warn when an invading army appears outside the city gates. The city's inhabitants, dwelling happily inside the walls, cannot see the invading army and rely on the warden's call to arouse an armed response. If the warden's cry is empty, calling attention to an army that does not exist, like the stress of plants grown outside of their season or the stress of animals slaughtered outside of the sacred harvest, the now stressed and aroused inhabitants struggle for no purpose. We struggle, often. Eating locally and in season tells your body how to live, how to handle stress, what to feel, and so much more.

Bacteria, it seems, are not surprised by our hypotheses. Through what is known as quorum sensing, some bacteria produce certain molecules that control populations in other species.[48] Some bacteria and fungi "become virulent," write pathologists Joseph Baur and David Sinclair, when they sense "particular flavonoids indicative of their preferred hosts."[49] Mammals are just bacteria and fungi that took their soil with them, as it has been said. To consider that mammals could very well have also adapted to this non-nutritive feedback loop, especially given Yun's work around energy and adaptative learning through consumption, is to consider mammals as an integral aspect of the world we inhabit. As heterotrophs, organisms without internal energy production that rely on other organisms for food, like plants, this would only seem natural.

Truth Yet Unseen

If this section presents anything it presents questions: what is stress and how does it accumulate in the body? If it has been shown to transfer intergenerationally, between parent and child, could it also transfer between species, between the consumed and the consumer? If a phytochemical's bioavailability decreases when stress is present, what does that tell us about nutrient density in foods? What role does the Xenohormesis Hypothesis play in stress transfer and local food systems?

But the science is yet unclear. I have written in the past that science is like two friends who know what the other thinks and often gets it wrong. Science is a wonderful tool in acquiring data but, occasionally, understanding some deep truth only requires a faith that deeper realities exist, like friendship. Nature abhors a void. Science has proven that much is true. And if that is true then the deep voids of interspecial inheritance passed through consumption, eating and nourishment, the relationship between time and space is filled with truth yet unseen but not unknown.

Memory is something known but not seen. Death is to life how breath is to life—inhaling, new worlds are born and exhaling, old worlds become new. Memory is calling. She is calling husbandmen and hunters.

"What do you remember?" she asks.

The Place of Peace

We went to bed that night with the moon, the creaking porch chairs still echoing between our ears. The universe felt close, her arms, her near light, wrapping us in a cosmogonic coverlet. We rose the next day anew, reborn in some ancient way, ready to reflect the light of a distant and ageless star.

We knew, deeply, rooted in the ancient well of our gut like ivy, that something lay beyond our small market gardens and small-scale pastured poultry enterprise. We had studied permaculture with Geoff Lawton, the New Zealand educator, and had established large keyline based silvopastures of fruits and nuts and nitrogen fixing species of comfrey, sea buckthorn, and locust. We had created a local, egg delivery service. We had named it all: *Síochánta Baile*, an old Irish phrase meaning "the place of peace that I call home."

Peace. Yes, that is what it was and that is what we were searching for. The more we let go, the more our small, human-scaled systems emerged in ways we never could have planned, designed, and our hearts drifted, like loose limbs bouncing the water, into the woods, into the wildly waving, untouched peripheries of that place of peace that we called home.

We also knew that the agriculture that began our journey was not to be the system that allowed it to mature. Regenerative agriculture and permaculture are fine first steps in the restoration of relationship and the reawakening of memory—from Earth and her waving hair to our two and four legged cousins to us, her simple and so dependent mammal. But something else was growing, not in our market gardens or mobile chicken houses, but growing inside us, that ivied well in our gut, that would soon emerge into what we would call kincentric rewilding: a relational land ethic of letting go but not stepping back, of rewilding ourselves, with the land, an energetic, and increasingly singular body.[x] A co-creative tellback.

A few months later, I received a phone call over dinner from a real estate agent in Virginia that we had contacted to keep their eye out for some properties priced well enough. Land values around northeast Ohio (where we were located) would afford us a couple of acres, no more.

"Daniel, hello. You need to drive down here." His voice was demanding, unlike his profession.

"You found something?" Morgan looked at me, half floating above her chair.

"Just come." He said.

The next day we were in Virginia, standing in a clear cut. Trees were falling around us and others were silent and still vertical, slightly, only for a moment more, like weeping men in an ancient battlefield. Mammoth diesel engines roaring ruts into the soft Earth, crying. The land was a sad play of neglect.

In ancient times, it was (and still is) the home of the Siouan of the Monacan Nation. More recently but yet many years ago, the landscape was a fox-hunting horse farm that then transformed during the early nineties into in a rotationally overgrazed and conventional Charolais cattle farm that then, during the century's transition and after the Charolais operation failed, became a Black Angus seedstock operation that, as you could guess, also failed, and the landscape was forgotten. A decade later and no doubt under financial strain, it then found its last and ultimate home before us as a clear cut and deforested wasteland.

We closed for one third of the land's market value and we closed in two weeks. There were two houses on the property. One of which was overly sized, like a pimple. It experienced neglect for over a

---

x "Land Ethic" as a term, as I understand it, was coined by the great writer, thinker, and conservationist, Aldo Leopold. His essay, *The Land Ethic* speaks volumes and is worth a read.

decade before we got there and we would spend nearly a decade more cleaning it up. We have since joked that the "big house" came free with the farm, a gift and a curse.

We arrived as the land's saviors, for we were ready and primed to farm in nature's image, with regenerative agriculture in our saddle-bags and permaculture primed at the hip. Nearly ten-foot-tall and persnickety herbaceous perennials, such as goldenrod, pokeweed, bull thistle, dogfennel, ragweed, and poison hemlock, covered so completely the landscape that we had to climb atop our rickety farm truck to see anything at all. From that elevated view, we discovered falling fence lines, spring-fed streams, and once-graveled farm roads that we did not even know we had.

We also discovered erosion ditches eating their way inward. Gullies were forming in the once clad and hilled respites and the ancient datums and their reliefs were silting the lower, now strug-gling wetlands. It was a latticed land of explosive movement—the tops of the hills were falling downwards, the lower valleys began to resemble the tops of the hills, and trees and their briars seemed to burst from the torn and mangled ground, like mines primed to explode. The loggers had turned ancient years into modern dollars and they slithered, leaving a diesel colored trace in their wake. It was a bundled and jumbled mess of life.

We watched our first, June sunrise atop that truck's cab and dreamed of nature's return. Memory was growing. Its seed was planted but she was not yet ready to awaken.

Wildness was also growing, but we had some unlearning to do. The land, its memory, would soon speak, soon emerge from the eroding soil beneath our feet, and change our lives forever. A tell-back whispered through the winter's harsh wind would soon ignite a great fire. That came next.

And so ends this branch of the *Stagtine*.

SECTION I: OF MEMORY & TIME

II

IN NATURE'S
IMAGE

SECTION II: IN NATURE'S IMAGE

A Section, Inspected

In which a February blizzard speaks through a bull named Paddy—a story that commences the Wildland's process of letting go, of "Open Grazing," as we step away from regenerative farming. The story skates over ice as it considers control's hold over farming, over life's flow. The narrative invites the reader to consider what separates rocks and humans and plants and cows and how life communicates through a cognitive animacy conveyed behind cellular and community pathways. The section concludes with the idea that to run with them is not to hope in particular outcomes, but to release outcomes entirely in the hope that being human is enough. It is nurturing the animacy of life and its complex consciousness through becoming what we already are.

The Sunrise

Paddy, or Padraig, is a bull in the emerging Wildland. One February morning he was in his paddock, above the barn, as was considered appropriate on farms. It happened that he was unhappy and lonely in his position and strode, violently, to tell us so, threatening our lives and disrupting our best laid plans.

A flash of prismatic orange and red and opal blue ignited above the winter grey hills and hovered before it declined; The dawn's brilliant colors rising to sing up their sun. But only momentarily. Frozen droplets of snow purled from cold, grey clouds to even colder, greyer mud, knitting into a heather quilt that covered everything our eyes could see.

"Grab that line, quick!" I instructed in a tired drawl. The wet, morning cold was already weighing heavily on me. "He's coming back on us!"

"It's stuck! It won't budge!" Morgan cried as she worked to reel in the line of electrified grazing wire. The thick and now freezing mud clogging the spindle of the reel as it went, shocking her with its ten thousand volts. A plastic reel constructed from plastic strands laced with metal threads to carry the electrical current—the modern farmer's great tool and the wet, winter farmer's great curse.

A light sparkled across the mountain from one of our few neighbor's kitchens—over a mile across the river valley below and up a few hundred feet of the near sheer rock cliff on the other side. It was morning and they were busy making their coffee and living, as normal humans do, in their normal human ways.

"Is *this* normal?" her voice resounded across the mud, and landed with a fat, final slap—more a tired plea than a question.

I did not respond. Her question produced no ripples.

The cold engraved the dawn's departing darkness with crisp, thin edges. Weather you can feel between your fingers. If it gets colder, it will descend as an enflamed numbness into your fingertips. If it gets wetter, no one has a chance. There is little worse than freezing rain kissed bitterly by harsh, westerly winds. We would all soon freeze from the outside in, cracking as we go.

"Is *this* normal!" Morgan's voice cracked with emphasis as ten thousand volts pulsed through her veins.

Agriculture's Algorithm

My sweat froze as it splashed upon the bark-colored snow and my stomach rippled across its recently frozen surface. The snow seemed to fall from the ground up, like sparkling springs that froze when seen. A thin, painted stillness that covered the colder grey of February. Big, fat clumps of frozen water rebelled against the devolving days, and pocketed the amassing snow into distant continents. A curled, grey-white land: the dalmatian of winter.

Fear mixed rudely with exhaustion and the mucky smells of the wet, winter paddock festered like moldy potpourri. I stood still, my feet locked in the mud and my stomach curled inside of its cavity. Morgan and I were at work too early, trying to calm down our bull, but it was cold and we were tired. The sun had not crested the eastern hills and my boots were trapped in the mud. If Paddy charged, which felt imminent, I could neither move nor dodge his gladiator-like blitz. We had put him in this arena, and he was going to fight to the death.

"Is *this* normal!" Morgan's anger again pleaded, her tone dropped the last syllable. This time, there was no question about it.

I could not respond. The weight of farming mixed rudely with the unexpected cold of the early morning and they both pressed too heavily. Our bull's frozen pains lived in the soils and they held tightly onto my boots. My frightened stomach dropped from my body and drifted away over the ice, but the rest of me could not move. I was stuck.

Three days' snowfall had converged with Paddy's frantic pacing and last night's evening warmth produced a sinuous union of sticky sludge and slow-moving slush. But this morning's dawn-infused freeze now capped the trail of his earthly pain with a sheet of thin, melancholic ice.

It was a linearly bisected landscape between the cold and that which is colder. Between the mud and its ice. A dark-eyed junco with its frost-heaved wings spread in farewell bolted heavenwards from the base of a bull thistle on my right. She was flying north and must have taken rest inside the thorny thistle through the night. But she was late and she did not stay long.

While we had worked on farms for many years, Morgan and I were new to farming on our own and we had done what good agrarians do—what we had been told to do. We had separated the bull from the rest of the herd in order to control breeding and limit calving to a specific window of time in the spring. *This is biomimicry, you see.*

Deer and their ancestral cousins—bison, elk, and pronghorn—all regenerate in the spring when the warmth has returned and the food is aplenty. Managing our domestic counterparts to also calf in the spring is *natural farming* and *farming in nature's image,* we were told.

This also makes nutritional sense. Spring calving ensures that high quality and lush forage occupies the herd's diet when lactation's nutritional burdens crescendo with the calves' incessant demands. Spring calving coordinates the nutritional needs of the herd with the nutritional operations of the land. *This is good animal husbandry,* we were told.

Yes, this produces high weaning weights and fat cows that breed back in the summer months to do it again and again and again. *This is good for your farm business*, we were told.

This is calving in sync with nature—and this was our problem.

To effect a short, spring calving window, a farmer must affect the bull's exposure to the herd. Agriculture is entirely this simple. There is no science or complexity about it.

We may think our school years' education in math was worthless but agriculture and the herd's reproduction would call you a liar.

While mathematics may not stir your blood, it nonetheless regulates its flow. Algebra's algorithms are agricultural, for, as mathematician David Berlinksi writes, algorithms are the procedure of the effective.[50] What is farming but the making of Earth to be an effective, replicable, and scalable procedure for profit? Farming in some full sense is the domestication of breeding—regardless of if it is a seed of wheat or a seed of bovine. To farm is to manage what grows when, where, and in what. Yes, like an algorithm.

Ask yourself this: how many decisions do you, perhaps a farmer yourself, make on the daily that pertain to the production of food for sale? If we produce food and it does not sell, we call it a waste.

But how many decisions do we make that pertain to the production of sacred offerings to be gifted away? People often talk about feeding the world, arguing about production, allotment size, and calories produced per unit of value from acre to animal. But the world we are fixed on feeding is the human world, always only the human world. Farms suffocate under the capitalistic necessities of modern life and their many decisions are shaped by our desire for profit or our proclivity to feed humanity with little regard for the nourishment of the life all around us: the mycelial communities, the apex predators, their scavenging shadows, the murders of crows, the circling vultures, the wanting opossum and skunk.

How many foxes have we killed because they were eating our chickens? When chickens eat bugs, we call it natural farming. When foxes eat our chickens we call it a farm-business problem. Algebra's algorithms are the procedure of the effective and we manage the scales. Agriculture, in all of its modern forms, yearns for an effective version of nature. An efficient nature for our sake, always only our sake.

Two-hundred and eighty days before you want calves to start being born, you put the bull in with the cows, and two-hundred and eighty days before you want the calves to stop coming, you pull the bull out. Like a water spigot, farming in nature's image is as simple as turning it on and turning it off. It is algorithmic. To breed, we manage the bull's exposure to the herd—that is the input variable—and then we manage the natural and flirtatious tendencies of life's ebullient pulse to affect the outcome—that is the rule of the mathematical function itself.

Heedless of nature's image, our unnatural giant unnaturally paced the fence line. Bovines are herd animals, like humans are tribal animals and our cousins, the coyote and the mountain lion, are pack animals. Life exists when the herd, the tribe, and the pack exist but it can only exist well when the herd, the tribe, and the pack exist completely. Our herd was forcibly heft in two to control their breeding and our winter's rotation of the main herd—their controlled and planned migration from paddock to paddock—had drifted too close to the separate bull paddock. Life's sensuous passions drifted, like my stomach, in the ice-chilled air. Perhaps some of the herd was in heat or, perhaps, he just missed his friends. The *Bovine's* bawl steadily sounded against the dawn and the *Hominidae's* anger enflamed the dark hours.

Our bull's passion animated the morning with a strange energy. He ran and kicked and bawled across the paddock with a spirit unfamiliar in February. His head dropped. His ears flared. His eyes peered eerily into my own. Time stood still. But I knew he would not.

The Muck

"Morgan!" I cried. "My boots! They're stuck!" My body freed itself from my voice and its words were a faraway, detached cadence in the cold. Desolate fear settled as the desolate, farmed gladiator screamed in my direction.

Morgan had already scrambled to the paddock's gate and was panting atop of it. She was covered in freezing mud and had already shocked herself too many times on the electric reel to give another damn.

"He's coming!" she exclaimed.

I could not move.

Our bull Paddy, or Padraig, was often a very kind giant. During our farm's breeding window when he lived with the herd, he was their lead and he was our management's focus. He would come at our *woop woop* and the herd would follow. Bulls get a bad rap in popular images of agriculture. They are often pictured as mini-van-sized monuments of testosterone and anger with eyes enflamed and muscles fueled to charge. But these bulls have never had a place in our management. Life is hard enough and life spent fearing death or injury is not a life we have ever been interested in. Why are they so mean, anyway?

On farm tours, we would lay with Paddy in the shade while he chewed on his cud and we would scratch his nose to demonstrate his domestication to our onlooking guests. *Look at this,* we would say. *This is farming in nature's image.*

But nature slogged aggressively in my direction. The darkness of the morning grew darker and Paddy's plangent pains heightened. Hours of attempting to calm him down, to move him elsewhere, to repair the fencing he had destroyed when he got out and ran down the road, endangering our small community and the commuting passersby, had failed. Our work and commotion had only made it worse—the patched fence was not strong and would not hold another charge. His anger mounted with the morning. And now I was about to be his piñata, but tethered to the ground instead of hanging overhead.

Paddy's head dropped, his ears flared, and his hooves were beating toward me. Deep, black eyes affixed on my core. His elemental bawl echoed against the empty tomb of my stomach as I attempted to heave or break my feet free, the snow convulsed, the ground churned, the ice creaked but nothing gave. A mass of charcoal and steel blasted toward me.

Bovines are herd animals and Paddy had no herd. He was a testosterone-fueled gladiator of earthly pains and farming's pursuit of profits and he had no release, he had no rest.

Her energy regained, Morgan again yelled with everything she had, as though her words' waves could knock me free from the frozen mud. To no avail. The rising wind carried the sound away.

I attempted to run, but nothing gave. My boots, stuck in sludge, gave a death-like gurgle. Diving to one side, I felt my feet leave their boots and my body reunite with its rippling stomach, landing only feet aside from Paddy's skull-crushing force. I half crawled and half stumbled to the paddock's gate, dried thistles and nettles biting my knees as I went. Paddy regained himself and again lowered his head. I hurdled over the paddock's gate and fell to safety.

Landing on the other side, wet, cold, and shoeless, I laid with my back against the soggy and half-frozen Earth and screamed a scream that released my built-up adrenaline but not the kind of scream that did any good.

The sunrise. The nascent light. The wetted cold now coloring my shirt. The dark eyed juncos laughing *dit dit dit* as they flew away. The tender purling of dead grasses against the headward, winter wind, their stalks still erect and singing hymns of summer's hallowed, golden days. Then nothing. Silence.

Rocks and Reason

"What is the difference between a rock and a human?" asks a conservative college dean to his freshman class studying Aristotle's *Ethics*.

"Speech," returns one student, eager to impress.

"No, not speech exactly," the dean returns. "Think deeper. What does Aristotle say?"

"Humans have knowledge because we understand, more fully, what it is to flourish," answers another student.

"Better," whispers the dean, looking off into the theoretical distance.

"This is what Aristotle calls 'the good'" answers another.

"Good," the dean responds. "This is good. But what is the highest good?"

The students fumble through their books that lay on the table in front of them. Some flip endlessly. Others flip to certain dog-eared pages that are nearly entirely dyed with their roommate's neon, yellow highlighter. The room begins to sweat, as though the janitor, who is busily dusting the bookshelves in the back of the room, is playing with them, twisting the thermostat for fun.

"The good is itself desirable, only by itself, and for its own sake," emits one student in the front of the class.

A general exhale releases a portion of the room's heat and the students near the back of the room roll their eyes and pivot in their chairs. They are completely confused. They are nursing majors and their *good* is medicine—that which strives to save life and not to separate or define it.

"Yes, that *is* good," the dean says as he reclines, placing his hands, now crossed, on his stomach. "So, what is the difference between a rock and a human?"

Silence. No one, not even the nurses in the back, dare to answer.

"Reason," the dean asserts. "But it is time and class is done. We will continue this next week."

Winter's High Clef

This long-ago conversation echoed across my mind as I laid there and as Paddy looked at me, sadly, through the gate. After some time, I opened my eyes, but Morgan was not looking at me and, timidly, I was not looking at her either.

"That was close," I murmured.

"No," she returned, her gaze still somewhere else. "That was dumb."

A light snow fell, and a brief upward gust of tired breath tore through a nearby beech, its yellow leaves cataract down into the winter's duff. Paddy stood at the gate. His breath, like smoke in cold air, smelled of the long winter, an open tomb, the pallid inertia of short days. It hovered, strangely and unnaturally, as if in question.

"We'll need to get my boots."

"Yes," she agreed. Her eyes still focused on some object in the distance. "If you die, I'm selling the farm," she half giggled, half admitted, as haphazardly as one who tells jokes under their breath, knowing that they are not jokes at all.

Creaking tiny icicles trebled like wind chimes as they murmured and fell from the empty sugar maple branches above my head. Winter's high clef writ in water. Paddy's rumbling bellow and breath shook everyone, everything, everywhere.

"You cannot sell the farm," I whispered back, the air slowly returning to my lungs. My eyes fixated on the falling needles of ice.

"Then this needs to change."

SECTION II: IN NATURE'S IMAGE

Which Way?

Reason. The animacy of life. It is that by which we understand through sensory information the environment around us and that by which we are made capable of a response. Or so we are told. But, if Pascal is right, it is also that by which the shabbiness of the mind sloughs off its mastery.[i]

Feedback loops without reason are like speech in the wind. Of little worth. But a good attempt, nonetheless.

It is this idea that also animates the farmer's penchant to control life—breeding. If humans alone can employ reason and humans alone are needed to interpret life's ebbing and flowing and responsive feedback loop, then humans are also alone. It is our sad power for we alone have it and it makes us quite lonesome.

Reason and the ability to act reasonably is what separates us from rocks and soil and grass and livestock. In this way, argue all of the thought leaders and founders of the better agriculture or energy movements, it is also good for humans to exercise our natural, colonizing right over rocks and soil and grass and livestock. We can call it management, to make us feel better.

But is this true? If it is, our penchant to control breeding will save the world. Because it is effective, girded by humanity's prized reason, and infused with good intentions. If it is not, it will destroy the world. Because it oversteps Creation's complex symphony, re-

---

i Blaise Pascal, the early, seventeenth century French mathematician, philosopher, and Enlightenment malcontent wrote in his Pensées, "Reason's last step is the recognition that there are an infinite number of things which are beyond it. It is merely feeble if it does not go so far as to realize that."

places purpose with efficiency, and denudes life into that which is reasonable and that which reasonably manages. Is Pascal right? Is reason the fount of our mastery or is reason the release of mastery altogether? This is the question.

Aristotle divided sublunary life into three classifications: plants, animals, and humans and gave each a corresponding soul-type. Plants, he wrote have a vegetative soul; animals have a sensitive soul; and humans, we have a rational soul. He ascribed the weight of their difference in the observable fact of their effects.

Plants reproduce for the continuation of their kind and they do nothing else; animals have a certain level of observational capabilities but occupy the lowest possible levels of cognitive and cerebral function and lack both vice and virtue—and so "neither has a god;" humans are rational and our rationality allows us to think, to believe, to experience, to love, to know, and, most importantly for Aristotle, to rule.[51]

For, what is man but a "political animal" and what is the citiless man but an animal "low in the scale of humanity?"[52] The natural or primitive man, Aristotle contended, is animal in soul and is thereby a lesser man.[ii]

In his 1854 *Fragment on Slavery,* Abraham Lincoln demanded a retuning of this Aristotelian tradition. Comparing figure "A," who is lighter skinned, with figure "B," who is darker skinned and thereby enslaved by figure "A," Lincoln led a simple inquiry. Is it "*color*, then," he asked? Does the "lighter [have] the right to enslave the darker?" We could, in our modern and "regenerative" agricultural situation, otherwise inquire: does the more rational have the right to enslave the less rational?

"By this rule," Lincoln continued, "you are to be slave to the first man you meet, with a fairer skin than your own." This would continue on and on, over and over, with masters becoming slaves to the next lighter-skinned neighbor until the lightest skin was reached and it would be they who ran the world.

Socially, these views have their own and important weight.

ii This idea will be more sufficiently unpacked in Section 4.

Ecologically, if human-recognized rationality is the potent weight behind our ability to force, to have dominion—to enslave, that is— nature to go in this direction or that, then you, my smart and more rational reader, may force me to grow or go in the direction of your choosing. Social problems are ecological problems.

To the western mind, cognitive function is only found in the central nervous system's occupancy within the dynamically folded grey matter of our very cerebral cortex. This is the scientific definition of cognition—the admixture of a central nervous system and its cortex. Lack this form and you lack its function. Have this form and measure your mastery.

Which way would you have me go?

Production and Profit

I laid with my back against the mudroom floor in complete exhaustion. Paddy's February antics left us cold, wet, tired, and second guessing everything. We had worked entirely too hard to manufacture abundance—to cultivate it, to control it—and it was steadily eating away at us. Through us.

Doubts, sliding in like eels. Slipping like cracked eggshells in glass bowls. The yolks pulling down, down, down their calcium-white shields away from this crazy world.

"What does everyone else do?" I asked as I tried to shove the doubts back. I sidestepped.

Farmers eat production and breathe profit. Like smokers, we often suffocate but we never die hungry. And I could almost hear the machinery of Morgan's mind churning inside her skull. Machine minds for machine problems. Manufacturing solutions.

She was looking out of the kitchen window. Looking over long clumps of naked trees, like ancient hands erupting from the underworld that bracket muddy and farmed out fields and valleys. Black rows of red cedar mark old fence or property lines. Impenetrable layers of tangled briars and vines under them. Sometimes, the winter blackened cedars square off old family graveyards or forgotten and now fallen family homes. Here, in this moment, Morgan was looking over the forgotten backyard garden, now overwhelmed with time and neglect.

Out in the world, the actual world beyond our farm and beyond the kitchen window's forgotten garden, waits legions of sanctuaries. Oak forests covered under ivy and iridescent light; the deep springs of shade from the lone pines in the river valleys, laggards from the once glacial world; meadow gardens full of bright yellow and deep green wind; empires of briars and laurel hedges through which birds and butterflies float, endlessly, thinking only of nectar and berries.

Two worlds. One falling apart.

"We will figure this out," I whispered, as much to myself as to her. I spoke before she had time to answer and my hands found her shoulder. It was cold. "We will," I said.

Tilling Ourselves

Morgan and I spent the next few days thawing and thinking all too deeply on this great task of ours. The land's saviors, we had a problem to solve.

We first attempted to separate some yearling steers from the main herd to bring Paddy some company. But it aroused the main herd in unsuspecting ways, for it changed their community's nature and it changed the way that nature operated upon their community.

Calves and their older cousins started crossing the polywire-made paddock's lines before our non-growing season's grazing plan allowed for, and the stockpiled grass started to run thin. We would run out of grass months before the spring would return. Removing the steers reorganized the herd's family units and created a void for the young bull calves to fill prematurely. But Paddy still aggressively paced his fence line.

After the steers failed, we considered bringing in our herd of dairy goats. But we soon learned that there is nothing for goats to eat in the half-frozen and soggy tundra of Virginia's winter and so we brought them back into the woods to forage on acorns, pine needles, and bark.

In the haste of this movement and some slack in our management, the goats prematurely escaped Paddy's paddock and rummaged around the farm for a bit. Hours later and with many an unfortunate word said, the goats were once again in their woods and Paddy was once again alone and pacing at his fence line.

Nothing helped. Life had been reduced to its Aristotelian qualities and, no matter the soil health we were building or the complexity we sought or the idea that we were saving the world, life, in the fullest sense, was becoming an outsider on Earth. We controlled it. Deported what did not yield a profit. What did not fit our enforced asceticism.

What lived, lived because we said it could. What bred, bred because we allowed it to. What grew, grew because we managed for it. Like rifled lead, we tore through what we touched and, also like rifled lead, we were a tool in the hand of industry's army.

Exhaustion occupied the extent of our rope and its fibers had worn out. Our cultivation, our farming, was tilling ourselves into Earth. We were spent. Tired. Lonely. We were beaten. Punished. Nature's return through *natural farming* was harder than we had thought and she was constantly in our way.

The etymological root for cultivation extends deep into the dead heartwood of western civilization. It stems from the Latin verb *cultivō,* and means "to till" or "to move" or "to toil over."

I well remember the mudroom floor's cold tiles against my back. I was cold but without the spirit to move. Complete exhaustion had set in. *What are we doing?* In some strange, full sense, the cultivation of Earth was killing us and we were also killing her.

In that moment, farming's weight compressed us to our core and its parasitic friend, biomimicry, was slowly making its way out, chewing and churning as it went. The wetted cold exhausts the body in ways that nothing else really can and I think the same is true for farming. To be so in need of control—to place *this* animal *here,* for *this* reason, to accomplish *this* particular *thing*—is taxing work. Debilitating work. Work.

In this way, farming flirts with both flaccidity and drudgery. You do not work all the time but, when you do, it is often when you would rather be sleeping and this often happens altogether too regularly.

Silent days passed. Only platitudes smattered emptily against the walls.

"We just need some rest."

"Yes, a recharge. Then, we'll be fine."

"Everything happens for a reason."

"Yes, and we'll all live happily ever after."

Then, silence—incomplete, fretful, unnatural, untidy. The clock ticked. The refrigerator in the next room flipped annoyingly on and off. Our neighbor's half-filled grain bin, over a mile away, kicked up and its low humming in an otherwise humless world drowned around us. The fire crepitated with an airy whistle and then clapped and popped as its cellulose gave way.

"I don't know how much more of this I can handle!" I burst one afternoon. I was embarrassed immediately. The obvious is sometimes better left unsaid.

Paddy's incessant pains had destroyed multiple metal gates, a hundred feet of high tensile wire fencing, a water trough, a couple weeks of our tired and cold lives, and our interest in farming. We had spent weeks chasing or prodding him back in his paddock and night after night we fell asleep wondering where he would be in the morning—in his paddock, somewhere on the neighbor's land, on the road?

Worse yet, this was only to be a chronic condition in our "regenerative" life and not an acute illness. Farming in some full sense is the domestication of breeding—regardless of whether it is a seed of wheat or a seed of bovine. To farm is to manage what grows when, where, and in what. But Earth was calling and her inclusive and patient weight weighed heavily upon us.

"I don't know how much more of this *we* can handle," Morgan returned.

Paddy was teaching us, rudely. But he was teaching.

SECTION II: IN NATURE'S IMAGE

Mycho-What?

One evening, a few hard days later, around an evening fire that crackled beyond its custom, Morgan opened an old textbook across her very pregnant belly. We had spent the previous holiday season reorganizing our home's library and cataloguing new titles. Memories of college fashioned astride memories of childhood and home, a youth categorized genre first and then alphabetically.

"I read this in college," she said, a sad reverie.

"Look at this one," I returned. It was taped and held together by a prayer and smelled like my mom's hand cream. *The Door in the Wall.*

Good and bad memories alike alighted like a mockingbird on the chimney and also like a black vulture on the naked black walnut. But that night, sitting across the evening fire, something, some thought, maybe even, some memory surfaced and Morgan found herself holding a particularly old book. Forever ago, a lost dream from a lost time, she had studied molecular science in college on a full track scholarship and graduated with a degree in biology. She finished her degree in three years and she did it two years before I did. She is two years younger than me and, to be honest, also ten years older.

"What's that?" I half inquired, holding a book of my own and without looking up.

Its worn and dog-eared pages seemed familiar to her touch and she fumbled through them like braille. Delicately and without looking.

"Nothing," she returned. Her eyes fixed on the fire. The flames seemed to dissolve in her pupils like rifts of clouds that heave the sky into a speckled, Dutch blue. Inverted islands of memory.

Ancient notecards from chapters she cared not to remember fell to the floor. Collections of blues and yellows and oranges arrayed across the floor. Symbols on their top right corners, demarking short answers from essays from multiple choice questions.

Eukaryotic kingdoms? one card quizzed on its front.

Animalia (us), plantae, fungi, and protista.

"Fungi? That has its own kingdom?" I questioned as I helped pick them up. "I thought they were classified like plants?"

"Plants have chlorophyll, not chitin," Morgan remarked. Annoyed by both the question and her answer, as if the resurfacing knowledge itself was an unwanted guest in the already stressed and tired room.

Mushrooms are? One orange card inquired.

Fruiting structures.

Mycelia are?

Feeding structures, like mouths.

What fungus was discovered in 1950 and best senses light, wind, and gravity?

Phycomyces blakesleeanus.

The fire cracked and Morgan's pupils tufted into some high altitude of memory, like cirrus, and she returned to her book. She discovered a folded insert tucked neatly into its middle. A class handout most likely. *Net transfer of carbon between ectomycorrhizal tree species in the field*—a 1997 paper published by Suzanne Simard.

Skimming the paper's neon, yellow highlights, Morgan read aloud, "The amount of carbon exchanged between *B. papyrifera* and *P. menziesii* is indicative of a tightly linked plant–fungus–soil system." She paused. *Plants exchange carbon through fungi?* Her eyes skimmed further into the paper. "A more even distribution of carbon among plants as a result of belowground transfer may have implications for local interspecific interactions, maintenance of biodiversity, and therefore for ecosystem productivity, stability and sustainability."[53] *Interspecific interactions. Could this also extend to intraspecific interactions, like reproduction and breeding?*

The fabric chair that held her was yanked through some drain below the floor and all that was left was naked silence. An open mouth staring at a now silent fire—snuffed out by some creative energy.

"Daniel. What if we have been asking the wrong questions this whole time?"

"I'm not following you," I returned. Nervous where she was taking this.

"I can't believe I'm saying this, but we need to learn more about plants and fungi."

SECTION II: IN NATURE'S IMAGE

Interspecific Intentionality

Leading forest ecologist and best-selling author, Suzanne Simard has paved a gentle pathway through the once-closed and frost-born forest of the vegetative soul.

In her 2021 book, *Finding the Mother Tree*, Simard summarized her life's work, demonstrating that trees talk to each other—that, in the networked and highly-connected communities of forests, roots and their fungal friends co-create a life that pulses and pulses with intentionality. In an interview with the Yale School of the Environment, Simard summarized that it is "sort of like a below-ground pipeline, that connects one tree root system to another tree root system, so that nutrients and carbon and water can exchange between the trees."

Interactions between organisms is emblematic of Earth. This is the network of life. Even Aristotle's division of sublunary life understood this. But fungi facilitate and speak of a deeper connection. If anything, they also question our ideas of what it means to be "a thing." Fungi seem to facilitate or form a shared circulatory system between all of life, blurring the lines as they go, slithering by, busy in their work, our life.

This was questioned in the late nineteenth century, matured by Swedish botanist Erik Björkman in the 1960s, and then developed in the field by David Read and Suzanne Simard in the early 2000s.

This wood wide web, fungi's deeply woven and layered fabric connecting and covering life, is a seemingly ministerial but not reductionist system of community and connection that benefits the fungi, the soil, and the many plants rooted in its warm and healing womb. Perhaps the most surprising property of life's fungal web is its ability to enfold organisms together.

Winning is Not the Point

Communication is everywhere. This is not a substantive finding. Read today's popular nature essays and witness a deeply interactive world. Even lab scientists with their lab rats understand this.

When the wind blows, seeds are dispersed. When seeds are dispersed, they land upon distant landscape in strange ways, inanimately and unintentionally of course, we are told. They grow until some human intentionally decides otherwise. Most importantly, they grow alone, mining the nutrients they need and competing with those around them for those resources.

But Reed's and Simard's observation of intentionality within a plant's communicative pathways through its fungal circulatory system has opened a new language that extends beyond a particular species classification. And it changes everything.

Simard found that a plant's root tips are clothed in fungus and "any water the roots would be accessing, or anything soluble in water for that matter, such as nutrients," filter through the soil and its joining fungi as a two-way energy switch. From the root *myco*, like fungus, and *rhiza*, like root, Mycorrhiza fungi perform a function in Earth's womb by stepping beyond their own biological nature and becoming the roots of the plants themselves.

Arbuscular mycorrhiza go so far in this selfless act of becoming that they grow inside of the roots and within the very cells of grasses, whereas ectomycorrhiza grow on the outside of the root's cells in trees and shrubs. To make matters even more complex, *monotropoid mycorrhiza* grow as epiparasitic pegs in the host plant's cell walls but they never actually penetrate them.[54] Arguably the most famous *monotropoid* is the enigmatic Ghost Pipe, or *Monotropa uniflora*, that extends their pallid-white fungal and flower-topped phallus out of the forest floor and under beech and oaks during the early to mid-summer here in Virginia.

Fungi, like animals and plants, make up a kingdom of their own. The largest single organism on the planet—that we have yet found—is a fungus that lives in Oregon that weighs hundreds of tons and spills across two and a half thousand acres. It is believed to be between two and eight thousand years old!

Fungi are complex organisms with ancient associations. Different fungi do different things like digesting pollutants and nibbling on rocks to making medicines that heal and poisons that destroy. In 2017, a team led by anthropologist Laura Weyrich discovered in the El Sidrón Cave in northern Spain that Neanderthals over fifty thousand years ago self-medicated their dental abscesses—bacterial infections of their teeth—by ingesting fungus. Inferred from the archeological and DNA record of dental remains, Weyrich concluded that ancient humans intentionally let herbaceous material mold and then consumed the resulting natural antibiotic, Penicillium.[55] At the molecular level, argues mycologist Merlin Sheldrake in his bestselling book, *Entangled Life*, fungi are "pharmaceutically prolific" and humans are similar enough to benefit from and share our mycelial cousins' "biochemical innovations."[56]

Some fungus even augment Earth's atmosphere. Fungi explode spores—reproductive packets like a plant's seed—through what botanist Levi Yafetto calls hydrostatic squirt guns. *Podospora*, a genus of fungi found in herbivore dung, has been measured to explode at 1.8×10^6 m s^{-2}, or 4,026,485 miles per hour. That is five thousand times faster than a modern jet needs to fly to break the sound barrier and create a sonic boom. The volume of these spores equates to nearly five hundred blue whales.[57] This airborne and fungal mass is found in clouds and triggers weather patterns such as precipitation. Most strikingly, this great and entangled and explosive mass lives at your feet and we rarely even notice them.

Ecologists consider beneficial relationships between species as either symbiotic, commensal, or mutualistic. Symbiosis is when two species come together for the benefit of one or both; commensality is when two species come together for one to benefit and the other to remain unchanged but unharmed; mutuality is when two species come together for everyone to benefit. But Mycorrhiza fungi in all their complex forms do something else—they do more than co-create or co-exist with a plant's root systems, they step beyond themselves and become the plant's root systems.

Although the reason is scientifically unclear, it seems that it is more efficient to invest energy in befriending fungi than to invest energy toward the growing of more roots. Plants invest up to thirty percent of their energy (carbon) in their fungi friends. Mycorrhizal fungi are fifty times finer than a tree's finest roots and can grow nearly a hundred times farther. This is because fungal networks have thin walls, lack cellulose and lignin, and thereby require less energy to develop and sustain themselves. But this is also because friends make light work of life and fungi seem to be the best of friends.

The fungi, who lack photosynthetic abilities, trade with trees by sending their mycelium throughout the soil to harvest nutrients and water and bring those nutrients back as plant available forms to the trees in exchange for photosynthate. The fungi utilize this sugary meal to expand and sustain their great wood wide web of mycelial threads and tunnels. As they expand, the nutrients and communities the plants have access to also expand and the system becomes increasingly complex, communicative, and resilient. It also becomes confusing—where does one tree start and another end? Community and its gift, the two-way energy switch that sustains and enmeshes the eons.[58]

Mycology, consciousness, communication, and soil born gift economies extend even deeper into the atmosphere of existence.

Renowned mycologist Paul Stamets recently observed the connection between long wave sound and mycelial operations. Long wave sound—thunder, deep bass, and especially drums—travel longer as rich vibrations through the environment. As they travel, they reverberate the mycelial networks below the soils like strings on a guitar or violin. This resonance stimulates the hyphal networks to grow and spread, which in turn extends nutrient pathways and feedback loops. This long wave effect wallops like a tsunami through the ecosystem and increases the nutrient-uptake of local plants, either enrichening their near-ripe fruits or causing more fruits to grow (or seeds, leaves, nuts, or meat). Stamets demonstrated that the thunderous, human celebration of life echoes through Earth's eternity and the result is nourishment for all—the soil, the plants, the fungi, the humans, and everything in between. Dancing around the autumnal harvest fires with drums beating and feet stomping, Earth and her mycelia grow and give in a complex and communicative symphony. Consciousness settles, also like a tsunami, across all life, everywhere.

What if the modern pleas to "solve climate change" or to "save the earth" ultimately erupted as more late-night and fire-induced drum circles? What, if this is true, do we eat when we eat fruits or seeds or leaves or nuts or meat? Why, we eat the drums and their waves and their ceremonies writ in the fungal grit of Earth. What if the solution was more spiritual community and less agricultural work and management?

"The plant is fixing carbon," Simard described, "and then trading it for the nutrients that it needs for its metabolism." Vegetative life, seemingly, is an autonomous relationship where the plants harvest nutrients and communicate with their neighbors by trading with the fungi at their feet. That is, plants are seemingly conscious in their actions and are, most importantly, conscious actors within the great play of an autonomous economy—their family's great and wooded hearth. Relationship does not necessitate a holistic reciprocity, however. Is a plant's relationship with fungi only for increasing the efficiency in its own growth, as Aristotle argued? Is it only for the maximization of nutrients? Or is there more at play here?

It is important to differentiate cognition and adaption. Consciousness in regard to external stimulus may be one or the other, or both. But simple, evolutionary modes of survival, while important, are not revolutionary.[59] Adaption suggests automatic response. A humble reaction, a knee-jerk. Cognition, on the other hand, anticipates response. A vision-directed change, an understanding of the future. Charles Darwin called this the "root-brain."[60]

Through a time-sustained analysis of Douglas fir and paper birch trees, Simard observed something entirely magical. She observed cognition. As her team worked to place shade nets over the Douglas firs, to reduce or completely limit their photosynthetic abilities, they realized that photosynthesis, which should have dropped as the tree's solar exposure dropped, remained static in the firs. Planted next to a birch, the Douglas firs grew without the sun. They grew without the ability to photosynthesize. They grew. But how? Scientifically, this cannot happen. But it did. Aristotle rolled in his grave.

Simard had stumbled upon the great conversation of life, like a dancing child stumbles over the time-exposed and now slowly eroding oak's root into a face full of maitake mushrooms. Simard realized that the birch was passing nutrients to its friend, the shaded Douglas fir. These nutrients were in proportion to the amount of shading placed over the fir. As the fir needed, the birch gave and as *much* as the fir needed, the birch gave accordingly. This revolutionized everything. The great birch was keeping her friend alive and she was doing so willingly and intellectually. For, when the autumn came and her own leaves dropped, the nutrient flow switched. It did not stop, as you may expect in an unintelligent system like a car's engine that stops when the ignition turns off. No, the flow stayed on and the flow turned around and went in the other direction. The Douglas fir began feeding the now defoliated birch with nutrients, excess carbon, and the net relationship through the seasons and between these two friends was a sustained satiation through the intentional relationship of life.

In further support of cognition over adaption, Simard's student, Kevin Beiler, authored a study in the late 2000s mapping the spatial structure of this mycorrhizal-maintained collective. Beiler found that, while these carbon-pollinating networks cover tens of meters, not everyone is connected equally. Older trees have more connections with their neighbors than younger trees, indicating that time is a determining factor in communicational abilities—age, wisdom, learned knowledge. "Large trees," writes Beiler, "play a foundational role in facilitating conspecific regeneration and stabilizing the ecosystem."[61] Because of this and using these older trees as hubs in the decentralized nodal network of forest socioecology, every tree in the wood wide web is connectable in three steps, or jumps, from canopy to canopy or root to root.

This reciprocal connection's import furthers as we consider

whether life is a zero-sum equation, as some modern ecologists and their unfriendly economist colleagues argue. Zero-sum is a term used to describe systems where wealth is neither created nor destroyed. Instead, what is had and won directly asserts that the other players in this "game" irrefutably do not have and thereby lose. In other words, life is finite and its operations rotate around a fixed, finite axis—or game—and the winning of this game is a matter of collecting and amassing things, like money or energy.

But what Simard and others have demonstrated and what our ancestors have long understood is that life's network of interactions is not a *winner takes all* sort of affair. Resources are neither limited nor finite because time is at play. Yes, your hand, let's say, can only hold so much. This is its finite limit. But how much could your hand hold over a thousand years? How much could you hold if you had millions of supporters, friends giving you their hands, holding you, holding them?

This is relationship and its responsibility's infinity. It is the magic of co-relation and conscious interaction that transforms once finite resources into infinite realities of reciprocity. It is a give-and-get system where life is slowly built and balance is found over the long-term.

"Over and over," writes Simard, "the experiments showed that carbon moved from a source tree to a sink tree—from a rich to a poor one—and that the trees had some control over where and how much carbon moved."[62] If life is a game, then winning is not the point.

When you look at them, they look at you. When you see them, they see the all of you—the birch, the fir, the air, the fungi, the birds, the carbon, the crow-ravens circling above, ready to consume that which consumes.

There is no mastery in our actual world. Only gifts. We must amend our focus from dominion and growth and species dominance (even with good visions) and instead consider what undergirds the life of the system as a whole, from the ground up. Anything else is atonal.

Cellular Consciousness

But Simard is not alone in her findings. In his book, *Plant Behavior and Intelligence*, Anthony Trewavas demonstrated intellect and autonomous life at the molecular level in a plant's tissues. Trewavas found that a plant's cells have memory and a knowledge of themselves—a culture beyond the petri dish. The knowledge of oneself, or what psychology calls "self-knowledge," includes information about one's "personality traits, typical emotional states, needs and goals, values, opinions, beliefs, preferences, physical attributes, relationships, behavioral patterns, and social identity," writes professor of psychology from Mount Royal University in Calgary, Alain Morin.[63] As such, the self-knowledge that plants and their smallest cells possess does not represent a self-process per se, as photosynthesis may be a self-process, but rather the result of a complex, self-reflective, and social process.

It is a fine-tuned and directed cellular process involving memory, vision, and a sophisticated understanding of current and future needs.

In this way, vegetative plants both as single organisms and members of the greater, vegetative community, have fitness against environmental challenges—like Simard's solar shading of Douglass fir and birch—and they assess with intelligence their surroundings. They remember past events and recall past responses. Most importantly, this intelligence and cellular assessment is conscious—that is intentional, directed, purposeful.

Heidi Appel and colleagues demonstrated through their analysis of thale cress (*Arabidopsis thaliana*), a small plant from the mustard family native to Eurasia and Africa, that this innate, cellular memory and self-understanding allows plants to become strategic alchemists in their own defense. Her team re-created the vibrations of a munching caterpillar and observed that the plant amplified its production of toxic mustard oils (*glucosinolate* and *anthocyanin*) and then quickly routed those new compounds to her leaves. The thale cress did this before she was attacked—demonstrating that this was not a chemical response but a strategic alchemical defense. When Appel's team re-created vibrations that mimicked the wind, rain, or song of birds, however, the plant's physiology did not change and her alchemical weapons remained sheathed.[64]

Another study, looking at Volatile Organic Compounds (VOCs), demonstrated that plants through associative communities and their sensory processes provide biotic and abiotic dynamics for overall system survival.[65] Sagebrush (*Artemisia tridentata*), for instance, warns wild tobacco (*Nicotiana attenuata*) when it becomes damaged by grazing herbivores by releasing a number of alerting VOCs into the air (researchers claim that 60cm is the maximum distance that these alerting VOCs travel—or travel with potency).[66] Wild tobacco, sensing the good Samaritan's warnings, produces phytochemical repellents in their leaves, deterring herbivores and other browsers.[67] In other words, plants help other plants survive and maintain their defenses.

It has long been considered that sagebrush is not good feed for cattle, considering the high levels of terpenoids in its leaves—a secondary compound that upsets rumen digestion. What if intelligent, grazing herbivores understand this connection—that, by grazing sagebrush during the growing season when other forbs (like wild tobacco) are growing around it, the defoliation of the one plant increases the overall phytochemical load of the others, reducing and restricting the overall palatability and feed volume of the location. But in the winter, with less plants to warn, they graze the sagebrush. Learning to optimize foraging opportunity is, in some basic sense, a basis for survival. To make matters even more interesting, all of the research surrounding cattle and sagebrush occur during the winter months—when all other vegetation (again, like wild tobacco) is dormant and the shrubby Samaritan has no one to warn. One research team found that winter grazing of sagebrush by cattle over a three year period produced more grasses and forbs in the following years.[68] The more balanced and vegetative milieu was created through cattle grazing a plant that, chemically speaking, they could not stomach. But they did—when the overall defenses of the system were at its weakest, or most basic or simple. And the system's health slowly returned. Like two Roman consuls who shared the power, these systems alternate and balance over the years until some emperor enters the environment. Us.

Life speaks of relationship. Of a time-tested and learned adaptive response and intelligence that co-develops within animal and plant kingdoms alike. Without it, the harvest becomes predation and its members become the slaves to the emperor.

Renowned cognitive scientist and philosopher of biology, Paco Calvo summarized life's cognitive function:

> Plants, on the other, have to make it in life as rooted, slow-moving organisms that have to grow creatively instead of just walking off. In order to survive, they need to integrate many different sources of important information—about light quality, direction, which way is up and whether there is something or someone in the way—and use it to control their patterns of growth and development. Plants are constantly, and tirelessly, swaying their organs, responding to uncertainties such as soil structure, predators, or competitive neighbors. Plants have to plan ahead to achieve goals.... They proactively engage with their surroundings. Like animals in the bloodied tooth-and-claw wilds, plants couldn't afford to do otherwise.[69]

Vegetation's cellular memory produces secondary compounds when attacked or questioned and they mine particular primary compounds—macro and micro minerals and nutrients—when they need to grow.[70] They think, observe, reproduce and love, grow according to their own visions, and they do all of this while being rooted in place and being good neighbors. We transitory humans have much to learn from them.

Plants demonstrate an intrinsic life force that is also your life and my life.[71] Really, fundamentally, if we are to be honest with ourselves, it is their conscious life that allows our own to live and ours is a blessed gift that they give willingly, for now.

In his Pulitzer prize winning novel, *The Overstory*, Richard Powers speaks through the character of Bill, a forest ecologist and father of Patty, a girl born with both a speech and hearing impediment. "Real joy," Bill explains as he and Patty travel from farm to farm and forest project to forest project in his old truck, "consists of knowing that human wisdom counts less than the shimmer of beeches in a breeze." He continues, "The only dependable things are humility and looking."[72]

What plants and their communities lack is what we recognize as intelligence, a central nervous system, but they do not lack the thing itself. If anything, we lack looking and we lack what they happily and jealously possess: life in community and life in nothing else. "To see takes time," writes early twentieth century modernist and recalcitrant painter Georgia O'Keeffe. Seeing takes time, yes, "like to have a friend takes time," continues O'Keeffe. Do plants merely reproduce? I think not. We need to work on being better friends. We need to spend more time looking, not working.[iii]

What is the difference between a rock and a human?
Wrong question.

---

iii The human eye generates, it is estimated, nearly 10 billion bits of data per second. Danish writer of popular science, Tor Nørretranders, wrote in his 1998 masterpiece, *The User Illusion,* that a mere 0.00016% of this information and data is actually utilized within the consciousness of the mind. The eye may see, the mind may generate bits, but little of this becomes usable, the science says. This is why meditation and breathwork and other mindful activities yield enigmatic but not surprising results—when life slows and when life lives differently, bits of information, memories, feelings, and visions arise to the fore and they arise from the depths of our deep states of consciousness, like information locked in lockers once-secure in the underworld of our soul.

Husbandman to Hunter

We saw our farming lives as nature's savior, as rational man dictating and demanding nature's marvelous return. But Paddy opened another door, or another gate. We had long pushed for green grass in the spring and we had long pushed for soil health and enriched vegetative communities through stocking densities and the mathematical management of time—through tight and moving mobs of cattle, sheep, and goats.

Yes, our soils increased and the vegetative communities developed with it. But we never found a herd that invariably effected and was intimately affected by its environment. While we thought our grazing mimicked the natural landscape, her co-creative and fluid energies—her fungal circulatory systems, for instance—never welled to the surface and a putrid, ecological stagnancy like bog water infused the landscape.

"Then, what do we do?" I asked, again embarrassed.

"What if we do nothing at all?" Morgan whispered just above her breath. As much a question to herself as a question in response. "If fungi transform individuals into an enmeshed and tangled web of life," she thought out loud, "maybe even life forces that are animated and extended with the spirit's and the wind's vibrating energies, then what are we doing when we pull the bull out of the herd?"

"Are you asking what *is* reproduction?" I questioned. Trying to follow.

"No. I am asking—" she allowed the thought to mature, to birth a new reality, "—why are we getting in the way?"

Skating on Ice

All of winter is left to nurse its yearly wounds and stumble and weep and sleep through the cold, grey dawn, awaiting her rebirth.

We had long worked through the grey dawns and we had long questioned the point. Living seasonally was important to us but we worked when the winter slept, shoveling heaps of hay that stand uneaten amongst the muck. As if a great tide swept in and took its fine time draining away, Earth rises to meet the hay midway.

Life rises as it freezes, like agriculture rises to meet the ecological miracle that they tell us looms lovingly in the distance. If we all just work hard enough. We will see it. The miracle. Just keep looking. Keep working. Hard. Harder!

The next morning, with fungi at our feet, we did what felt like the impossible. We opened Paddy's gate, like a hydrostatic squirt gun, and did what all of our mentors and all of the podcasts and all of the books and all of the grazing conferences told us not to do: we released control.

Opening the barn's paddock gate, Paddy erupted downwind. He immediately and happily ran right past us, and our smiles and their joys followed. I cannot remember the day or the time but I well remember the joy. Morgan was laughing as we both tried to keep up with his playful, bucking gate. I remember how her icy breath struggled to compensate its joyous energy spend and I remember how her many laughs were marked between inhaled heaves for air and exhaled explosions of life. A loving laughter.

Like two lovers lost in love's lucidity, we laughed as we ran and we ran together—the three of us.

"Is this allowed?" I questioned, laughing as we ran.

"Is anything?" Morgan returned, obstinately.

I remember my boots skating over the icy, February landscape and I remember feeling weightless, like the dark-eyed junco emerging from her ashen inertia. We were late but we were finally moving. Our fixed and focused attention on soil health and its regeneration lifted heavenward and a peculiar lightness that was also a particular permutation of life's true chaos settled on the scene and we approached the main herd's gate.

Paddy's happy plunge halted at the gate and with a subtle twist of his neck. His eyes looked into ours. Time stopped, for a moment, or many moments, and he looked at us. He was not asking for permission. As though a grown child leaving home, his was a look of deep remembrance and a yearning to actualize what his body and its ancestors long knew—autonomy.

He stood still as I nudged passed him. He did not even twitch. My coat brushed his jet black curls and my adrenaline-energized blood rushed heavily through its veins. In the silent cacophony of remembrance, his ancestors screamed and danced but he did not move. He was a marble monument of muscle. A teacher waiting for his student, patiently.

The gate opened and he walked through it as though he walked through a grove of chestnut oaks, evenly and kingly. We shut the now singular herd's gate and turned around and walked away. We did not wait to see what happened. Paddy was now a permanent member of his herd. The moment said enough. We never looked back.

The drums erupted; the fungi pulsed; the heavens seemed to open up and life, in its more-full, unadulterated form, descended. The commons of Earth became less enclosed.

Entangled

While the landscape ever evolved to meet new conditions—modern climate change and the increase in summer-long droughts, for example—the herd under *our* control could not. It was like a tree without her fungi, without her friends, without her singular nature and entangled existence.

It was locked in place and we held the key. The growing of soil and plants and beef is a fine thing but it had steadily become the only thing. Our management was focused on mimicking natural and wild breeding calendars and our holistic management lacked holism in the *actual* sense. It lacked her complex, dynamic and beautiful story of change. It lacked the understanding that humans are not the only species that have reason. If anything, it is modern humanity's lack of reason that is threatening the world.

The land was our resource, but we were not her relation.[73] In the spirit of Lincoln, if we do not release control, we will be controlled and, if we do not release our hold over abundance, our own abundance will also be limited. Is it a surprise that our modern and decadent world yet struggles with the social issues of control and colonization? Is it a surprise that our modern movements around the creation of a better and more abundant world yet plod through the ecological boulevards of the colonizer? Is it a surprise that Paddy won the day?

After closing the gate, life opened in front of us. A great chasm of opportunity developed as its energies gathered, like a wave in a storm, like the sunrise, like fungi in the soil. Life opened. Inviting us to jump in.

All life depends upon the freedom to move, to be. But what if we've focused all too much on the movement and its management and not the freedom and its being?

What if humanity's control over the herbivore's evolution through overt domestication and selective or restrictive breeding is only a manifestation of our *own* faltering patterns of internal degeneration? Ungrounded ourselves, we attempt to find security through the controlling of others. Fungi and vegetation's intrinsic and cognitive cellular memory tell us, however, that life may only exist, in any true sense, when it exists together, connected, and when its connection is more like an undifferentiable and completely entangled mess of thread.

The same is true for herbivores. From the molecular cells of Paddy to those in the vegetative plants that are soon to become a part of Paddy, nature is intelligent. She is intelligent, make no mistake. Her innate intelligence is a fact that exists beyond human acumen, like galaxies of quiet stars. But she is also helping us to understand that she is intelligent, for our own sakes. For our own health. She is very kind.

Nature holds and releases, gives and gets, grows and dies, and moves intentionally, consciously, purposefully. Nature's intelligence is her relational capacity. The fact that we lack the linguistic skills to communicate with her does not impugn the self-evident truth that she is intelligent. If anything, it speaks to our own lack of intelligence. But the human penchant to be the center of everything is not new. Even the ancient Greeks had their *Omphalos*—their "navel". The center of the world, it was the home of their Delphic Oracle, their civilization's astral umbilical cord.

Old but not innate. This penchant is set and developed by the systems around us. We control breeding because we do not control the harvest. Local farmers and commercial farmers alike produce nourishment on demanding calendars that bow to the modern systems set by industrial capitalism's watch and the infinitely deep wisdom of the United States Department of Agriculture (USDA). We control what breeds and grows when because the systems around us control what is harvested when and how what is harvested is harvested. There is no room for complexity. No room for life. No room for Paddy in our modern motel. The manger only grinds.

Celebrated psychiatrist and Oxford scholar, Iain McGilchrist argues that it is humanity's evolution of a frontal lobe that sets us apart. It supports our ability "to stand back from the world, from ourselves, and from the immediacy of experience." But, instead of seeing this as a shared trait in the living world around us, McGilchrist argues that without this ability—the frontal lobe and "necessary distancing" capabilities—humanity would "be like the animals." Animals, he writes, cannot stand back from the "immediacy of experience," but humans can. Reason, in this way, is locked away, for us alone.[74] If wildness is the autonomous acceptance of the basic conditions as they are and these conditions are otherwise known as being present, then it is McGilchrist's frontal lobe that is our demise. For it allows us to leave the animalistic present.

Another story of separation, another day of control and strip mining.[iv] From Aristotle to McGilchrist, we must decide if *Homo sapiens* are mammals or mini gods. Are we created in the divine's image to stand special and above or created in the divine's image, like everyone else, our cousins, to kneel alongside?

If plants and their animals communicate intelligently, live in communities intentionally, grow and not grow according to their known and self-understood purposes, have true self-knowledge, and operate their lives under a cognitive animacy and autonomy, then controlling that life and its diverse expressions is to limit Earth's existence. It is to put her in a cage. It is to step beyond ourselves, our own purpose and existence, frontal lobes be damned.

Like loggers that churn the morning air and Earth's transcendent beauty into something more temporal, something less real. A life controlled is a life less real and, soon enough, it will become a life not at all.

---

iv This is not to dismiss the entirety of Iain McGilchrist's work, as his book, *The Master and His Emissary: The Divided Brain and the Making of the Western World,* is a truly pivotal work on the subject and influenced me greatly.

Since that cold, February day, we have run one herd as one unit. The modern world places many barriers to control's complete release. This is not lost on us. The simplicity of the solution, releasing our control over the cattle's breeding, is also not lost on us. You mean, after all that, you just opened the gate and let Paddy in? You mean, after all of that pain, you now just run one herd?

Letting go is against our civilized nature. The medicine of churning machines clogs our hardened veins and instills in us tendrils of its technology. It suffocates work upon our rest. We become bored with simplicity. We become bored outside our "constant state of wretchedness," writes Pascal. Simple solutions oft agitate the burdens of life because it is simplicity that wakes us up, distills the noxious medicine, and rives hoop from stave and breaks spells finally, like ruptured oil barrels.[v]

It was that simple? Yes. Sort of. The nature of release is complexity clothed in great simplicity. When you release breeding, you release strategy, management, and genetic flow. You also release the timed and organized ability to harvest. You release your timely control over the cycles of gestation, the strategic and profitable union of particular genetic traits, and the rhythmic flow of new life. You release the ability to manage a "finishing herd" on wonderfully rich forages that increase their "kill weights," forgoing the beef's marbling, customer-expected taste profiles, and optimized profits. You release the ability to schedule the birth of calves and kids and lambs when it makes sense for your management or the season. And you release your colonization over Earth's cognition. You release Earth from her cage. You release the ceiling of our relationship as you open up the emergent connections that are made possible only within the autonomy of an intelligent community—the herd. Cows breed when they desire. Are we to live in a world without desire?

Instead of focusing on soil health or vegetative communities or

---

v Pascal (see footnote i) wrote in his Pensées, "That, in fact, is the main joy of being a king, because people are continually trying to divert him and procure him every kind of pleasure. A king is surrounded by people whose only thought is to divert him and stop him thinking about himself, because, king though he is, he becomes unhappy as soon as he thinks about himself." This unnatural state, this general abhorrence of simplicity, leads humankind "to seek rest by way of activity and always to imagine that the satisfaction they miss will come to them once they overcome certain obvious difficulties." The connection between Pascal's thought and the modern movements that posit agriculture as some miraculous solution to either the climate crisis, modern capitalism, and more cannot be here overlooked. We abhor simplicity because we abhor silence and rest. We abhor the idea that, maybe, we are not Earth's savior. Like kings, we surround ourselves with the coverlets of work, of doing more, so that we do not realize what we are, truly. (Source: Pascal, Blaise. Pensées. Translated by A. J. Krailsheimer. London: Penguin Books, 1995. pp. 38-40).

breeding calendars or breed registries, our relationship with the land has emerged to understand, thanks to Paddy, the land as the land. The land as herself. And the land as us, her body writ in a bloody grit. Not life in this direction or that; not a regenerative life as opposed to a degenerative life; but life. Nonjudgmental. Nonlinear. This is the voice that echoes over the lands. This is the voice of Paddy, inviting us to let go. There is nothing to search for, there is only to be, to see, to witness the wonderful veins of life wandering with Earth. There is only to let go and to love that which is found when you hold nothing at all.

"You are ruining what our ancestors worked so hard for—well-domesticated animals," voice some and "you must be wealthy if you do not need to maximize production," echo others who are probably more intelligent and probably better at managing cattle than us. They are definitely richer than us.

We often struggle to reply to such comments. We sit back in silence and sadness. *No,* we think. *We just don't have a right to enslave the cow, or life for that matter, to profit, to regenerate the errors wrought by our own species.*

Anishinaabe writer from Lac Seul First Nation, Patty Krawec wrote, "when we return to ourselves, we undo the colonialism that has gotten inside our heads."[75] Holding and wearing nothing at all, our mucky boots and wet clothes strewn on the mudroom floor, Morgan and I stepped back and dropped everything. The Wildland's relationship with open grazing was born. But we had some learning yet to do.

And so ends this branch of the *Stagtine.*

SECTION II: IN NATURE'S IMAGE

III

PHENOTYPIC
RELEASE

SECTION III: PHENOTYPIC RELEASE

A Section, Inspected

In which the near catastrophic field birth of Nelly speaks—a story illustrating that, while releasing control over breeding is a fine first step, to run with them is not to step back but rather to step into. A trust fall forward, unknowing of the outcome, a becoming of community with the land and the animals as the land and as the animals. The story bounces between Nelly and short asides on the nature of wildness, how big and fast solutions precipitate small and slow problems, causing confusion and chaos, and how our long-forgiving Mother is starting to shrug in her decisions. The section concludes with an examination of phenotypic plasticity, the palate feedback loops that undergird the conscious movement and behavior of life, inviting the reader to consider whether what ecologists have called the "degenerative animal behavior" of overgrazing is really just an over-domestication of their phenotype, causing adaptation issues and not a call for more management.

SECTION III: PHENOTYPIC RELEASE

Summer Drumlins

Nelly, daughter of Nancy, was first born after the cantrefs of cattle consolidated. At the time of late spring in a valley under shadow, she spoke and her words created new worlds.

A strange perfume carpeted the soon summer meadow and an eastern breeze lifted flower petals like a child lifts rocks.

Little, white wings fluttered in little tornados across the waving sea and settled, together, like children, at the base of a dying black walnut. *In loving memory*, they wrote in colors that gently worked to cover the black soil under the dying, black giant. The walnut's juglone was now silent, the chemical its roots release to eradicate what grows around it is no longer needed when she stops growing, when she has nothing left to say.

Starlight enlivens from the outer records of heaven the sleeping hills in glancing, tangled shadows but sunlight, close and personal, calling us by name, brightens in shape shifting, sinewy light. Life settled like the petals of spring or the pebbles of old, forgotten brooks under this warm light and the step-motion strides of Virginia's hot and humid summer burst with activity.

What was once a land replete with empty stillness became an earthen pregnancy of opportunity with golden pendants of beech, a season or two old, flickering in the speckled light of the new canopy and a light wind rustling upwards, filling the void. All conjoined in this land of new life.

It was a bright, ambrosial May morning, when wildflowers man-ifest as aging daffodils and dandelions and covered the winter-torn drumlins of meadows and dreaming forests with the first colors of summer. Amber hued the day. A speckled breeze hewed the hills.

A calf was born. But all was not well.

Nancy

My hand closed around the tab of my boot. Elowyn, our oldest daughter, stumbled and fell forward into a crawl and Morgan dropped in behind us. The room was big enough for one and we struggled with three.

"Your daughter is ready for work."

I stopped my efforts and affixed the cream, leather moccasins to her little, amber feet. They sparkled as the shoes twisted in the morning light that cast through our home's only eastern window. Morgan smiled, intensely like sunlight competing with itself.

My hands returned to their task and they worked pant cuffs into my boots as I sewed them up, together. *Can never be too careful.* I thought about ticks and chiggers and spiders and field mice in the tall grass crawling up my pants to wreak havoc in places where havoc was not welcome. Morning chores with a baby in tow was not yet a feat we had mastered but Elowyn made it easy: just let her out, she was born ready to go. Even today, many years later, you can plop here anywhere in the two square miles of the Wildland blindfolded, spin her about, the world turning on its side and her stomach spilling into her throat, and she can still tell you which way was home.

"That way, I thinks, I go that ways home." She is pointing exactly home, south-south-east not south-east mind you. We are crouched together, below the sapling line, harvesting maitake mushrooms from an old, tired white oak in a woodland valley three hundred acres away from home. Mountain laurel towers over us and the sun was hidden behind a dense canopy of white pine and white clouds. She was born ready for this: she remembers trees that house owls and stumps that mushrooms and their fairies live in, she is her mother writ in different ink and her grandmother in a different age and she is our little, honey-loving and helping Wynnie.

She settled into our farm's life like a half-broken filly settles into a saddle, chafing at the strop, learning to trust the process, but never losing the wild blaze behind her eyes.

There was an unusual haste about us, this morning, like the air itself was leaving the room. Something was not quite right. The filthy, mudroom floor was caked in a clam-colored cold and Morgan's gut was uneasy. Her smile at the two of us on the floor quickly turned into something else: fear or fright that fear was imminent. We had been on calf watch the past few days and Nancy, an aged and richly pregnant cow in the herd, had been slow and uneasy. She had kept herself separate from the herd, inhabiting a lowland valley crested with cedar and clad in crownbeard, a yellow, broadleaf wildflower. Beyond lay long slopes of small knolls, tumbles of Indian Currant—a small, native shrub—carpeting Earth's floor. Beyond grazed the herd. Nancy was alone.

The valley of her choice was quick in its descent. It delved into a hollow of refuge. To be there was to be there fully and one could not see into its void without being in it, completely. A spring formed its eastern boundary, a perfect hiding place, a place of peace she called home, for now. Our neighbors, who used to farm this land, always told us that an old homestead once occupied this holler but no one could remember where—a foundation, a memory lost, like a mountain and its spring water, flowing forever into the hidden valley of time.

The open grazing system that Paddy birthed the winter prior seemed to be working but it gave us less visibility into the herd and their happenings. They ran as one unit—calves, cows (mothers), steers, bulls, yearling heifers—and as they did so our control over their running increasingly weakened. Family units emerged in un-expected ways and a spirit emanated from their combined mass and animated a peculiar movement that we could not manage, much less control. They were different, less domestic. They began making their own decisions.

Nancy's would be the first calf born after this amalgamation and its emergence, but something was not right.

SECTION III: PHENOTYPIC RELEASE

Children of Apes

"Give me a wilderness no civilization can endure," writes Thoreau. But we have put wilderness in a box. The same, slamming velvet box that once housed our diamond and gold rings.

We set wilderness over there, behind that fence. Like a local, used bookshop, wilderness draws nostalgia on the passerby but we keep walking on, for used bookshops contain poor lighting and poor lighting struggles to make anything glitter. There is nothing of value there, inside those old, papered walls. Those pallid words of forgotten worlds.

But our own walls are now closing in. They are pallid in their own ways. The privilege of modernity is beginning to crumble as we realize that the glittering technological age that garishly ushers us into a migraine infused blindness that is really just the age of human ascendency is not compatible with a finite world, a living world of limits. We are told that we are on the front lines of the Anthropocene, that our work helps The Cause, that we are saving the world, that the chancellor needs our blood.[i] We open our eyes, just above a squint, and find that we are not unlike the unlucky youth of old, those barely molding under mounds of rusty Earth, standing in aisles of death, trenches good for nothing but trench foot. We see a world on the edge. We see a world that we do not want. We see an end, a death seeping and streaming like a toxic,

---

i In his Pensées, Pascal writes, "The chancellor is a grave man, dressed in fine robes because his position is false." This is "why we have found might when we could not find right." We have robes to spare. We have youth to give. (Source: Pascal, Blaise. *Pensées*. Translated by A. J. Krailsheimer. London: Penguin Books, 1995. pp. 23.)

green ghost into our cratered Earth, our piss-stained trenches, the shit welling up around us, our western front.

Not unlike the soldiers of the first World War, we are discouraged by the popular travesty of green movements without purpose and purpose without any movement. Today's movements are the conscripted youth of another war. We have returned to the unimpeachable industry of amassing conferences that inspire, papers that conflict, truculence against the machine but not defiance against its source. We have largely given up the attempt to ground this work, once amassed in theory, into any larger, more solid, living, or complete reality. We say Earth needs saving, that her climate is in a state of emergency, beckoning the end of the world as we know it. Billions will soon be homeless, refugees of climate disasters. We say holistic agriculture will save the day and then we complain when it does not adequately fill our pocketbooks, as if five-hundred-year-old white oaks or million-year-old meadows care for our capitalism, our papered profits.

We created this: not the climate but capitalism. And now it destroys us: not the climate but capitalism. Like Ilúvatar spoke to Melkor as he led him into the Void in J. R. R. Tolkien's *The Silmarillion*, "And thou, Melkor, wilt discover all the secret thoughts of thy mind, and wilt perceive that they are but a part of the whole and tributary to its glory." Like Melkor, we will never meet this glory because we have long missed the tributary. Like Melkor, our minds are dark. Our existence as moral beings seems dependent, like oceans on moons, upon the existence of an order of things. Trees grow up and out to touch the light; grasses wave when the wind blows; acorns fall in their time. Nature's order forms our own. This is reflected, like light on moons, in what wells up within us, what Charles Taylor calls in his great work, *Sources of the Self*, "desires, sentiments, and affinities."[76] Earth is the source of truth but knowable only through the individual self's experience of kinship—community. It is not self-expression that creates self-understanding, but self-understanding through a community's expression, interbeing, and communion with Creation that all is created. The self understands itself through nature because nature is the self. But this can only be true when the interbeing of Creator and Creation are well joined and celebrated—the divine vocation is order's foundation—but industrialism and its capitalism is the monistic materialism of separation and it is ravaging Earth, separating her people.

Taylor laments, "To see the full complexity and richness of the modern identity is to see, first, how much we are all caught in it, for all our attempts to repudiate it."[77] Our minds may create but it is the gods who lament and look down and it is the gods who allow it all to happen. For now.[ii]

Big solutions inhabit what can only be small problems and big corporations with big ideas and big desires rush in to colonize what is left of the local environment, the local youth. The chancellor calls all of us to arms.

But nature, clothed in her hidden diamonds and as my friend Rob Lewis writes, "nature, word with roots still covered in soil," sits quietly. She was never invited to the conferences. She was never asked to speak. She was never allowed to write the papers.

Our desert-occupying and blood-birthed civilization is a vulnerable organism. Organism? Yes, for our hands created it and we were created, at least recently, out of it.[iii] But our now cultivated world is the measure of our success and its ensuing catastrophe is the measure of our demise. We yet swim outside the gods' tributary.

As anthropologist Paul Shephard writes, "we can go back to the Pleistocene because, as a species, we never left." Our western legacy is a strangely pious attention to the creation and destruction of things, like gods. Even in the writing of this book, as I discussed my viewpoints with a colleague, they questioned, "yes, but what should humanity do? *Be one mammal*, I got it, but what should this mammal do?"

We are wonderfully gifted but to be good at something is not quite

---

ii Charles Taylor writes in the preface of his work, *Sources of the Self,* that the enlightened and modern "moral philosophy has tended to focus on what it is right to do rather than on what it is good to be." (pp. 3) Taylor continues toward the end of the book, writing that "we are aware of this significance through our inner nature [the need of interbeing]. In that the good to which nature conduces is now a purely natural, self-contained good, and in that the proximate moral source is a self-subsistent order or interlocking beings, to whose principles we have access within ourselves." (pp. 315) Source: Taylor, Charles. *Sources of the Self: The Making of the Modern Identity.* Cambridge: Cambridge University Press, 1989.

iii Consider Chapter 2 of J. R. R. Tolkien's *The Silmarillion: "Of Aulë and Yavanna,"* wherein Aulë, "unwilling to await the fulfilment of the designs of Ilúvatar," created the Dwarves in secret, mining the first of the Seven Fathers of the Dwarves in the mountain halls under Middle-earth. But Ilúvatar responds negatively to this co-creative act, asking, "Why hast though done this?" and "For thou hast from me as a gift thy own being only, and no more." The extension, here, for us, is to consider the difference between co-creation under divine Creation and complete autonomy to create whatever we may. Co-creation does not imply freedom of creation. (Source: Tolkien, J. R. R. *The Silmarillion.* Edited by Christopher Tolkien. Boston: William Morrow, 1991).

the same as loving it or being loved by it. Thomas Huxley in his 1860 Oxford Evolution Debate with Bishop Wilberforce famously asserted that he would rather acknowledge an ape as his ancestor than be a priest careless with progress.[iv] Like Shakespeare's Hamlet, we have "lost all [our] mirth" and the modern, human world "seems to [us] a sterile promontory" and a "foul and pestilent congregation of vapours." Progress and its foul and pestilent world are driven by forceful acceleration.[v] Time runs downhill, it collapses under its modern priests' careless weight.

From the first flakes of stone tools to their iron counterparts took nearly three million years. From the first iron tools to the hydrogen bomb took only three thousand. The Paleolithic era covers around ninety-nine percent of the human story and the biological evolution and cultural development that flows through its patient veins is a story of slow change: the world one was born into was, more than not, the world of one's death. While climatic variations punctuated a culture's history and punctured a people's mythology—ecological disasters, famines, tectonic shifts, and so on—generation by generation, life flowed imperceptibly between birth and death, dawn and dusk. This is the "pace of nature" that Ralph Waldo Emerson wrote about. Life lived in *true* reciprocity—from the Latin *reciprocus,* meaning backward and forward simultaneously.

But progress and its profit were at the tent flap and cultural development eventually outpaced biological evolution and the destructive feedback loop that Rebecca Costa in her book, *The Watchman's Rattle* called the "cognitive threshold" took hold.

There is a "crucial relationship between evolutionary change and the modern human condition," writes Costa. Biological evolution is often uneven and slow, driven by mutations and environmental selection. Adaptive faculties progress over millions of years through time-sustained intimacy and place-based development that change

---

iv This debate was not transcribed at the time but this paraphrase gets to the gist of Huxley's thought.

v In his Pensées, Pascal writes of knowledge and the natural state and pace of the mind. "The world is a good judge of things, because it is in the state of natural ignorance where man really belongs. Knowledge has two extremes which meet; one is the pure natural ignorance of every man at birth, the other is the extreme reached by great minds who run through the whole range of human knowledge, only to find that they know nothing and come back to the same ignorance from which they set out." (Source: Pascal, Blaise. *Pensées.* Translated by A. J. Krailsheimer. London: Penguin Books, 1995. pp. 22.)

and emerge with the local ecology as a whole. Biological evolution cannot happen in a vacuum.

Cultural development, on the other hand, often outpaces its local ecology and runs awry before human cognition even embarks to understand it. "The point at which a society can no longer 'think' its way out of its problem," writes Costa, is the state of standstill and collapse. While culture and its progress are numerically cumulative, innate intelligence and communal development either within a species or across multiple, symbiotic species is not. Cultural development *is* a vacuum.

We formed the combustion engine and now we are burning to death. We globalized the human community and now we, the lonely billions, die unescorted into granite-white graves and with no families or tribes at our side—only the beeping of our vitals lull us into our eternal sleep. We made fire our slave only to develop better weapons for defense and now we have blast craters for mountains and our tectonic plates shake us away, like a dog with fleas. We made energy and homes out of old growth forests but suffocate to an ugly, pale, and young death.

Victims of our own success, we cannot evolve our way out of this. Progress, the seductive success, that leads to disaster. Long has this ruin crouched in the doorway, our tent flaps flirting with its destruction and long has it longed for us. Evolution has nothing to do with it. Deserts may be the gravestones of civilizations, but rebirth is a powerful thing and we are drifting eastward.

But rebirth is not progress. Make no mistake about it. This book that you hold in your hands is not a book that seeks a revolution in how agriculture is done. It is not a book that seeks a revolution at all. It is not a book about progress. We do not need a revolution. Agriculture is not our problem.[vi]

We moderns have a strange relationship to the Pleistocene, as best-selling titles such as *A Hunter-Gatherer's Guide to the 21st Century* or *Why We Need to Be Wild: One Woman's Quest for Ancient Human Answers to 21st Century Problems* well demonstrates. We look to the Pleistocene for answers to our modern problems like we look to medicine or alcohol. But modern medicine is the third-highest cause of death in the United States and alcohol is the fourth.[78] We look for answers from our soft beds and air-conditioned homes that are constructed from toxic chemicals and herbicide-infused, genetically modified, and monocrop pine forests. We look for answers through electro-magnetic frequencies that throw our very-electrical body into microwaves and we do this on machines constructed from precious minerals that level mountains, displace indigenous peoples, and are mined by enslaved children. I write this on a computer, no less.

The Pleistocene began nearly three million years ago, which is, geologically speaking, only a wink in Earth's history. But in human terms, the Pleistocene is the deep and rich abyss of our species. The modern civilization of the last half a percent of our species' life has become our lifeblood, to some strangely biological degree, but civilization is struggling—it has always been struggling.

Nelly

The dawn was deep into day when we descended into Nancy's valley, creeping slowly, past the cedars and behind the crownbeard. Morgan carried little Elowyn in a pack and we held our breath. The late, May morning carried petals and early season grass seeds along the ridgelines to the walnuts but nothing stirred in the deep valley. Breath and its breeze were held, the moment seized everything. Wynnie was rapt, spellbound under the moment's purity, her little hands scrolled around Morgan's arms in a radial love, like two trees growing into each other. Her eyes were fixed on the gooey mass whimpering in front of us. She was the first to see.

There, under Nancy's feet was a little, black calf, shivering like a leaf in the rain. But Nancy was rigid, her heart pounded through a single thread, a slow pulse, a weak murmur of life. Germinate streaks of the valley's light colored her crescent, high cheekbones and clear fluid, perhaps a tear, cascaded into a free fall to her feet. *Pain and Joy,* I thought.

"No, something is wrong." Morgan said aloud, seeing into my mind. A tendril of panic arose in her before her eyes could recognize the dire paint on this life's canvas and she walked forward, cautiously.

She inspected the calf, a heifer, and found it deeply malnourished. Nancy's teats were dry and her udder sullen and sunken. To survive, the calf needed colostrum, the first-milk or what olden farmers called beestings. Colostrum provides a calf's first macro- and micronutrients and supplies peptides for antimicrobial defenses and immunoglobulins for immune system support.[79] It wakes life up, like the morning chill or the bite of a bee's sting. Without it, after a period of days, the heifer will die.

"Nelly," Morgan said, turning to Wynnie. "Her name is Nelly, daughter of Nancy." Her voice was stiff, inflexible, as if her desire for the heifer's life could find manifestation in meaning, in naming. She turned to me. "I can't find her placenta or anything left of it. Nelly looks like she's been licked dry, probably born sometime last night or early this morning, but she doesn't look like she's nursed at all."

Nancy's afterbirth never delivered, a rare but not unseen reality in the world of cattle farming. After a cow calves, it cleans: the calf, licking it dry, and its placenta, passing it and then, most often, consuming it. On rare occasions, the placenta can hang from the cow and drag for days. Cleaning typically happens within an hour of calving but cleaning requires the calf to nurse—the maternal magic, a hormonal crescendo from womb to mammary that releases the afterbirth and prepares the colostrum. But Nelly was not nursing and Nancy's placenta was stuck.

We brought them water, praying that time, peace, and space would provide a cure. I dipped a rubber tub into the spring to their east, an ancient stone rim patched in brambles, now wholly covered under moss and mold. Oak leaves piled in ranks and rusted the new water as it flowed into the tub. The spring was shallow but fresh and flowed, gently, like an elder's slow hand. The swift growth of sycamore—a tree known in ancient times as *sūkomoros,* the fig mulberry tree—covered an old junk heap only strides downstream, a sunken pit, an iron-colored life of welter and waste. Another engine, half a tractor's axle, an old cook pot, a shard of glass, five thousand more. I wondered how many had come before me with buckets, with thoughts, with fears.

We took turns and visited them hourly throughout the day but nothing changed and the calf weakened. From our limited but rhythmic observations, Nelly never got up, never walked around, never tried to nurse. Nancy stood and paced, slowly, in a small, moon-shaped crescent orbiting her calf. Then, she lay down herself.

Staying down, her head dropped. Later in the afternoon, we called the vet in a panic.

"She needs an antibiotic," he said before I could deliver even a quarter of the story. "A retained placenta could infect."

"Will antibiotics help deliver the placenta? Then, she'll be able to produce milk for the calf?" I was thinking of root causes and not surface solutions. But I was also thinking in fear.

"No. But it will save the mother."

SECTION III: PHENOTYPIC RELEASE

Amber Messengers

We stood, together, in Nancy's dusk-shielding valley and stared emptily at each other, praying for an explosive conjoining of mother and calf. The vet could not come out for another three days and we knew that, if something was not done soon, someone soon would be taken. Carried early from us, into the second world.

We researched solutions in old and worn nutrition books that we unearthed from old, paper-walled bookstores over the years and unpeeled scientific journal after journal trying to find associations between what we were seeing and what others, before us, also saw. A clam in an ocean of mollusks. One sentence in a journal from 2008 mentioned the role of Sulfur, a macronutrient, in the synthesis of proteins and catabolic stress maintenance (whole-body loss of muscle protein).[80] Was Nancy suffering from a catabolic response, impairing her internal maintenance and management of stress? Sulfur is also yellow and I had heard an old timer in Ohio mention years prior that sulfur deficiencies can be seen in the yellowing of flowers and plants in meadows—that vegetation yellows or deepens its already yellow nature when it grows in sulfur deficient soil.

Amber wildflowers rippled on the ridges around us. The spring daffodils that often grew as white reminders of the passing snows were this year, yet unnoticed by us, not white at all. They were green and yellow spears of spring. The crownbeard at our feet, an autumn blooming and native, yellow wildflower grew this spring in a yellowy-green. Earth was providing the ocular of opportunity and our eyes began to open.

Was it possible that Nancy's health problems were rooted in a mineral deficiency that also colored the landscape around us?

In The End

At the iron gates of the colosseum to the red-stained, marble halls of American Empire, to the incineration chambers of fascist racism, to the Spanish inquisition or the burnt streets of Salem, we have no choice but to abandon the hope that civilization is the underwriter and patron saint of progress and morality.

Life today is perilous. As we climbed the ladder of progress, we kicked out the rungs below us. There is no going back, in the fullest sense, without jumping off the ladder entirely—there is no nice way about it. We can look back to the Pleistocene to construct best-selling and social media attuned books that speak to the masses from our air-conditioned writing desks, but we cannot *actually* go back to the Pleistocene without deeper change—the jumping off the ladder kind.

Ninety-six percent of all biomass today is comprised of huddled humans and our equally huddled gardens and livestock. The wild—that is, everything yet unfenced and everything not yet castrated, tagged, measured, and fattened—makes up a lonely four percent. The wild has become a rounding error in ecological calculations. Where is nature? Her bones have long decayed under our feet, any traces of her truth threatening to be lost in the digestion of earthworms and nematodes. She is hiding. She does not like ladders, never has. But she is not silent.

We have long cheated our children, trading leisure for luxuries, gods for gadgets, and dirt for chemically infused cleanliness. When our rampage has come to a final end, our toxic corpses, which neatly occupy equally toxic landscapes, will be unearthed by archeologists who wear hazmat suits and work with radiation detectors, not trowels.

"Nuclear and chemical warfare were their destruction," one voice will echo across a university seminar hall on some distant planet.

"No, life," another will return. "They called it life."

The wonders and relations of Earth have been, are being, and will be perfectly replaced with things less beautiful, less real, and less raw. Earth weeps, she has long wept, and she is about out of tears. She will only hold us for so long. We have colonized her past, present, and future with a slavery both explicit and implicit in the creative and "world-saving" operations of our *new* mother, Mother Culture. But even this, a mother strangely of our own making, will only hold us so long. Debt and energy and chemical production have become the world's top predator and the prey is steadily running out. We have enslaved Mother Earth to erect the glittering Mother Culture and now both are turning their backs on us. We can never go back. "The way is shut" and "the dead keep it," echoes King Theoden in the *Return of the King*. Or was it another lone voice from the back and dimly lit corner of the university seminar hall on that distant planet?

The age of civilization has long ended, its embers smoldering over students trapped in the physical structures that enclose them and now grow out of them, like flame. We have a facile contempt for incarceration but not crime.

Our long-forgiving Mother is starting to shrug in her conclusion that letting the children of apes run the workshop was a fine and fun experiment for a while, but in the end, was a bad idea.

A Fresh Breath

I called our local feed store and asked for a bag of sulfur.

"You making meth?" they questioned hesitantly.

"No, I'm saving our cow's life." I replied stubbornly, caught off guard by the forwardness of her question. They sold us one small bag, nothing more, just in case I was lying. We paid in cash.

Morgan and I did not know if pure sulfur would kill or heal. We did not know if Nancy would even take it. How do you feed sulfur to an animal? Do you mix it in something else, like grains? We had not thought of that, nor did we have the grain to try.

Late that evening, standing stupidly in her valley, doubt delved its way deeper into our guts and we paused. We had poured pure, yellow sulfur into an old rubber bin and I held it in my hands like an offering to some distant god.

"Put it down and let's go." Morgan was tired and I think it all felt a bit too intimate, too personal to her own body's hardships in nursing little Wynnie the past few months.

I did and we left. Stepping slowly backward, our eyes fixed on Nancy like they were fixed on a Queen in her hall in another age. We walked slowly home, quietly, only Wynnie's cooing echoed in the darkness.

The next morning, fearing the worst, Morgan and I crested the hill of cedar. Our stomachs lived in our throats all night. Would Nancy take the sulfur? Would it kill her? Would it heal her? We felt alone, unequipped to manage animals, ill-informed by lost generations before us, unready for life.

"If only your grandfather was here," my mother would often say to me. "He would know what to do, you know? He could touch the soil and it would grow tomatoes. He put copper and old, iron nails and pipes in his garden long before you all decided that it was cool." My grandfather, an ancient Croat, died of a brain aneurism, unexpectedly and instantly in his basement when he was sixty.

If only, I thought as Nancy's black mass appeared in the little, dawn light before us. She was standing and the rubber bucket of sulfur lay upside down in the crownbeard. Our heart sank. I reached slowly to turn it over, expecting to see a pile of yellow powder mildewing the soil below. But nothing was there, just dry grass in a sea of dew. I crawled on my knees and lowered my head below the canopy of yellow-green vegetation, searching for the pure, yellow particles. There was none.

"Daniel!" Morgan cried from behind me. "Look!"

The new dawn and valley light colored the germinate streaks of Nelly, now on her feet and perched under the crescent shape of Nancy. Startled by the attention, Nelly pulled off the udder and looked at us. White fluid cascaded into a free fall to her feet.

Pain and joy, I thought.

Morgan grabbed and squeezed my hand.

I squeezed back.

Nelly smiled.

Soul Friend and Beginnings

Tradition is not the worship of the ashes but the preservation of the fire, like pursed lips.

In my genetic memory, I have over thirty words for meadow, but I have never walked in one. Long has assimilation been worked finely over the irons of civilization, its metallic song echoing against falling trees and their hills. The songbirds left with their people and the meadows followed. Oral history became pagan mythology and our language was nearly forgotten. We were colonized by civilization thousands of years ago. Today, my feet trod realms unknown to them, unfamiliar, and I am worlds away from my ancestors' dreams. My hands work in unfamiliar graves.

Purling waves that rise, in our language, is *tonnadh*. It is also a word describing death by poison. *Tonnach* means tempestuous, *tonach* describes the work of an undertaker, and the verb *tonaim* means 'I close the mouth of a dead person and prepare them for death.'[vii]

Waves, from the root *tonn,* are important in ancient Irish mythology. We have the phrases and tales of *Tonn Tuaithe, Tonn Rudhraighe,* and *Tonn Clíodhna.* In his recent book, Manchán Magan connects these three phrases as "supernatural forces that thunder" around Ireland's island perimeter, "protecting the land, binding and controlling existence." Waves are creative forces. But

vii While studying the Irish language, many online mediums serve great use. Manchan Magan's book, *Thirty-Two Words for Field: Lost Words of the Irish Landscape,* published in 2020 by Gill Books is a wonderful and wonderfully entertaining resource and is utilized here for this chapter.

they are also grounding. They serve as a raft in our creation story.[viii] *Lugh*, god of sun and light, skill and art, and member of the *Tuatha Dé Danann,* a group of supernatural beings and earlier residents of the island *Ériu* (or modern-day Ireland), sailed to this land on waves that "thundered a welcome."[81]

Tonn Tuaithe carries a peculiar and ancient memory in her auditory and cirrus rippling. It is a phrase that describes a wave that calls back the landscape through ripping ice: the glacial events of the Last Glacial Minimum (LGM), more than twenty thousand years ago, when the great cascades of ice sheets receded and carried debris from the northern coast of the island and placed it in Church Bay. In *The Second Branch* of the *Mabinogion*, a collection of oral yarns carried by the Celtic *cyfarwydd* (storyteller or bard) that were first written down in the mid-fourteenth century, the god-character *Bendigeidfran* walks across the Irish Sea's land bridge between modern day Wales and Ireland, for "the sea was not wide then" and people watched as the mountains and their forest moved and walked the waters.[82] This ancient oral tale holds the life of between twelve and nineteen thousand years of ecological history, before the waves of *Tonn Tuaithe* crashed in, curling the lands of Wales and Ireland apart.

It is memory older than civilization, infused in a culture and language and writ in the heart of a people whose connection to the land and the waves crashing and purling at their feet is at once present and primeval. The linguistic similarity between *Tuaithe* (describing the glacial waves that created the land), *Tuatha* (describing the folk of the land's gods), and the word *Túath,* (meaning community), should not be overlooked.

From the vastness of the heavens to the unformed floors under the infinite duff of the deep woods, humanity shines an intimacy assembled from a quick smile, a turning glance. We have become so good at solving problems that we have well purchased the narrative that ours is a species that masters tools, that thinks intelligently. But, on our worst days, a human smile can lift us up. Even our tools fail at

---

viii See also the Introduction of this book, detailing Amergin's song.

this simple task. On the coldest days, a smile provides great warmth. This is not because we are anything special, with these two eyes and a nose perched atop stretched and splitting lips, this divinely bland and bipedal creation, but because it is especially us: me, looking back on me without my judgements, my fears, my hidden truths reflecting back.[ix]

This is, in some sense, the ancient Gaelic phrase *anam cara,* meaning "soul friend" or "friend of my soul." In their ancient and Celtic ways, nearly lost after a thousand years of domestication and forced assimilation, my ancestors understood the soul as an uncaged spirit, a divine light that flows in and through us. *Anam cara* is friendship beyond ambition or pompous pageantry. It is truth nestled, like a little mouse in the duff, comfortably, safely. It is a quick smile, a turning glance, the warmth of a thousand fires.

The ancient Celtic mind suffered not under dualism—it did not separate to understand, it did not trade imagination for articulation. It worshiped the circle and understood light as a kin of the darkness. *Anam cara* is this kinship, something that cannot be cleft from its landscape or disentangled from her infinitely affectionate embrace. It is a culture of connection where the face is the divine animation of the soul's articulation, an echo of what lies beneath, like Nancy and Nelly's germinate and milk-covered smiles. Our *anam cara,* our soul friend, resonating the germinate streaks of the valley's truths back at us and teaching us what to do next: let go.

And it is in this echo, this reconnection with our ancestors, with those holding this wisdom among us, and those wild cousins that stand stalwart against our progress and who are yet living and rapping in a cage of bones at the base of our crumbling ladder, this bursting memory, that nourishment and its wild reciprocity really begins. Kincentric rewilding is a journey of letting go, like learning your ancient language. It is at once real, at hand, in front of us and also progressively reawakening inside of us, unfolding from

---

ix Humans do have one, strange feature about us: we have white in our eyes. This is a strange, sociocultural adaption in our development over the eons. The white allows us to see the dark pupils that swim and dilate in their veined spheres. It allows us to determine where another human is looking, how they are looking, and more. It also allows humans, to some degree, insight into each other's deeper emotions and attentions. We are social animals, that much is true, and it may also be equally true that our socialness is scalable with our abilities to see, to read the open books of our neighbors, to cooperate interpersonally—that is, communally. Source: Hare, Brian. "Survival of the Friendliest: Homo sapiens Evolved via Selection for Prosociality." *Annual review of psychology* vol. 68 (2017): 155-186. doi:10.1146/annurev-psych-010416-044201.

our core, slowly, ancestors and their dreams walking around and cementing our feet in the sod.

Phenotypic Plasticity

Humanity's modern penchant is control. Nutrient deficiencies are solved by adding nutrients. Health problems are solved by calling health professionals. Cattle are destroying the world, some argue, but it is humanity that built the fences; humanity that constructed the regimes mortared by property rights and boundaries that restrict and reduce life's actual freedom. It was humanity that forced them there.

But what if Nancy was telling us not of her nutrient deficiencies but of *our* delinquency? What if the problem was not pasture management or nutrient balancing or the eroding and denuded soils beneath it all, but the lack of place-infused genomics writ over ranks of generations? A problem of the ungrounded, those whose ancestors sleep in distant graves.

In 2019 I wrote an article for *The Permaculture Research Institute*. I argued that animals are master nutritionists, for they daily sift and sort through hundreds of species of trees, grasses, forbs, shrubs, sedges and rushes, each vegetative life infinitely unique even amongst families. If yellow Indiangrass grows alone, it grows in a particular way and possesses a particularly unique combination of primary and secondary compounds available for herbivores at certain times of the day or during certain weather patterns. If yellow Indiangrass grows in a meadowland, rich in undulating diversity and amongst a multitude of supporting forbs and legumes and slightly shaded by a community of supporting trees or shrubs, it becomes something else entirely. The nutrient profile of vegetation changes and its palatability for grazing herbivores transmutes either positively or negatively given the community, the soil, and the time or season in which it grows.[83] To know is to know communally. To know separately is to know only sadness.

To be alive, animals must recognize this. But to be alive and well, animals must be able to understand this—that is, they must have memory and cognition—and they must be able to relate to it. Life's ability to act autonomously and intelligently *is* life.

A friend and mentor, an *anam cara,* Dr. Fred Provenza has long sought to unravel our linear and regenerative models. In his monumental book, *Nourishment,* Provenza discusses the *instinctual* and *acquired* cognition intrinsic in the healthy operations of our wild and living world. In his chapter, poignantly titled "Challenges for Guests," he argues that what modern man and its science calls "idle wanderings" of grazing herbivores is really a nutritional study of the highest intellectual order.

With internal self-understanding and external observational fluency, grazing animals satiate their undulating nutritional needs by sifting through the great diversity of chemical and biological foodscapes. This behavior, it seems, simultaneously challenges their hereditary wisdom (the ancestral knowledge passed to them from their mothers) and forms their budding instincts (adaptive epigenetics developed through their own lives) that allow them to do more than simply survive, but thrive in our dynamic and ever-changing world.

Provenza is not alone in his analysis. Following their observation of a group of goat kids infected with ten thousand gastrointestinal larval nematodes, Juan J. Villalba and colleagues documented an immediate change in grazing and foraging propensities in antiparasitic plants, such as *Pistacia lentiscus,* or the mastic tree. The infected goats performed "therapeutic self-medication," Villalba wrote. They were able to understand the problem and find the solution. Root cause analysis is something humans struggle to complete, or at least to complete well. But these goats excelled at it, immediately.

Gastrointestinal parasites manifest their effects as anemia, hemorrhages, weakness, increased mortality in both the young and the old, decreased milk production in does and sexual vigor in bucks, and severe weight loss, often leading to death.[84] Upon infection, the goats, young and inexperienced, immediately turned to anthelmintic plants containing high levels of tannins and self-medicated proportionally to their needs. Tannins are produced by plants as a defense mechanism—a palatability-limiting agent to reduce grazing or foraging pressures of undulating ungulates—but these goat kids employed as medication what the antiparasitic plants deployed as defense: a symbiotic relationship for the restoration of a holistic, balanced health. Plants produce chemicals for their external terrain's defense and animals, to defend their internal terrain, employ biochemical alchemy through grazing and selecting their diverse diets.

How did they associate weight loss with increased parasite load? How did they understand their own infection levels so as to self-medicate properly and in proportion to their needs?

Generational genomics. A learned and given process, the orosensorial and post-ingestive feedback loops of the tannin-rich plants educate and form a medicinal behavior that becomes nested in genes. Villalba's research discovered an interesting anomaly. Goat kids from another breed that were not infected with gastrointestinal parasites consumed the antiparasitic plants "irrespective of infection."[85] These particular kids' prophylactic and wild alchemy was the manifestation of ancestral relationship via an adaptive landscape genomic. Their understanding was not their own, constructed from individual processing but was a collective understanding, passed through genes. Today's prophylactic grazing was the outcome of yesterday's learned medicative successes. Grazing is ancestral dreamwalking.

Provenza's research corroborates and extends these findings. In a 2010 paper in the *Journal of Animal Science,* a group studying the interrelation of maternal nutrition and fetus development found a direct relationship between maternal nutrient deficiency during neonatal development and muscle mass in their offspring.[86] If a mother experiences malnutrition while pregnant, that experience is handed, directly, to her offspring.[x] Health is intrinsically linked, they found, to both one's ability to self-medicate and one's ancestral

x See Section I—intergenerational linkages through mtDNA of Holocaust survivors and their children.

ability to self-medicate over many generations. Health is given in genes.

We see this same reality in humans and this should not surprise us. In her book, *The Hungry Gene,* Ellen Ruppel Shell demonstrates that, in children who were born to mothers pregnant during the winter and famine of 1944-45 in Holland, they were eighty percent more likely to develop chronic diseases, diabetes, and obesity later in life, regardless of other factors. Individual choice matters but even individual choice is imbued with generational flavors. Provenza calls this a "predictive adaptive response," that works through "developmental plasticity in utero and early life to modify form, function, and behavior in ways that confer survival."[87]

Affective and Cognitive Loops

Phenotypic plasticity, that is, the ever evolving and observable characteristics where your given genotype and your environment converge, is the intergenerational play of evolution in place. As animals exhibit grazing instincts over an undulating diversity of resilient, vegetative communities, their orosensorial and post-in-gestive feedback loops become wisdom's nested wellspring. Its weight is multigenerational grazing instincts. Time and an intimate connection with place are required for evolutionary adaptation to occur well, for health to exist at all.

Connected to the particular nuance of their ancestor's place through their genes, young animals well adapt to new stimuli because the new stimulus is really just old pressures with new solutions. But here is the problem—in researching plasticity's role in adaptive evolution, Anna C. Vinton and colleagues discovered in a 2022 paper what they termed, *phenotypic lag.* This is the time that exists between the *mean phenotype* and the *optimum phenotype.* If this lag is too large, the species will collapse. That is, if the evolutionary genetic convergence between a species and its environment is disrupted or moves too slowly in respect to the movement of natural climate and microclimate evolution or change, that particular species is threatened with extinction.[88]

While animals may be great nutritionists, their education requires a community-infused genomic whose success depends upon the intimacy of that relationship—their relationship between them and their ancestors, between them and their current landscape, and between them and the ever-changing nature of tomorrow. The behavioral modifications that follow an animal's affective and cognitive feedback loop results ultimately in an adaptive landscape genomic built through a herd's collective wisdom and transferred through the herds collective genome. But this only happens in time, and this only happens when time plays well with family—Vinton's *phenotypic lag* threatens a community's life when the herd's collective communion decreases. Separate the herd and you separate its river's rich and deep watered convergence with its *phenotypic optimum*, its Chesapeake bay, its legacy.

Just as yellow Indiangrass grows differently in different communities, so also do the herds of herbivores affect their herbivory. "By learning from mother and peers...behaviors become part of the foraging culture—the collective nutritional wisdom," Provenza writes.[89] As each conscious cell in every plant's tissue is consumed by each conscious cell in every herbivore's tissue, the autonomous and great multitude of life is conjoined and made singular in the embrace of the community's nourishment, as the many undergo a marvelous and singular death and as the many are reborn as the nourishment of all.

This wisdom is passed within the herd via relational osmosis and reproduction—collective nutritional wisdom—but it is only sustained when the herd is allowed to be a herd. The Douglas fir can only feed the birch if they grow together and grazing herbivores can only become master nutritionists and conscious actors in their lives if they are raised together and then allowed to graze together, in their own ways.

Phenotypic optimum is the convergence of life with that which is well living: ancestral lineages and families written in the landscape herself.

SECTION III: PHENOTYPIC RELEASE

Overgrazing as Passivity

Releasing breeding and running one herd, Paddy's call the previous February, in some large sense stirred our sortie into a more-wild paradigm of farming. Nancy's valley, on the other hand, called us into deeper connection, for she showed us that, while we had released some of our control, we still held onto the reins.

If *phenotypic plasticity*, an animal's social and genetic ability to adapt to its microenvironment through time-sustained microprocesses, is a species' ultimate survival mechanism and characteristic for thriving, well-being, balance, and health, our management has to change. And then, it must emerge with the life around it. Nancy showed us, delicately but not ungently, that our system of agriculture played on the edge of our degenerative penchants. We were trying to become better at harvesting; better at getting improved outcomes in soil health and biodiversity and carbon out of our atmosphere; better at producing grass-fed and finished beef; better at honing our management to optimize the vegetative landscape's energy flow and solar conversion; better at cycling nutrients. But we were also becoming better slaves to the industrial and linear machine of progress—Costa's cognitive thresholds be damned. We were about climbing the ladder, rungs be damned.

The registration of our greening agriculture in the halls of scientific theory as an axiomatic system constructed in the image of natural process reflects a barren architectural passion. Like a roughed-in shelter, it is marketed as good enough. But good enough for what?

It is far from a home, with generation's toes tapping on the beaded and beaten oaken floors and a fire rapping in the time-blackened hearth, its broth boiling over and winter tales carried by the hush of candlelight above it all.

Our herd was locked in *phenotypic passivity* and they were locked in place. What they were was not a product of intergenerational genomics playing happily through a *phenotypic plasticity* that chaotically and lovingly converged with its local environment into an emergent abundance writ in the ancestral wisdom of life. They were agents of production. Not children of Earth.

Overgrazed and Understocked

Whether you read *Regenesis* by the environmental activist George Monbiot who argues for a farm free future or *Saying NO to a Farm-Free Future* by small-holder and cultural critic Chris Smaje, who, perhaps obviously, argues for a farm filled future, you will witness a narrative whose climate and local place saving sights are fixated on grazing animals. According to their 2013 report, *Tackling Climate Change Through Livestock,* the United Nations argued that global livestock and their supply chains emit an estimated 7.1 gigatons of CO_2-eq (carbon dioxide equivalent) per annum, or 14.5 percent of all human-caused emissions. Fossil fuel spend, sector wide, accounts for about 20 percent of sector emissions.[90] This means that both the animals themselves and the ways in which they are commercially raised, moved, slaughtered, and sold well contribute to our modern "climate crisis."

But this is not a new or modern debate. John Acocks, a South African botanist, and author of the 1951 classic, *Veld Types of South Africa*, was one of the first to document the connection between cattle and the landscape's desertification. Working in the early 1930s within the advancing Karroo desert, Acocks studied the increasing ecological and social degradation of desertifying land and famously argued, "South Africa is overgrazed and understocked." That is, too few animals are on lands for too long.

Overgrazing occurs when herbivores remain in a given area for too long or return too soon and repeatedly consume, graze that is, the same plants over and over as they attempt to regrow. The process looks like this: after the initial grazing and defoliation event, the plant draws on its root or crown energy reserves (think a bank account or battery on your cell phone) to regrow its leaf material. After a certain period, the plant recovers sufficiently to transition its growth's supply from root and crown energy to sunlight energy and photosynthesis begins. As its new and recovered solar panels (leaves) optimally work to transform solar energy into oxygen and glucose (photosynthesis), the plant also replenishes its root and crown energy. Its cellular memory is gearing up for herbivory. Overgrazing is when repeated and sustained grazing pressures prohibit individual plants from undergoing this root-to-sun-back-to-root cycle and, after enough time under this abuse, the plant dies.

When you drive through a rural landscape and notice grass growing like putting greens, this is most likely because it is tired, blade by blade it sleeps, and not because it was just grazed. Its landscape is dying, slowly, from its roots to its fruits.

Domesticated herbivores, the experts tell us, select their favorite plants first and, after those are killed off, the animals steadily work through their next favorites and so on until all that is left is sparsely populated communities of undesirable plants. In brittle environments, where precipitation is irregular, this leads to desertification; in non-brittle environments, where precipitation is more regular, this leads, most often, to forests or desertified shrublands.[xi]

And so, who do we have to blame? Who are the monsters of the mudsill? Some today argue that grazing herbivores are inherently evil players in the climate arena. But Acocks and his future colleagues argued that it is not animals but our human management of their grazing that makes the difference: the mismanagement of time and movement within conventional grazing methodologies is the problem, he and others argued, and not the animals themselves. This same idea is well captured in Diana Rodger's 2020 book and following Netflix film, *Sacred Cow,* as, "It's not the cow. It's the

---

xi To learn more about the "brittleness scale" and its important weight in how it effects biochemical decomposition, see Allan Savory's *Holistic Management, Third Edition: A Commonsense Revolution to Restore Our Environment,* Third Edition, Island Press, 2016.

how." Animals do not cause desertification or climate degradation, but the mismanagement of animals does, it is argued. The solution, while it takes many names today, is called non-selective grazing.[xii]

Conventional grazing methodologies that supposedly deteriorate the environment manage for low stock densities that produce low defoliated landscapes with low nutrient cycling and high percentages of standing and underutilized herbaceous material. Over time, this wasteful and low functioning system steadily evolves into decadent shrublands where farms and their profits struggle and, eventually, all settles down, like a tired retiree, into a bankrupt dessert.

Non-selective grazing emerged to save the day through the management of a high stock density of grazing herbivores to produce highly defoliated landscapes with high nutrient cycling and low percentages of standing and underutilized herbaceous material. Over time, this "regenerating" and "high functioning" system steadily evolves into abundant grasslands where farms and their profits thrive and, eventually, all settles down as a developed home to feed our billions.

But is this narrative true? From grazing to profit, conventional to non-selective, is *any* of this true?

Degraded Wisdom

Nancy and her valley showed us that we had been asking the wrong question from the beginning. What if, when Acocks saw degeneration among selective grazing regimes, what he *really* saw was the degradation of the herd's grazing instincts and wisdoms in a world wrought by human control? What if overgrazing is just *phenotypic lag*? What if ecological degeneration is really just *phenotypic passivity*—communities of life unable to adapt to their surroundings? What if herbivores lack adaption and relationship, not management?

"We've come to rely on fences and grazing systems rather than culture to influence diet and habitat selection," argues Fred Provenza.[91]

---

xii It also goes by management intensive grazing, mob grazing, rotational grazing, high-density grazing, non-selective grazing (NSG), adaptive multi-paddock grazing, or total grazing. I am sure I have missed a few but you get the point.

What if we focused more on co-creating a *phenotypic optimum* centered around extended families, relationship, epigenetically derived balance, place-based knowledge, and culture and freedom, in place of competition, excessive breeding, and rotational fence systems? What if *phenotypic optimums* could yield a world teeming with life? We have bred grazing herbivores to do only one thing: grow. We have focused herbivores on eating only one thing: the grass we plant or the grass that happens to be in their paddock that day. We have engineered herbivores to exhibit only two characteristics: taste and size. And we have neglected nearly everything else. Some breeders argue for heat tolerance or marbling (remember Section I), but all center on production.

Remember, overgrazing is when herbivores destroy their food source by re-grazing herbaceous material that is yet regrowing. It is time we begin asking ourselves: why are we comfortable claiming that nature, left to her own, destroys herself? Only modern humans are that dumb. Yes, only domesticated humans would engineer herbivores to be little, destroying humanoids.

Phenotypic plasticity does well to describe our own problem, I think. Morgan and I started farming to save my life. That was it. Saving my life in the most basic sense was the extent of our desires and vision. But in doing so we enslaved the animals to heal the soil. We brought in cows from cultures not of this land and told them to regenerate. Nancy's internal problems were sedated with sulfur but not released until her phenotype was free to ebb with the land, to build, together, with its soils, and to undulate and select freely from the resulting vegetation. How can animals learn to self-medicate and epigenetically adapt to landscapes if they are forever told where to go, how to live, and what to eat? We were focused on non-selective grazing to prevent desertification or the forest's return. We were good stewards of the land's resources but missed altogether that she is not a resource. We were destroying the adaptive landscape genomics that sustain life. Kincentric rewilding was emerging, whether we liked it or not.

Release Ourselves First

That morning's revelations overpowered our purely intellectual paradigms, a sunrise cresting over a once obscured valley.

The landscape was at work to resolve its sulfur deficiencies. That much the yellow wildflowers and their yellowing grasses well knew. But Nancy was locked in place, she had no *anam cara*, no soul friend.

The release of breeding was the first step of remediation. Paddy showed us that. Releasing the herd from our management's control and progressive penchants came next.

Later that afternoon we changed the name of the farm from Timshel Farm to Timshel Wildland.

"What is a wild land?" Morgan asked.

"Wildland as one word, I think. *Wild* is not an adjective. It is her," I said, my arm pointing out the window, hoping a squirrel in the nearby walnuts would pick it up, be listening, would care.

"Isn't that just giving up? Like, we now just do nothing and release everyone?"

"I reckon we have to release ourselves first."

Rewilding is many things to many people. For our purposes, it is that which holds life, wildly and autonomously. Many "rewilding projects" begin by importing once-native species. Others commence by erecting ten foot tall game fences to restrict what comes in and what goes out. Even others begin by herbiciding everything to start fresh—removing native plants and their peoples.

Nancy had other plans. She invited us into relationship: to run with her, to accept the basic, imperfect conditions as they are, simply, openly, honestly, as holders for all of life to imbue with its colors, songs, vibrations, sounds, communities, forms, feelings, and energies. Then, from that humble and slowly-filling place, she invited us to accept our role as conversationalists, partners, co-creators—Earthlings in the truest sense. Inseparable from Earth, we are life. When we learn to run with them, we accept the equal extension of responsibility with our two and four legged cousins for the future of the world.

Leave your subduing at the door.

To run with them is forgoing, to some large degree, the visions we have—regardless of our desires. When you run behind a herd, you can steer them, push them in this direction or that. When you run in front of them, you can manage their speeds. But, when you run *with* them, you waive all of this goodbye, your control, your visions for the world, your mastery over the outcomes, and simply become what you already were: them, us, Earth and its Earthling.

Rewilding and running with them, in these early years, also allowed us insight into a new paradigm with new questions. When making decisions, we began asking: what is the framework that allows us to ask this question? And then, once determined, asking: is this action defensible given this framework?

For instance, we as a modern and groundless people strive to heal the climate. What is the framework that allows us to desire this? Our modern abilities to do so, of course: to affect the weather through strategically polluting it, to harness hydroelectric power and solar energy by blocking rivers and cutting down forests, to utilize fossil fuels to plant crops to make fossil fuels, to mine metals from mountains for industrial manufacturing to heal eroding hillsides, to produce tractors to plant biodiversity, and so on. Our ability to heal the climate comes from our ability to destroy it. Are we comfortable with this ability? Are you? Is attempting to save the climate an action that is defensible? In other words: is saving the climate worth destroying the climate? No seriously, I am asking...for a friend.

To run with them is the relearning of being human once more, one species amidst the great, rhythmic, and sometimes painful melodies of Earth. It is letting go but not giving up. It is releasing hope in order to find it again. It is, like smoke and exhaled breath, about life in the fullest sense and not life that is full of things. It is letting go by diving deeper, by stepping into. It is also about rediscovering the wild not as a place that holds our wonder or a place that holds our more primitive and less developed but happier lives. But a place that is our wonder, that is our place, that is our lives, but not owned by us.

If this is hard for you, know that it is and has been awfully hard for us. We drink from the same poisoned chalice. We live in service to the same machine that takes industrial capitalism for granted and Earth as resource as its guarantee. That, unlike the wind's wailing and the torrent's tears, this chalice, this machine grinds not the landscape but the roots of its peoples. And it is gaining ground.

SECTION III: PHENOTYPIC RELEASE

A Journey of Palates and Place

We early realized that, while many rewilding projects existed around the world, they all began with moving companies—they work to remove unwanted animals, people, and nature's actual chaos and then work to import native species to grow and run about within their prison yards of exclusion fences. To heal the rivers, they buy beavers. To heal the beavers, they buy rivers. To heal the grasslands, they bring in ancient breeds of cattle that look wilder than the ones we have today. But these ancient bovines bawl like everyone else and come in modern trailers and they come ready to be told where to go. A global phenomenon, rewilding is about wild species and not about species that grow wild together.

While these projects may have their worth, we decided that our path would be led by what we had: we would run with Nancy and we would all grow wild together. We would learn from them and they would learn from us. It would be a process, a journey of letting go, a progression of dismission not of species but masters, a step by step becoming of true relationship—rewilding is not a thing but a process. They chew the cud, we chew the fat, and we all grow wild together.

The Magic of Minerals

After releasing control over breeding and running one herd that grows and develops and lives together, loosed from the productionistic rhetoric of modern, agricultural systems—what we called open grazing—Nancy and Nelly escorted us to the next step: a co-creative and cyclical mineral program.

Plants construct their bodies from atmospheric carbon molecules and air, the latter comprising about seventy percent of a plant's makeup.[92] These elements combine with solar radiation to generate the biochemical marvel of photosynthesis. Soil carbon is a by-product of this plant physiology in motion, when a plant's root structures deposit carbon through root exudates into the soil like you deposit food into your larder.[93] The greatest carbon sequestration and storage system ever created: sunlight, air, and water dancing together deep into the dirt.

These root exudates release complex carbohydrates and proteins containing carbon. It is a community block party. This process enlivens and attracts bacteria and fungi living in the soils that depend upon these gifts along with a plant's cellular material that is cast away—or sloughed off, as some say—when the plant grows. But bacteria and fungi are low in the soil food web's trophic cascade and this process also draws protozoa and nematodes and even larger organisms like arthropods, earthworms, voles, and more. The nematodes and protozoa slither and slide with waving flagella and vibrating cilia to consume the bacteria and fungi, primarily for their carbon. When they, in their turn, are consumed or die, they will release the once-carbon molecules as transformed and primed plant available nutrients for the process to feed itself, what is called "nutrient immobilization," and repeat, eternally. Nearly eighty percent of a plant's nitrogen comes from protozoa![94] This is the rave of the rhizosphere. But this rave is energized by minerals.

Minerals are nature's alchemical tool that enables this miraculous process. They provide the fundamental enzymes that help catalyze solar radiation into storable glucose—carbon to be given and traded and consumed in the wonderfully raucous rave. The heart of this process is chloroplast and its blood is chlorophyll. But, without an adequate amount of essential minerals, the chloroplast weakens and the plant either withers or becomes attacked by predators.[95]

The primacy of mineral balancing that in substantial part nurtures the relationship of nutrition and herbivory has long been ignored. Pioneering research from Virginia Tech entomologist, LeAnn Beanland has recently demonstrated that insects attack plants containing simple amino acids, given that they are easier to digest and process than protein or sugars.[96] Sugars in plants provide "sweet immunity"—photosynthetically active fructose and glucose cells that flow through the plant within the phloem as the building block for cellulose and amino acid synthesis along with immunity.[97] When plants suffer from mineral imbalances, free amino acids increase ten times and their overall immunity descends, exposing them to a pest's predator pressure. Dr. Beanland and colleagues have demonstrated an inverse relationship between mineral balancing and pest pressure. Plants without access to adequate minerals are attacked and plants that have access to minerals attack pests. Packaged sunlight, minerals and their sugars are the magic of the meadowland, the sunlight's spell: the autotroph—the creator of life through nothing but love, community, and starlight.[98]

Magnesium is an essential constituent in this physiological and biochemical process, inhabiting the core of chlorophyll and aiding in the production and deployment of photoassimilates, activating enzymes, and synthesizing proteins.[99] Other minerals, themselves just electrically charged, combined molecules, provide support for a multitude of other cellular processes. It has been postulated that healthy soil is nearly forty-five percent minerals.

Nobel Prize winning biochemist, Linus Pauling argued, "You can trace every disease and every infection to a mineral deficiency from unequally yoked energy fields." They moderate and regulate the soil spirit's tetrahedron: chemical, physical, and biological life. Minerals in the soil, to a degree and in both associative and direct ways, contribute to its nutrient richness. Charles Waters, the founder of Acres U.S.A, argued in his introduction to Dr. William Albrecht's work, *Soil Fertility & Human and Animal Health* that, while minerals are one aspect of the soil health, they act as the "gatekeeper."[100] Combined with soil organic matter, arthropods and animals, inert material, and microorganisms—a mere teaspoon of healthy soil contains nearly a billion bacteria, yards of fungal hyphae, thousands of protozoa, and dozens of nematodes and holds nearly fifty-nine percent of all life on Earth.[101] Primary minerals are Earth's long term source of geochemically derived nutrients that result from the weathering of feldspar and micas, and secondary minerals result from the low-temperature, charged reactions that surround this weathering.[102]

Any deficiency or imbalance in the minerals in the soil results in a deficiency or imbalance in its vegetation and animals, humans included. Just as minerals were an essential function for the creation of energy through soil and its plants, they are also required to break down the digested material's chemical bonds to release such energy. Any deficiency in minerals within one's diet will accompany an equal deficiency in total digestible nutrients within the foodstuffs. Without proper mineral balancing in the soil, the bioavailability of nutrient-dense foods plummets.[xiii]

A Focus on Forage

Our land, degraded and deforested, lacked this biochemical alchemy of balance. The music in the rhizosphere was quiet and the dancers were sleeping. Rocks may weather in the aqueous womb of Earth, producing minerals to co-create with the life around them a catalyzed energy from sunlight, but the rocks were exposed, lifted to the surface through erosion and diesel engines that tore roots heavenward from ancient forests and her meadows. Health teetered on the scale. If wild animals, through *phenotypic plasticity* creating a generation-infused and place-centric adaptive landscape genomic, can deftly assay the nutrient qualities in their surroundings and self-medicate accordingly, reviving and then releasing this deep instinct, the animal's discriminatory palate, was pivotal.

Up until this point, our management provided a balanced mineral mix for the herd. While this is the streamline in agriculture today, it does not come without problems (Nancy sure agreed!).

Take for example a cow that consumes forage that is deficient in magnesium. We call this grass tetany: when spring temperatures and heavy rains boost cool-season grasses' growth so that their nutrients

---

xiii Like stress, as we saw in Section I. Both stress and minerals directly contribute and regulate a substance's nutrient bioavailability. See "Interlinkages" chapter in Section I.

are diluted by their own moisture content, leaving the lush and green grasses deficient in magnesium. Over time, the cow understands its deficiency and walks over to the one-bag-mineral-program to consume its needed minerals. The perfectly mixed mineral ration contains the proper ratios of calcium and magnesium, among other compounds, but the cow is deficient in magnesium and not calcium. When she licks the mineral mix and consumes both calcium and magnesium, she becomes even more deficient in magnesium and so she again walks over to the mix and again licks the mineral and again receives the proper ratios of calcium and magnesium. This cycle continues until the cow is so deficient that the vet is called.

Too much calcium prevents magnesium from being absorbed. The cow started her journey deficient in magnesium and not calcium. Every time she licked the perfectly balanced mineral mix, her deficiency in magnesium heightened and exaggerated. Every lick of the mineral mix made her more deficient in minerals. This is what was happening with Nancy.

Beyond the mineral deficiencies that this system often yields, it also separates the herd's palate, their internal physiology, from the world around them. Minerals and the supposed health that follows are something they are given, handed by humans, and not a living force they interact with. If we could kincentrically rewild our palates, that is, if we could connect self-understanding, self-medication and the undulant and building community of life around us, talking to us, we could release mineral supplementation altogether. Release begins in the palate.

We began this process providing what has become known as cafeteria-style free choice minerals—a multi-compartment container that follows the herd from pasture to pasture and contains twelve different minerals, all in elemental form. If Nancy needed sulfur, she could go to the bin and get sulfur, or calcium, copper, selenium, iron, and so on. This system also helps remineralize degenerated soils. Up to eighty percent of the minerals a grazing herbivore consumes they give back in their manure. If the herd, today, grazed on calcium deficient forage, they took calcium from the container and gave calcium to the soil.

Every day, we worked to document what minerals they had taken and the species of plants that grew in that region. We combined this data with soil tests and created a complex metric of what minerals existed where and what minerals failed to be uptaken (rave of the rhizosphere, remember?) through vegetation's photosynthesis and its soil food web. It is important to consider that, while minerals may be present or balanced in the soil, if no plants or surrounding microbial communities are willing to mine and exchange them, if their rave is silent, these minerals are of little use to herbivores. Certain meadows may have adequate minerals but no vegetation to uptake them; certain meadows may have inadequate minerals but great vegetation to mine them. Health is balance and health is only found in community.

Over a period of four years the herd's ability to match their internal physiology with their external biotic realities collided and their grazing as "lawn mowers" transformed into their foraging as master nutritionists. Cows tend to graze clovers in the morning and grasses in the afternoon given the flow of protein throughout the day. But ours started consuming unpalatable forbs—weeds, you would call them—that are considered toxic or unpalatable to cattle along with tree bark and shrubs. Grass became an afterthought. We stood amazed as one bull, Nuadu son of Nelly, walked up to a mature white oak tree and snaked aside its leaves with his pale, purple tongue and consumed the branch instead, wood and all, like a goat. The herd began sifting through large stands of poison hemlock, one of the most toxic plants for animals and humans alike in the greater Piedmont ecoregion, nibbling on the clovers and forbs growing below. Some even began consuming the poison hemlock!

With their own internal and social emergence erupted a simultaneous surfacing of vegetative biodiversity.

Now that you see us, a chorus of voices echoed across the healing hillsides, *for who we are, we will stay, we will be with you.* Kincentric rewilding was at work.

Life seemed ready for the next step. Utilizing daily observations, soil tests, and years of notes, we began strategically restricting the minerals that we knew the herd would need that day. If they were grazing a pasture where historically they would have devoured sulfur, we took away the bin of sulfur. If they were grazing a pasture where historically they would not touch any minerals, we would take away the bin entirely. Through grazing, they were sampling soil, associating the digestive feedback loops between their palates and their place. Through internal and social *phenotypic plasticity*, they were self-medicating and sampling the biochemical alchemy around them. If the mineral bin was present, it would be a crutch. It was an educational tool and the students were ready to graduate. Removing it gently would slowly force their reawakening instincts to focus on forage, not us, as the medicator of the meadowland. When they needed calcium, they turned to dandelions; when they needed magnesium, they turned to plantain.

Remember our earlier conversation about grass tetany when the spring grass grows apace from its mineral acquisition and results in magnesium deficiencies? Plantain, a forb high in magnesium, even in the spring, is one of the earliest spring plants to grow. It is as if she knows this, is here for this, and is waiting to be seen. One to one and a half dry matter pounds of plantain—*Plantago Major,* to be precise—has been found to satisfy the magnesium needs of a well-framed, modern cow.[103] If the plants grow in soils deficient in organic matter, microbes, or minerals, it could take up to four dry matter pounds. A well-framed cow can easily consume thirty dry matter pounds of forage a day and so these numbers are entirely attainable, if plantain and the cattle's palate are both present. If you needed an impact on why *phenotypic plasticity* and kincentric rewilding matters, this is it: if an animal will die if they are not supplemented with magnesium in the spring by their human masters, and that magnesium supplement is derived from modern industry mining and pureeing mountains into powdered minerals, "nature" is just another word for a life dependent upon the modern industrial complex. Nature knows, nature holds, but nature must be let go in order for her to do anything at all, or anything in love. Plantain is there, waiting, speaking, patient, freely willing to give, waiting.

Our adaptive oversight, over time, indicated that we needed to increase their Vitamin A supplementation when they grazed in the heavily clear cut and eroding lands, given the psychological stress that fifty-acre blackberry stands produce. Vitamin A is an essential nutrient affecting many metabolic and physiological systems, namely vision, gene transcription and a bolstering of the immune system—all of which they needed in greater degree when thorned canes towered over them. We also expanded the bin to include selenium when they grazed within the old tobacco and dairy fields. Selenium is simultaneously lethal and helpful to plants and animals but it plays a critical role in antioxidation, feeds essential soil microorganisms (*archaea*, a prokaryote similar to bacteria), regulates vegetative metabolism, and detoxifies the system of heavy metals.[104] Inside the cow, it facilitates Vitamin E absorption, defends the animal's cellular metabolism, and is essential for glutathione peroxidase activity, or the repair of oxidation of lipid materials, fats and hormones specifically.[105]

We all were learning, slowly, emerging together. Letting go is not stepping back. It is diving into right relationship with Earth and all her Earthlings. But it is a process, a journey. A journey that we as humans also needed to go on as well—learning to self-medicate and wild forage (Book II of *The Wildland Chronicles*).

Removing this educational crutch was the first step in releasing our control over their palates. It is important to note that forcing domestic animals to self-medicate through vegetative feedback loops in landscapes deficient in biodiversity is like asking an infant child who cannot even crawl to feed themselves—immoral, neglectful, and totally missing the point. It has to be a process—an intentional, loving, and intimate process of letting go where, step by step, we all become more free, more animate, and more living.

Over many years, the herd reproduced and grew as its surrounding biodiversity exploded and through it all a conscious and cognitive community combined at the confluence of time and place, of Earth and her animals, awakened and danced. Today, we only provide rock salt in the winter. It is moldy by spring.

And so ends this branch of the *Stagtine*.

IV

LOST HERDS, WOUNDED LAND

A Section, Inspected

In which a herd of goats speak through death, pain, and true joy—a story illuming that open grazing must in fact be open. That we must forego the progressive mythos of our modern minds that pin competition as nature's driving force and to understand that, in its place, lives extended families, relationship, purpose, and kinship. The chapter flows from the trials and victory of Mara, a matriarch in the goat herd, to the examinations of the nature of soil health, the cyclic and prehistoric nature of agriculture, and the need to rise as hunter-husbandmen. The section concludes, walking readers through the ancient mammalian landscapes to break the spells of herbivores as mobbing, moving, and mowing engines for our regeneration. The reader is invited to consider: what if we truly let go and ran with them?

Phalanx and Flowers

Mara, matriarch of the goats, had three sons. One afternoon, as often happens with those in need, she escaped her limits and dwelt in the dark woods. She returned after two sennights to speak with us. We listened.

A light cleaving the clouds harkened upon an oak tree. Its branches spilled silvery dew upon the ruddy backs of a herd of goats, themselves lost in a breakfast of oak leaves and oak nuts. Light, water, and attention falling downwards, a moderated melody, a ballast of the belly.

Behind, the hill rose slightly and found a deep browning bed of this year's grasses. Goldenrods, fleabane, and the geometric master boneset held pinnate against time and remained tall, their once great, summer flowers slowly rusting into reproduction. Beyond, a thicket of greying forest, young and new, scurried up a steep bank, charging the cedar phalanx planted atop the next ridge. Some ancient battle repeating itself, some ancient feud awakening every night, the cedars winning. The hill is never taken.

It was here, under the oak tree and upon a forgotten meadow where a row of spring poppies used to grow that the goats decided to stop and pass the afternoon. Atop the oak a lone lark threw threads of many colors, germinating the last of summer's song into the air. The goats stayed at it for some time and after a few mouthfuls of some smoked jerky that I carried with me, I settled down myself into the meadow's grasses, closing my eyes. I awoke to the late sun. She was steadily sliding down the eastern forest, skiing rays of distant, orange light upon their grey trunks. They were nursing their wounds from this morning's charge up the hill. They had lost many good trees. The cedars had turned them back, routing a fine defense.

"The sun is medicine. Right Dad?" Weymouth, our second child often asks as he rips his shirt off, exposing his oak pulp stained and sapling thin frame.

"Medicine, that is right."

The surgeon's tent, the meadow's medicine—the sun healing feuds and their forests, I thought, rubbing my eyes clean of sleep.

My face flushed with sunburn and wind. I checked for the goats. They were still foraging under the oak.

An Evening Journey

We crept down into a shallow and flat river valley, trampled by time, crushed by charging trees, or smoothed by some great current, we did not know. The water flowed gently and the goats lapped in turns. They approached the river as a child approaches fire, drawn indelibly but slow, remembering the pain and progressing limpness of the startled cottonmouth. Time tested muscles tensed and their hooves moved unhurriedly. Their latitudinal eyes scythed through the shrubbery and pierced east and west and then east again. Their horns spiked shields above them. A coyote hunting pack or a meandering black bear sow may lay just downstream.

Or maybe not but who is to know? The rash are dead in reckless graves and so we cannot ask them.

We skirted the far side of a frog pond, the upturned, clay bottomed root ball of a great red oak whose crashing end fashioned a shallow home for reptiles and a stable perch for birds. We then steeled up the adjoining ridge and the valley's water mixed rudely with the meadow's acorns and cultured a ballasting liquor in their bouncing bellies.

Everyone walked single file behind the lead buck, Néit.[i] He seemed to be following some inner map and he held our trust. *Has he been here before?* I wondered. About midway we chanced upon a trail made by deer. It rose, patiently, in steady turns up the confused back of the ridge. The upward side always cutting the hill

---

i The Celtic god of war. Pronounced *Neh-CH*.

downward—hooves, the first Earth movers. Cedars gathered around us but the trail found the way, winding up and then down as we climbed but ultimately out. *Maybe they got directions from the deer?* The evening light of the loosening canopy mixed and mingled with the cedars at the forest's edge into an orange hued red and then into a pale green of another autumn meadow.

Pyros, we called her, the meadow. A ten-acre pocket, really, in an otherwise forested block of the Wildland. Limestone bedrock marginally clothed in capped dirt and American Persimmons, *Diospyros virginiana*—the autumn pyros, the tawny-tinseled epilogue of summer.

We arrived once ascended into a grove of crawling honeysuckle, once more thick in autumn. It climbed the closest Persimmon to the forest's edge. Japanese honeysuckle was introduced in 1806 on Long Island to bring beauty to an otherwise concrete land. But it ran away, as plants often do, and has become an edge habitat and early successional nuisance for most. She often twines saplings and shrubs into an ornate mass of green and yellow speckled with snowy white. Known in China for thousands of years as *Jin Yin Hua*, she also treats wind-heat in the body.[106] A pathogen of the Yang type, Wind's direction is upward and exogenous. Wind ails the upper body, causing headaches, coughs, and sore throats as defensive Qi weakens and pathogens invade.[107] She also contains chlorogenic acid, a natural flavonoid and powerful antioxidant currently associated with neurodegenerative diseases.[108] She is a fine friend of the forager and veils every tree in the meadow, like brides.

Whatever their reason for coming, before long the goats foraged their fill and the sun settled into her final set. Everywhere over the field and under the shifting shadows of the honeysuckle hedges lay the ragged remains of summer. The cold grew as the sun set and goats and trees once more were on the move. The day's camp concluding. The last fires setting steel for the last battle. The cedars quiet, waiting.

We started our walk home. This time I was the lead. The sun shone like corporeal flame clipped between fertile darkness and fecund starlight. We descended straight into the valley, jumped the river downstream from before, now a swift trickle leaping and lifting pebbles over a deep-riven bed, and climbed the gentle bank back again, keeping the oak on our right. Another meadow, another moment, maybe tomorrow we could do it again.

Earth fell ever eastward and down into another valley's pond where shelter and the night's milking awaited us. We walked in silence, shifting like shadows, the pale echo of hooves on rocks the only sound. A murder of crows perched on the polished needles of a towering pine but said nothing. Dead silence.

The leveling, last shafts of the set sun beat awkwardly, wobbling like drunken trees in the autumn wind and broke, finally, into flickering fissures of grey and green ribbons. Darkness had come, falling into the deep dusk.

Morgan busied to ready the milking parlor. We had work to do. The wind rose. The goats milked. We cleaned up. We tucked them away, safely, from the wind and her coyotes. We walked home, alone. The warm, meager milk sloshed in the jar.

Soil and Saber-Toothed Cats

Harmony is combined self-expression adorning one, great melody. So it is also with Creator and their climate.

We are approaching a colossal collapse, I believe, and we have some decisions to make. Since the early twentieth century, the human population has quadrupled and its environmental load has increased more than forty-fold. What we experienced during the COVID-19 era illustrated, regardless of how you fall on the particulars, Rebecca Costa's "cognitive threshold" for human problem solving. We ran this way and then we ran that. We jumped higher and fell flatter. Ecologically, we are steadily degrading our biosphere with industry and green energy projects that attempt to heal it.[ii] Agriculturally, we are steadily building our soils by creating pastured CAFOs of mobbing herbivores who are subservient to our will and slaves to our desires.

Kincentric rewilding is not equivalent to the essence of the wild. Plenty of books about rewilding and relearning to live a wild life occupy the best-selling bookshelf ends in large bookstores and live long atop Amazon's algorithmically curated lists of recommendations. But they talk about the wild as a thing, over there, with an

---

ii Articles displaying research and field findings mount against the ecological use of industry to heal ecology, from solar panel waste in landfills to those sent to third world countries instead. No matter the mineral mines in the Congo enslaving hundreds of thousands or the discarded acres of used wind turbines. You can block the rivers as well; the salmon don't need them. Do they? It is also important for us to consider the toxic radiation of alternative technologies. From EMFs rising in solar fields to water usage in AI technology. In its latest environmental report, Microsoft disclosed that its water consumption spiked to nearly 1.7 billion gallons in 2022. Cornell recently claimed that "the global AI demand may be accountable for 4.2 to 6.6 billion cubic meters of water withdrawal in 2027, which is more than the total annual water withdrawal of...Denmark or half of the United Kingdom" (arXiv:2304.03271).

essence living in its thingness. "We must learn to become wild once again," they write as though "the wild" is clothing that we can don if we want to. If we just try hard enough.

But we will never experience her ultimate expression so long as we merely conceive and push forward her idea, put up with her as a practice that some implement around us, or evade her entirely. As long as we remain tethered to her in some abstract form, her essence remains locked away from us. "Names can name no lasting name," the great Taoist master wrote and the essence of something is held not in what it encompasses, but in what allows it to encompass anything at all.

Life is not what we see, but what holds our sight holds our life.

This is in the same way with soil. The purely accurate is not yet the true. Truth seeks true relations and it is out of this pure relationship that material and essence and creation work together to construct what is accurately and commonly known as the truth. Soil health and the many modern movements that have been constructed around the soil's suspected importance in regard to the healthy future of mankind (it is always in regard to mankind's future) is something that appears purely accurate to us but it is not yet something that is true.

Since the European Enlightenment or even before, we have been comfortable to represent cause as that which fetches something's nature. After fetching something's nature, cause may also be that which puts that something to good use. Cause is both the fetcher of the deed and the application of the good—the using of the tool. We are familiar with modern tools—hammers, technology, electricity. But the cause to fetch the hammer alongside the cause to put the hammer into good use is also a tool.

Time's play over life's death and chaotic rebirth is the sticky substrate out of which "the soil" is born. This complex matter is co-responsible for the soil. It is a microbe enmeshed aggregation of life and death, fungi and bacteria that emit a gluey glitter that both cements and repels the soil's particles and plays an essential role in protecting organic materials from biodegradation.

Soil health is indebted to this multimember process for it is out of this that the soil in some true form exists. But the soil's debt is not to fungi or Actinobacteria generally, for these particular members contribute as the matter comprising the soil's health here, in this place, and not the matter of the general place across everywhere. Matter is a local property and soil is indebted to its local friends.

The idea extends. The health of the soil is indebted not only to the local matter it contains but also to the aspect or form created by the local matter that allows it to contain anything at all. Remember, essence is what allows us to hold and not what we hold.

Science enjoys reductionism like an alcoholic enjoys alcohol or a college student enjoys inebriation—not intrinsically but in effect. The effect of linearity upon the human intellect is in the same way as it is with alcohol—it reduces overwhelming complexity to manageable realities, if only for the moment.

The modern, "save the climate movements" talk about and view the soil and its health, it appears, from this singular perspective: the effect of soil health is the strong future of humanity; the effect of soil health allows consumerism to continue without destroying the world but also without changing the heart of the world; the effect of soil health allows the depredation of modern life to appear less desecrating; the effect of soil health is a better world for humanity, now; the effect of soil health is a better world for me, always me; the effect of soil health is the admixture between a "better" world and, in all reality, the same world as we were born into—where the reign of industrial capitalism and its greed gets simply more rain, more fuel for its production.

If the soil was to save us, we would yet have the industry that originally colonized the soil and we would need the soil to rise up again and continue saving us again and again and again, like we need pistons in our cars to keep pushing and pushing and pushing us forward. And so, what is soil? And what is soil health? Both the life in which the property is known as soil (matter) and the property in which the soil appears as knowable (its form) are in their respective ways co-responsible for soil. Even humus, the greasy black rot sandwiched between life's fresh death and death's fresh, new life is comprehensible only as the co-relation of matter and form, of death and new life.

We can call this its "soilness." But it is not yet true. To have self-knowledge is good; to have purpose is to be true with oneself.

The soil's limit or bound is its purpose. This is its ultimate frontier. Limits and bounds are not popular ideas in the modern world of everything. But the truth of soil is the truth of limits. Health, to be usable as either a word or an idea, demands a circumscription of soil as *this* soil as opposed to *that* soil. It demands to be known, personally. That is its purpose.

The Greeks have a word for this. *Telos*—the co-creation between matter, form, and bounded purpose within the duramen of life. Any reductionism of soil health as universally important is the degeneration of its true *telos*—a mockery of life and not its regeneration. This is because it extends that which is here to be everywhere, insulting bounds and limits like the university's inebriated bumbling masses often insult laws and their limits.

Soil is the co-relationship of matter, form, and bounded purpose, or Creation, that works in the local place, that is known in and only by the local place, and that is only relatable to its local place.

The soil may save you but she is beneath your feet. She is asking for your tears and not your toiling. The soil may save you but she needs you, the primate, and not you, the industrial capitalist and savior of the world.

A retuning of this narrative is the retuning and re-bending of our flat Earth. It extends the life of those around us by understanding their limits and diminishes our own powers of dominion but not our responsibilities as kin.

Isn't that what we really want? Isn't that what a good life should be about?

As I write this, Virginia burns. A tinderbox lacking tears. We entered extreme drought status last week and now, just twenty miles upriver, nearly four thousand acres burn. The week prior, about an hour northwest, another five thousand acres burned. Another National Park. Another week. Another day in the human dominated world. Rain left the Upper Piedmont nearly four months ago and our feet kick up dust. Our children think they are at the beach.

The soil may save us but sometimes I wonder if she wants to. We surely do not deserve it. It is time we actually meet her, where she lives, on our knees. Sometimes, instead of looking up at the night sky, we need to instead look down.

The steady warming of our climate, for most, threatens our ways of life, but the swift upending of Earth's current balance into its old routines of fire and ice is subtly sounding our town bells and is bellicosely knocking at our door.

The last ten thousand years have been a fairytale—a Goldilocks epoch of atmospheric balance. But this is changing, we are told. Not by the scientists, but our bones, if we listen. If Goldilocks leaves and Earth steps back into her old routine of hot and cold therapy, crops will fail everywhere, coastal cities will be overrun with torrents of waves that crash upon a starving people and recede with our civilized stress back into the ocean. The great lab experiment of a "civilized" life will come to a crashing and catastrophic end. Only then will we realize that we are just as vulnerable as the soil, the mammoth, the saber-toothed cat, and the bison.

Beauty and Darkness

We had purchased a herd of dairy goats from our midwife when Morgan struggled to nurse one of our children. We felt vulnerable, exposed, unnatural, like the sun failed to rise and left us searching for shadows, probing in the darkness for even darker forms that foretell the light. Something to give us hope.

Goat milk is similar to human milk and is easier to digest, to a degree, than the alternatives.[109] It has high levels of minerals (namely, calcium, magnesium, zinc, and potassium) and medium-chain fatty acids, an ingredient often added to infant formula that has been found to treat low levels of cholesterol in the blood.[110] Supplementing with the milk would help.

"It's a good idea," I admitted to Morgan over a breakfast of charred eggs. "Goats have wide palates and do well on wide forages. They eat weeds and such, I am told."

"This landscape is wide, yes, it is perfect for them," she replied, barely above a whisper. Her gaze drifting elsewhere, across the room, floating over sun speckled dust, landing on a sleeping bassinette under the window. The many cotton blankets calling in the dust and reflecting the sun, warmth holding that which is warmest. "I just hope it is deep enough."

A year passed but the struggle remained, albeit permutated into new forms. We struggled to pull any milk from the goats who struggled, equally, to produce it. While we daily rotated the herd between the forest's edge and its nearby meadow's undulating respites, we seemingly could not move them fast enough. They either jumped the temporary fences or died inside of them, eyes looking out, piercing beyond the electric impediment, soul drifting to where their feet failed to carry them. If they got out, which most did, they would winnow the forage on the other side, selecting a bite of this and a nibble of that, or they would go straight through the cracked door of the feed barn and gorge on chicken feed.

They needed more of something or something different entirely. We built large gardens of propagated comfrey, sunchokes, and lambsquarter to harvest and dry like tobacco in the rafters of the barn. We harvested thousands of pounds a year and, once dry, crumbled them into fine flakes to supplement their daily diets of fresh forage. We planted eight thousand black locusts on a keyline pattern to coppice and dry as "tree hay." Black locust is a native and nitrogen-fixing tree that grows well and fast and contains nearly eighteen percent protein.[111] The local feed store's grain for goats contains only fifteen percent. We also interplanted mulberries, American persimmons, tulip poplars, indigobush, and elderberry within the locust guild.

The week Weymouth, our son, was born, we planted thirty-two thousand white pine seedlings in the area of the farm that was most heavily clear cut and was still struggling to emerge with life, intending to let them grow a bit and then cut them, as they were needed, in the winter season, to feed fresh to the goats.

Years passed on. Some still jumped. Many died.

I came to the point right away as we finished moving the herd one afternoon. "Are we killing them?"

"No," Morgan said, unflappably, her hands busily worked a tangle from the fence. "God!" she exclaimed as one found the sharp end of a blackberry cane nestled in the knot. "They say to butcher the ones that get out—" She nursed her finger in her mouth, sucking out the pain. "Listen—is it, really, like actually, their fault?"

I nodded passively, unsure. "Farming is not ugliness with hints of beauty but beauty with hints of darkness."

"Well—" Her hand now searching the air for the goats, waving a bloody wand. "Maybe it is just beauty built on darkness."

"Or darkness with hints of ugliness—" I looked away. "—Duke passed this morning," I said embarrassedly, awkwardly, letting the words fall out into the world too brashly, too quickly. My head tucked down as my fingers felt the shame pulse through them as they worked the leather laces from the metal eyelets to relieve a briar from the sock inside my boot. A tear welled. Then many. Duke was an expensive buck we purchased only a few months prior—a registered, papered breeder with parasite resistance. The vet later told us that he died from the inside out. "Parasites, you sometimes just can't win, you know?" she said over the phone, nonchalantly, smacking her lips as she worked to topple her afternoon list of phone calls.

SECTION IV: LOST HERDS, WOUNDED LAND

Mara

The cafeteria-style mineral program that was working for the cows had no effect on the goats. Even today, pushing a decade later, goats seem to know the difference between soil mediated minerals and the machine moderated alternatives—those delivered through plants' biochemical processes and those delivered through modern industry's purely chemical processes. They do finely on the first, poorly on the latter.

But the land for too long had been abused and its biochemical medication was only slowly reawakening.

I led the goats that evening, under falling dusk, passing frog ponds and trickling streams, Pyros' honeysuckle still sloshing in their bellies, to the milking parlor.

We walked slowly, heads down. There is a popular belief, owing itself, I think, to the technosocial muse of dopamine delivered through swiping and scrolling and likes and views, that farming is romantic, filled with fluffy animals, and profitable. Or, that it *should* be profitable and these and other things. But this belief only further demonstrates our separation from Earth, for she promises nothing but that she will be here, riding the dawn down on the sun or rain or mist and she promises nothing more. Will we make it? Will anyone? The sun rises and she sets. That is all we know.

We had little expectation for the evening's milking but at the least we would handle them, continuing their acclimation to the stand

and milking system, and look them over. While I milked, Morgan would examine their hooves for rot, udders for mastitis, and would pull down their lower eyelids to check for anemia—scoring what she saw on a dust-covered FAMACHA chart that hung in the barn.[iii]

Morgan waited for us in the parlor with her a fresh batch of what we called "goat balls," a mixture of mullein, fennel seed, thyme, ginger, garlic, hyssop leaf, clove bud, cayenne, wormwood, and sprouted pumpkin seeds held together with organic molasses. An herbal punch to the parasite-beaten gut.

"Penny, Mr. Lafayette, Rose, Jack Frost, Piper, Sonny, Shenandoah, Sasha, Cher, Opal, Opal's Ogden and Olive—" her voice trailed off as her breath ran out. "—have you seen Mara?"

I scurried around the forty goats in the barn's stall, eyes scanning for a white and tan cleft doe. "No, I don't—I'll check outside." I replied. But she was not there—not in the barn, the barn's yard, the day's fence, or even in Pyros. I walked back with my flashlight rudely scanning an otherwise sleeping landscape, the eyes of frogs in their frog pond reflecting back on me, like a *Grimm's Fairy Tale*. No Mara.

"One quart." Morgan had just finished milking when I returned empty handed. "Forty goats. One quart. Daniel—listen—this feels like our fault."

"Thirty-nine." I said.

---

iii FAMACHA is a "measure of ocular mucous membrane color, which is evaluated with a color chart to determine anemia." Source: Food Animal Practice (Fifth Edition), pages 78-91.

Equilibrium and Agriculture

Equilibrium is a play between two contrary penchants. If one overwhelms the other, balance becomes lost and life drifts endlessly in the domain of the heavier object. If allowed to stay for a certain amount of time, the heavier domain retunes its senses and an observation of current metrics becomes the equilibrium of current arguments. That is, what is imbalanced seems balanced when disparity's dominance reigns for long enough.

Agriculture is the equilibrium of our age and extends deep into the perceived history of our world. Its modern modes developed (or redeveloped as we will see) in the confused haptics and heterogeneous cauldron of the *Younger Dryas*, a mini-ice age, or glaciation events, that lasted from 12,700 to 11,500 years ago. During this time, temperatures dropped to a -5 to -25 °C annual mean, or 23 to -13 °F average.[112]

Climate change in the Northern Hemisphere, especially in what is now North America, incongruously mixed with the great extinction events of the megafauna and the continent-wide dismantling of the Clovis culture into regionally developed and individual nations.[113] That is at least the story we are told. We lost the megafauna when our population increased, then the Ice Age receded and we turned to agriculture for security and its leisure, but, in the infant stages of that development, the world cooled once again (the *Younger Dryas)* and life slowed down, but agriculture's stable and stalwart hook was well set and it allowed life to carry on. This is our equilibrium: agriculture's dominance over scarcity secures humanity and creates civilization. But is this actually a balanced truth? Is it even true at all? If our hearts were weighed against the feather of Maat, the ancient Egyptian goddess of truth and justice, what would be the result?

We are agricultural, I think, because we were told to be. Anthropologist J. Lawrence Angel published in a 1984 paper an examination of skeletal remains of *Homo sapiens* before and after the *Younger Dryas*—before and after the uniform rise and constancy of agriculture. Angel's inspection focused on teeth, height, life span, and pelvic inlet depth index—an obstetric measurement concerned with birth canal size.[114]

What he found surprised the world. Agriculture produced less healthy people who were smaller, lived shorter lives, and, comparing the teeth and pelvic inlet depth indexes, which decreased by nearly twenty-two percent between the Paleolithic (30,000 B.C.) and the late Neolithic (5,000 B.C.), it produced a species, genetically speaking, that was on the way out. Angel also showed that, as the transition to agriculture completed between the Neolithic and Late Neolithic periods, the longevity of both men and women decreased significantly, to 33.1 years and 29.2 years respectively. It then remained this low until the rise of modern healthcare, in the late nineteenth century. Even more, Angel showed that male height dropped from five foot ten in the Paleolithic to five foot three in the Early Bronze Age (3,000 B.C.).

Angel is not alone in his findings. In 2002, an American team of scientists surveyed a multitude of human skulls ranging over the past 200,000 years of our development and demonstrated a parallel pattern. The human brain's size has decreased by nearly ten percent, our facial features (sociocultural communication) are less pronounced and softer, and our jawbones are paedomorphic—childlike even through adulthood.[115] Compared to our Neanderthal ancestors, modern humans exhibit rounder skulls with brief brow ridges. We are domesticated mammals. We are to Neanderthals what our poodles are to wolves: soft, unnatural.[116]

Unaided by archeology and science, only supported by silence, Henry David Thoreau lamented in his *Walden,* "Better if they had been born in the open pasture and suckled by a wolf, that they might have seen with clearer eyes what field they were called to labor in."[117] Let there be pastures and fields but suckle on the wolf.

Across every metric, human health declined with agriculture's rise. Surely, agriculture allowed populations to explode. It allowed civilization to dominate and colonize the animate and free movement of Earth. As nuanced hunters and farmers, we were one species on Earth. We were Earth People.[iv] As uniform agriculturalists seeking civilization, we became gods. And we fell in love with ourselves. Some aspect of our ache today is that we operate under a singularized culture—not two or three or three hundred thousand. We are claustrophobic and suffocate under a single penchant and mind. This single culture has somehow won over the rest and preempted all other prospects and potential cosmos. A sterile soul in a waveless ocean, nothing to console, nothing to dream, nothing to be.

One of the thought leaders in the "Regenerative Agricultural Movement" posted on their social media this morning that our "societal meltdown" will progress until we "re-connect" with nature. When we begin to heal the land, we will begin to heal ourselves, they wrote, and agriculture is the key. That is, our purely human-created society's decadence is proportional to our purely human-created agriculture's dominance over the natural world and fostering an agriculture that heals the land is the first step in healing ourselves. But is this true? This is the story we tell.

This is our story. One we are born into and one we strangely decide to continue, to keep on living. Agriculture saved humankind when the climate tried to kick us out nearly ten thousand years ago; agriculture is the stabilizing and civilizing force in the unstable and savage world around us. In the warming climate following the last ice age, farming and its resulting cities found ultimate peace and leisure in their wonderfully warm and new homes. The domestication

---

iv The Powhatans called the outer lands of low waters *Tsenacommacah*. The Monacan, who dwelt upriver, close to the heart of mountains, kept their name a secret. In 1608, John Smith attacked a Monacan group on their way to Mohaskahod, a hunting town, near the falls of the James River and took one man captive—Amorolek, a member of the Hassininga, who was wounded in the hostilities. Mosco, a member of Smith's army, inquired about the Monacan world. Amorolek returned, "[I know] no more but that which was under the sky that covered [me]." When asked who laid beyond the mountains, Amorolek returned, "the sun." While many indigenous nations call this land *Turtle Island*, those past, present, and future inhabitants of the landscapes depicted in this book do not. The late George Branham Whitewolf, a Monacan Indian Nation Assistant Chief, said in a 2008 interview that the word "Monacan" means "Earth People." Yes, Earth People.

of life followed and humankind began selecting desirable traits and molding the landscape to optimize the life of those new organisms. This, in turn, created cities and leisure and government and small villages became towns overnight and our population's dominance followed. This is what we are told. This is what we tell. But is it true?

Equilibrium's great play over our great, human age beckons our observational servitude and technocracy's incessant noise drums in the foreground. But its great inefficiency over life's relentless pursuit of *true* balance makes all of these demands as ineffectual as herbicide over weeds—temporary but never complete, for all grows and will grow once more.

The narrative that agriculture arose with civilization or that agriculture in some sense is required in order to save humanity from the climate crisis is a narrative that is out of balance—it appears true because it has long appeared true, a false equilibrium for a false people, disconnected from our ancient roots and gods.

In 2015, a joint international team of archaeobotanists discovered small-scale grain cultivation in the valleys around the Sea of Galilee in modern-day Israel that date to 23,000 years ago, or 11,000 years before our history even believes agriculture first developed.[118] A greater historical expanse exists between the Ohalo II culture's grain production in ancient Israel and the accepted rise of agriculture in the Middle East than exists between the accepted rise of agriculture and today. Let that sink in. In other words, think back 10,000 years when agriculture first developed and then double that amount of time and you still find agriculture, inhabiting the landscape, feeding humanity, nourishing. This is a staggering finding. It interrupts the accepted flow of human development and it stands against time.

Agriculture seemingly inhabited its landscape 23,000 years ago as a developed, discernable practice, which means that it ultimately began even earlier. It predates the Last Glacial Maximum (LGM)—the height of the most recent glaciation event of the Ice Age when the ice sheet and its cold was at its greatest. This means that not only does agriculture exist outside of human civilization in any modern sense, developing at least ten millennium before civilization developed, but it also stands outside of any human response to the climate. Agriculture was not a response to the climate but an animate force living under it all, through it all, like us, the all of us. Agriculture has a spirit of her own.

Over the eons, our climate has cooled and warmed and then cooled again. Now it is warming once more (it has done so nineteen times); humankind's villages, towns, tribes, and cities collected, fell apart, collected again and now are falling apart, maybe permanently. The *Homo sapiens* genome emerged from Earth's womb and mixed with Denisovans, Neanderthals, and *Homo heidelbergensis,* maybe even stranded and isolated groups of *Homo erectus* to create the modern complexities of human cultures, skin types, and more and now we have become an isolated and distinct species on Earth once again.[119] The gongs of modernity and its linear history ring loudly but the loving throngs of the ancients and their collective wisdoms whisper even louder. What Angel inevitably discovered was not the difference between hunter-gatherers and agriculturalists but between life lived in nuance and a life colonized by linearity. Paleolithic peoples lived in the great complexity between hunters and husbandmen.

Agriculture may have developed around 10,000 years ago but it was a redevelopment, it would seem, of a former agricultural penchant that preceded it. But this makes sense if we let our industrial and reductionist minds rest, if only for the moment.

We rebel against equilibrium's engine when we pause.

If agriculture is the care of particular life, then how did it take us hundreds of thousands of years to realize that when a plant grows it grows from seed? Consider this, hold it tight and realize its importance. Also realize how embarrassing it is. How did it take us hundreds of thousands or millions of years to realize this? That we can be as the birds and the rodents and the wind and we can move and plant seeds for ourselves? The wind and its perpetual flutter, the rodent's autumn harvest in their oaken larders, co-creates life and so can we. So have we.

But our modern climate crisis demands a rise in better agriculture and perhaps, even, a rise in our connection to Earth, but, while it is true that a better agriculture is generally a good thing, it is not a better agriculture that will produce the needed results.

Spencer Wells in his book, *Pandora's Seed,* wrote, "[the ancients] were unaware of what, by changing their fundamental relationship with nature, they were unleashing on the world. Instead of relying on nature's plenty, they were creating it for themselves."[120] Wells well understood that relationship matters but his argument appears inconsistent. Who are these "ancients" who chose separation? How is agriculture a separating force?

When we clothe ourselves, are we not divorced from a reliance on nature's weather? When it rains, the deer and the field mouse get equally wet but we stay dry in our North Face rain jackets. Is The North Face to blame for our modern crisis?

When we construct abodes or homes, are we not divorced from nature's torrents and open-aired banquets? When it is cold the water freezes and when it is warm the water evaporates, but we stay both cool and warm in our little, climate-regulated worlds. Are our homes to blame for our crisis?

When we create tools to kill and tools to heal and, more importantly, tools to hunt or gather (or farm), are we not divorced from "relying on nature's plenty?"

When the leaves and their grasses grow and when autumn blows Mother Oak's acorns groundward, nature uses what it has and accepts the outcome, and we come with buckets and pails and scythes and tools. Are our attentions and tools to blame for our modern crisis?

Whether you raise a cow for beef or hunt a deer for venison or harvest green beech leaves under the rising, spring sun for salad, it seems as though the finer details matter less than our kinship with the finer things—lives—living among us. The story of a better agriculture rising up to save the world so that we can also save ourselves is a continued narrative of separation, which erupts from the linear narrative that 10,000 years ago agriculture was born to simultaneously save and secure the world.

We rotate and cycle with Earth on the axis of life. The Hindu doctrine of *Manvantara* teaches that the world steadily cycles between four phases of increasing spiritual obscurity and the idea of a cyclic Earth reigns in most ancient cultures. But we stand with our linear history as we stand with the modern and very public virtues that we need to heal Earth to heal ourselves, as if the healing of Earth stood in our way to healing ourselves and as if Earth needs our help to begin with. All she asks, I think, is when her acorns fall that we are there, on our knees, with happy hearts and children wedded under games, with open hands and bare feet, ourselves, animated by thankfulness. *I see you. We thank you.*

What if we do not need to do anything but open our eyes and replant our roots? To become both hunters and husbandmen?

Mara #2

Mara emerged from the deep woods two weeks later. She was healthy, more vibrant than her fence-jumping peers, and nursing triplets. They were energetic and happily plump.

Goats often have twins or triplets but often fail to feed them all. Most commonly one kid gets the most milk and grows the largest and the others stagnate or fail to thrive from the outset. Some researchers have speculated that herbivores lower in the trophic chain often over produce during gestation and then limit those who make it according to nutrient access. The more nutrients the landscape provides, the more they will let survive. The less nutrients, the less survive.

But Mara's triplets were equal in size and nursed evenly, a balance of beauty, a garment of silk, brocaded and shuttle-woven.

She appeared at the milking barn right before sunset. We appeared moments later from the forest's edge with a herd of goats. We found her laying on the barn's concrete, three kids on top of her, playing, jumping, and she looked at us.

Hello again, her eyes seemed to say.

Hello again, Morgan bounced back.

Mara must have left the group during our evening walk to the oak and beyond and found a sharp valley, nestled in leaves and duff, and stayed put. Under autumn's falling cathedral she laid down, gave birth to triplets, found water and food aplenty, and relaxed until everyone was ready to return. Maybe she found a fallen tree or a ripped-up root ball to hole up for a while, warmly and safely. Maybe she struggled, greatly, to find anything at all.

We worked through the evening's milking in silence. We were speechless. We thought her long dead. Mara was last on the stanchion and gave nearly a quart of milk herself, happily. She stood there, released the milk, and walked off to her littles, licking and grooming them as we cleaned up the parlor. We cleaned in continued silence. Our words could not believe their eyes.

Morgan's lips puckered pulling the warm, glass jar from her mouth, mocking a sommelier. She swirled, sniffed, and sipped life's liquor again, smacking her lips, "It tastes sweet like acorns with subtle notes of tannins and pine and juniper fruits." Her eyes shifted, thinking towards a deepening dimple. "Now—what is that? Do I taste white boneset thinly mixed with goldenrod and teasel?" Her eyes fell back on me, glistening under the parlor's dim lights. The dimple remained.

"Probably the pungent fly agaric."[v]

We laughed until tears welled and then we laughed again, hallucinating a new world, dreaming.

---

[v] A magic, poisonous mushroom that many in ancient Scandinavia used for psychotropic purposes. It is toxic to humans but not to most animals and so the ancients fed it to goats or reindeer and then drank their blood, milk, or urine to dose on the hallucinogen.

Stories & Storytellers

What *really* is it? A troubled cool settles on warm days, a sense of unease, perhaps, a downward tension like rope on rusted iron, that as our powers as people increase so our desire to increase becomes our only power. We tether ourselves to growth and stretch and strain under the pulling pain. We let our limbs and branches fall so that energy goes only up, up, up. It is a familiar feeling, like grass underfoot, but it is also unnerving, like sharp stones that lurk in the deep green bed.

This is the mythos of modernity. Mythology once lived airborne, its power inflight between worlds, and it carried us with it. But we captured its force to harness its energy when we planted our feet in the rocky grass and when we stretched our bodies to the sun. We traded our mythology for mastery and in doing so we became slaves.

Mythology used to greet the darkness with light and now it lights the darkness, falsely. Much like soil, it is not yet true because it is not yet real. Like planted pine forests that grow a century in a decade, we are not even known to ourselves. No birdsong lulls us into spring. No migrating sows usher their young cubs over our golden duff. No slight summer wind enters our suffocating, over-planted ranks. We extend up and never look back down. We extend up, because when we don't, we are culled for pulp.

Some tales cast spells. Good tales rip them open, guts spilling, and blood staining, its sap oozing and purling down rippled bark. Good stories wake us up. As Thoreau said in his *Walden*, "I do not propose to write an ode to dejection" but to "wake my neighbors up."[121]

The schism cleft, our ancestors rise and walk amongst us. The schism cleft, we become broken and whole, ready for the sun to fill us but not ready for us to fill the void between.[122] We need stories, not climate saviors.

Mara #3

"What is the point of a farmer if she did it herself?" Morgan asked taking off her milk-splattered boots in the mudroom. "I am not a milk machine. I don't just squeeze the day for its nutrients."

"I don't know—I, I don't." A shrill alabaster of activity echoed through me, pounding new forms with every pulse. I had a headache. We were tired, like usual.

Mara startled us forward. We had taken well to walking with the herd every afternoon, allowing them to self-medicate and select what they needed but it was not working. Something was not quite right. No matter how much we supplemented their daily moves with daily walks and cuttings of comfrey and pine and locust, they were not healthy. We lost kids from every litter. We lost does in milk, mothers. We eked a modicum of milk from the others not to feed ourselves but the orphaned kids in the herd. No matter how many minerals we organized, disorder reigned. No matter how hard we worked, parasites and hoofrot worked harder to bring them down.

Their phenotype was domestication, optimums be damned, and they collapsed without overt housetraining.

The modern farm is an amphitheater of noise, and fragrance. In the spring, it smells of distended plans, infinitely long to do lists, and diesel oil. In the summer, exhaustion is scaffolded by the excitement of the first harvest. As temperatures cool, the spring's sounds and smells return, but summer never does. Autumn has arrived.

Autumn is the realization that stillness is good enough, for now. It is *Samhain*, the festival marking the end of another year, when the veil between death and life is the thinnest and ancestors walk among us, visiting, loving, remembering. The declining days silently swim between the odors of flame and salt on cast iron and a cold but conversant darkness lays on the unfamiliar end of the bed's many quilts. Stews and broths bubble against the early nights and dreams descend upon healing bones.

But in the spring, once or twice a week and only at certain moments in the lengthening days, the wind bears a low, humming smell of gasoline and diesel once again. The cast iron is put to rest. There is no time for them anymore. The flights of birds seem as much to fly away from the great river of machinery as they, only weeks ago, flew away from their southern roosts.

The hills of Appalachia are really just tired mountains, like old men who care not for glory or fame or prestige but just want to be left alone to their afternoon naps. Like tired, nodding men who require nothing but a gentle blanket of duff atop their morning rocking chairs. Our sun will soon rise. Their sun will soon set. But not yet.

During the Precambrian Era, long geological naps mixed with violent outbursts of youth to create what our species never saw: a land of high mountains and rocky and cloud-covered crags; a land of explosive change. Bedrock became boulders, boulders became pebbles. Miles of impending ice became lakes and suburbs of clams and their freshwater friends that flapped in their millions at the dawn, a sun-measured adductor arena. The days ended and the lakes became deserts and life slithered away into the increasingly small river valleys like the Rappahannock, the Rivanna, and the Rockfish. Spruce and their primordial monoliths fell and rose as oaks and another year or another day or another hour passed and life, like children on their mother's hem, passed with it.[123]

That is the funny thing about mountains and their hills you know? They are solid and strong but really, they are flimsy and fleeting. Forever flirting with time. But stories and their stones become alive when we become aware.

Like Mara.

Microscopic layers build across the millennia, like carbon molecules in diamonds. Curiosity alchemizes with memory and its atomic partner called *purpose*, element one hundred and nineteen. Over time, stones and stories become like boron—hard like a diamond but not as clear and too brittle to be a tool. Yes, stories and their stones are often mistaken for tools.

Like goats.

"We need to consider alternative options." I said, my hands lighting the first fire of the year, summer drifting into memory as the smoke purled above us. It was warmer inside the house than out and smoke always finds the kindest way up.

Morgan dreamed in the kitchen that lived on the other wall and looked beyond the shelter of glass into a world drifting before the coming winter. A squirrel jumped down and bounded across the autumn glade, slowly climbing a cedar, carrying only what it and the cedar's mid-trunk crook could handle. An opossum found its meandering way to wherever it was going and a kinglet and a warbler traded crowns. A lone junco perched above it all, their dark eyes peering down from their puff of grey and white feathers. The blessed crow-raven and the birds of *Rhiannon* sounded from their paradise and a heavenly fire kindled under the Cauldron of Rebirth.[vi] Morgan wondered if she was awake or still sleeping, still in the swift-flowing dream that was Mara's return.

"I—I don't understand, really." I said, breaking the silence. "So, you think she just—lived? Like, out there? The bear's den is not far from where we walked."

"We couldn't find her for two weeks, Daniel."

"Just because I couldn't—the momma sow just had two cubs." I

---

vi This theme is derived from *The Second Branch of the Mabinogi*, the second yarn of *The Mabinogion*, a loose collection of Welsh oral mythologies passed down in front of the Celtic winter hearth until written in mid-fourteenth century in two manuscripts: the *White Book of Rhydderch* (Aberystwyth, National Library of Wales, MS Peniarth 4-5) and the *Red Book of Hergest* (Oxford, Bodleian Library, MS Jesus College, 111). The Welsh word, *mab* means "son, boy," and the general consensus is that the original yarns were "stories of youth." *The Second Branch of the Mabinogi*'s story is set between ancient Wales and Ireland, where an Irishman, *Llasar Llaes Gyfnewid*, a huge and monstrous man, gives a cauldron to *Benigeidfran*, the king over Wales, whose name translates to the Blessed Crow-raven. The cauldron may be in reference to the ancient Celtic cauldrons of immortality unearthed across Ireland in numerous archeological sites. These cauldrons also parallel the Gundestrup Cauldron from Denmark, a gilded bowl nearly 4,000 years old which is interpreted, by some in the field, as representing immortality. The cauldron is passed back to Ireland after *Benigeidfran* gave *Branwen* daughter of *Llyr* to the Irish king, *Matholwch* to wed. Battles ensue after honor is stood in contest (a true Ulster Cycle era myth) and *Matholwch*, losing, places his men in the Cauldron of Rebirth, which heals their wounds and returns them to the arena of battle the next day, albeit without mouths to speak.

rambled, completely overwhelmed.

"Two weeks." Morgan busied herself slicing wrinkled onions from the summer's garden, now long forgotten in weeds. The stove's flame hugged the licked iron, like a hand holding an already bit apple to share, as summer herself splashed in, garbed in carrots, garlic and soon, sliced onions. The broth of Nigel son of Nuance, popped and splashed as summer filed in, rank by rank.

Morgan said nothing. Only her knife returned words. Our children played in the other room and cotton blankets collected the day's dust. The fire crackled.

"Every time. The fire speaks—" Morgan whispered, afraid, perhaps, to offend the new flames, "—it breaks spells and tells stories."

Awakening the Cave

If uniform agriculture is the equilibrium of our civilized, false age, then what about the husbandman's herds and their regenerative mythology of mobbing, mowing, and moving animals? First, we must understand the myth.

In 2014, I wrote a biography of Daniel Boone, the American woodsman, for my academic thesis.[vii] I wrote it, in part, because I was interested at that time in our culture's beginnings. Boone is the popular image of American expansion and he opened the west for white colonization.

I wanted to find out if that was *actually* true or just the constructed, hero mythology of our settler culture.

I had only recently returned from France's glorious Dordogne Valley, where I was studying the Middle to Upper Paleolithic cave art of early *hominins* from Lascaux to Grand Roc to Les Combarelles. Our work partnered with *Oniris*, the Nantes-Atlantic National College of Veterinary Medicine, Food Science and Engineering and we sought to slowly unpack the life, genetics, and mythologies of early humanity through their enigmatic arts and to consider why ancient humans painted animals such as horses, bison, mammoths, aurochs, lions, bears, deer, and wolves on deep and dark cave walls. Hunter-gatherers, history tells us, had no time for leisure or art or even to progress their phonology into a "true" ethnicity—stability

---

vii The text later transmuted into book form and was published in 2020 under the title: *Boone: An Unfinished Portrait*. While not an accessible or pleasurable read for most, the work offered an academically-acclaimed and reconsidered history of the early frontier.

through a written language.[viii] They had no time for artistic or civilized expression, only survival. But they did paint and they painted well and painted a lot.

I wanted to learn if that was *actually* true or just modern mythology welling up, like crude oil, from our incessant industry and indelible mastery.

The Bison-Bird-Man of Lascaux

Often called the Versailles of Prehistoric Man, Lascaux ranks as one of the world's oldest and grandest art galleries. Over two thousand paintings decorate seven galleries. The late Norbert Aujoulat, who studied these paintings for over thirty years and published *Lascaux: Le Geste, l'espace et le temps* or *Lascaux: Movement, Space and Time*, argued that each of the cave's major panels comprise a calendar of rutting—a seasonal sensation of cross-fertility. Aujoulat revealed that the major animals in every panel were depicted in their rutting coats: auroch bulls donning thick head hair (representing summer), hulking horses red and brown with tails reaching the floor (representing spring), stags bursting in the red carrying large antlers (representing autumn), and bison warm but thin under their winter coats (representing winter).[ix]

The majority of the paintings are from the upper Perigordian (Gravettian) period. This was a time of climate amelioration, known as the Achen Retreat, when the Northern Hemisphere's cold tundra receded and forested steppes were born. The ice-born mammoths were on the way out and the aurochs, horses, stag, and bison were coming in—their world's calendar was changing and their art, buried deep inside the womb of Earth, readied their calendars for its revolution. Art often rules over times of great change, aesthetics working out the world around us, knowledge becoming ocular as colors hue caves or canvas from the imagination out, from the soul

---

viii I pray the "air quotes" do their job here.

ix Bison perhaps held religious importance to the people around Lascaux cave, representing the winter period, the end of the year, the cold silence before the dawn. See Rusploi, Mario. *The Cave of Lascaux: The Final Photographs*. New York: Harry N. Abrams, Inc. 6-203.

to its society. These painters, artists or bards, gave a form to their culture. They did not merely replicate what they saw but created their world in symbols, in new dimensions of spirit and matter—a nature of being, lived and made alive through living. Are we any different today?

The art of Lascaux was produced with mineral pigments devoid of collagen and therefore have not been easily or reliably dated. Archeologists Sylvain Ducasse and Mathieu Langlais surveyed five reindeer bones from the cave that were clearly marred through anthropic exploitation—butchered and consumed by human—and found that they dated to the same statistical period around 21,000 years ago.[x] Each panel's polychrome painted scene provides rich insights into the dynamism of ancient life—from the Hall of Bulls where animals swirl around one's head as though fish in great, underwater schools or the Nave's *Panel of the Imprint*, a near fifteen foot engraving just above the cave's floor that contains three bison and twelve horses.[xi]

It is important to consider that not one of the nearly one hundred panels containing nearly two thousand individual paintings depict a scene containing herds of anything at all—twelve horses contained in a corridor is the extent of it. Given that these panels were painted during the Achen Retreat at the end of the Last Glacial Maximum, when large sheets of ice wrecked as they receded across the Northern Hemisphere, when the climate was held in a crisis of balance, when entire species were heading to extinction, and when others were coming into their own movement and moments, this is quite a surprise. We will come back to this a bit later.

Only one out of the nearly two-thousand paintings in the Lascaux cave system is of a human and it is a story of mutuality and fertility. Known as the *Shaft Scene*, the painting depicts two figures who are supposedly dead or dying. The panel is separate from the rest

x Dating resulted to 21.5-21 cal ka B.P., to be precise. Sylvain Ducasse and Mathieu Langlais, "Twenty years on, a new date with Lascaux. Reassessing the chronology of the cave's Paleolithic occupations through new ¹⁴C AMS dating", PALEO, 30-1 | 2019, 130-147.

xi Looking at the panel, the bison face to one's right and seem to plod along deeper into the cavern. But the great majority of the horses seem to run from the panel, heading to one's left, to the mouth of the cave. There is a clear split in this iconography, between the horses and bison, perhaps owing to the fertility calendar postulated by Norbert Aujoulat, where horses signify spring and are running out into the light of a new year. This is only speculation. German archaeologist Marie Köenig considered the ascending mare outline in the Hall of the Bulls as representing the morning sun and the descending mares signified the winter.

of the cave's art, occupying a nearly vertical, natural fissure—The Shaft—which descends nearly twenty feet below the cave floor to a hidden and perhaps sacred space underneath.

A bison stands over a bird-headed man and looks back to its stomach, which hangs outside of its body. A spear has been thrust through the bison's spine or its anus and emerges as its sexual organ below. Its stomach, ripped open by the spear, spills down its hind legs. The bird-headed man is rapt in a shamanic trance, or dead. A lone bird is perched just below the scene on a staff and looks away from story. The bird-headed man's penis stands erect.

A world away, the Lakota's *Wiwang Wacipi*, roughly translated as "gazing at the sun as you dance," enigmatically shares this ancient motif. In his biography of his grandfather, *Tatanka Iyotake,* or Sitting Bull, Ernie LaPointe wrote:

> In the center of the sixty-foot circular area, a hole is dug and *wakapa pi* (pounded meat), tobacco, and chokecherry juice offerings are put in the hole as gifts to the tree, which is then raised into position by leather ropes. Sharp-edged gravel is thrown inside the area to create more suffering for the barefooted dancers. ... A bough of chokecherry branches [are] placed in the fork of the tree. Attached to one end of the chokecherry bough is a small figure of a *Wiwang Wacipi* man with an erect penis. On the other end is a small buffalo figure, also with an erect penis. These figures represent fertility, a prayer that the Lakota nation and the buffalo nation will always be populous and fruitful.

The symbology between these ancient cultures and their kincentric connections to Earth and her wisdom should not be overlooked. The Lascaux Shaft's bird-headed man and the Lakota's sun dancer: perhaps the intermediary, the journeyer, between Earth and the second world, the spirit world. They share the spiritual connection between man and bison, the idea of cross-fertility, the shamanic role in indigenous society and culture, and the kincentric worldview.[xii] The Shaft and the ceremony. They both offer a crossroads—a journey

xii Wahinkpe Topa and Darcia Narvaez's 2022 book, *Restoring the Kinship Worldview: Indigenous Voices Introduce 28 Precepts for Rebalancing Life on Planet Earth,* is a groundbreaking and truly pivotal read on this subject. Wahinkpe Topa sun dances with the Lakota and carries great wisdom—his mentorship and care to carry my questions into Earth's ancient and loving hands I regard deeply.

one is invited to take if they are capable of suffering, of descending into the darkness donning its death, of dreaming past consciousness, of falling forward, of enduring pain to show kinship and love, and arising anew, reborn into the light of day. The bison is winter to the ancient Celts of Lascaux but the spring is coming, soon.

While these two, great peoples were separated by hemispheres, language, and genetics (as we will see in Book II of *The Wildland Chronicles*), their kinship with Earth eradicated the very human boundaries of space-time and, together, they both co-created and continue to co-create more beautiful worlds.

The bison-bird-man of Lascaux has plagued my attention for over a decade. The symbology, the ancient, stone canvas illuming potent portents for our own day when the climate is again running away from us. Our own Achen Return, calling us deeper, to ride down the dawn, into the land beyond, to follow the bison into the deep, the spirit realm. One last chance for kinship in a world cleft by capitalism, by enlightened culture, by civilization.

Making the Shoe Fit

During the writing process of my biography on Daniel Boone, between 2014 and 2017, my work pivoted, as these things tend to do, into a study of the mythology and cultural enigmas of the early American Frontier. I steadily worked to tease out why popular history positions the frontiersmen of Boone's era, and Boone himself, on pedestals of rugged individualism altogether imbued by the colonizer's unconquerable powers. I was interested in why the Daniel Boone of history was not, seemingly, the man of reality, in the same way that I was interested in why the ancient, "uncivilized" hunters of prehistory had so much leisure to color their culture with great art and symbology.

Ken Burn's 2023 documentary, *The American Buffalo,* quotes from Daniel Boone's autobiography, but Boone never wrote one. Boone confirmed this before his death and his son, Nathan, later confirmed this on record. Why do we put words in his mouth? They are our words, I think, and we need someone else to blame. Others argue that Boone's settler-colonialism is demonstrated in that, upon his death, America's supposed simple lover of the wilderness owned hundreds of thousands of acres in the west. But Boone died penniless and with only land enough to bury himself, for he never filed his legal paperwork for the land. He, like his critics, believed that the land could not be owned. He was not a perfect man, to be sure. Far from it. Very far. That much is clear. But he is also not the man our settler-colonial mythology has constructed.

Complex Shrines

The Neolithic society of Çatalhöyük in southern Anatolia is a fine, albeit strange, inspection point that will allow us to better understand these tensions.

Dating to around 9,500 years ago, it is believed that five to ten thousand people inhabited the great stone city. According to some archeologists, James Mellaart and others, Çatalhöyük depicts the earliest departures of the Natufian cultures of Palestinian hunter-gatherers into one of the world's first cities. But the people of Çatalhöyük did not leave hunting at the city gates. Mellaart's team unearthed what has become known as the *Shrine of the Hunters*, a free standing, three-walled monument flanking an open courtyard. Its artwork was finished shortly after the courtyard's construction, indicating that this was not random art adorning open walls but art the walls and courtyard were built for. The long frieze and murals depict humans alongside stag, wild asses, and fallow deer who have misplaced their heads. Around these animals stand humans. Some are painted red and carry weapons, while others are painted black and carry nothing at all.[124]

Çatalhöyük's *Shrine* speaks of hunters (indicated by the red pigment, perhaps covered in blood) and husbandmen (indicated by the black pigment, perhaps indicating the soil). It tells of hunter-gatherers, pastoralists, art, and leisure all inhabiting the same place for thousands of years. It tells of a community's collective work event, not to civilize or erect puppet masters, not to check humanity's supposed ambition or to create a government of angels[xiii], but to celebrate and to bring people together, much like Göbekli Tepe and Lascaux cave.[125] Not a struggle for survival but a snuggle for survival.[xiv] It is community without the civilization part. But its story as spell breaker is far from putative.

Around Çatalhöyük an ancestor cult developed and mysterious goddess figurines have been unearthed throughout the region. These small but deftly carved figures with greatly exaggerated hips and breasts may be emblems of female fertility or may reflect the high social status of women in their complex culture. Perhaps these figures depict the strong feminine spirit, the feminine divine, or are representations of ancestors that people carried with them, the inflated physiography a celebration of lineage.

But modern historians paint a different story—like those depicting Lascaux's people as hunter-gathering barbarians and the settler-colonial mythologist of today that paint European colonialism as manifest in the white destiny. In place of celebrating the potential role that the feminine body and spirit may have played in ancient cultures, they argue instead that, in prehistory, humans could not have understood the link between sexual intercourse and reproduction without the aid of modern science. So they tell us that a woman's fertility and following childbirth must have been, at this time, seen as a supernatural phenomenon. It is hard to write this sentence without laughing, sadly. And then crying.

The Christian apologist, G. K. Chesterton could not resist entering the conversation. In his essay, *Science and the Savages,* Chesterton reasoned that the "most pathetic of all the delusions" of primitive peoples is the idea of anthropomorphism. As long as a "tree is a tree," he wrote, "it does not frighten us." But it becomes something frightening, alien, and strange, "only when it looks like ourselves." The tree in nature is not alien or frightening. Man in nature, accord-

---

xiii From James Madison's Federalist 51, "Ambition must be made to counteract ambition" and "If men were angels, no government would be necessary. If angels were to govern men, neither external nor internal controls on government would be necessary. In framing a government which is to be administered by men over men, the great difficulty lies in this: you must first enable the government to control the governed; and in the next place oblige it to control itself." Marshall Sahlins, in his 2008 work, *The Western Illusion of Human Nature* discusses this subject at length. Source: Sahlins, Marshall, *The Western Illusion of Human Nature* (Chicago, 2008), pp. 72-76.

xiv "Snuggle for survival" is a phrase coined by biologist Martin Nowak. Source: Nowak, Martin, "Why We Help," *Scientific American (No. 1, 2012), pp. 34-39.*

ing to Chesterton, makes our knees knock. But this is the settler and industrial mythos: only civilized humans *truly* live and, if that is true, then a tree that is also alive as a human is alive also becomes immediately frightening, because it is also immediately out of place, like goddess figures in the dirt.

The Paradox of Progress

Did civilization and its uniform agriculture provide the needed cure, the industrialized alchemy, to solve the Enlightenment philosophers feared "State of Nature?" At some time during some day at some hour in the seventeenth century the parched tinder of innovation blazed to life. Thoughts ill-kept in tumbling, Greek marble became safeguarded in reawakened libraries and the physical sciences and their philosophies came into creation. Before, there was nothing, all was void. After, everything, and it was good. But was it?

Even Raymond Dart, the great Australian anatomist and anthropologist could not resist the Enlightenment's new creation story. In a 1953 paper, Dart wrote that our prehistoric ancestors were "confirmed killers: carnivorous creatures, that seized living quarries by violence, battered them to death, tore apart their broken bodies, dismembered them limb from limb, slaking their ravenous thirst with hot blood of victims and greedily devouring livid writhing flesh."[126] From David Hume's 1777 assertion of modern racism, wherein he claimed that "negros as naturally inferior to the whites," to Voltaire's 1733 letter comparing "the black wool on their heads" to a "race peculiar to that part of Africa, the same as elephants and monkeys," to the modern day Holocaust, where the management of the concentration camps was tasked to the SS's *Economic and Administrative Department* of Hitler's Third Reich, we must, I think, begin to consider that civilization and its supportive agriculture is not what we were sold.[127]

Inherent in these questions and beyond the outrageousness of their views, is a world they neither discovered nor saw and provides a strange view of evolution.[xv]

It is Darwin writ in the social textbook of the enlightened west. Lewis Morgan, an influential social theorist of the late nineteenth century, argued in his *Ancient Society,* that human consciousness, not unlike human biology, naturally and inexorably progresses through three stages of cultural evolution—from savagery (hunter-gather) to barbarism (substance agriculture), to civilization (written languages, law, and art).[xvi] This trajectory plays in the human species as naturally as biological evolution plays in the ruts of our ecology. As human society evolves, so does our language and art—it goes from Lascaux to the Louvre. As human understanding becomes scientific, so also our goddess cults and animistic naivety recedes into the darkness with the bison and the stag, running downhill, into the bowls of Earth, the annals of prehistory. "If man desires to find out the origins of religion, let him not go to the Sandwich Islands; let him go to church," writes Chesterton.[128]

But churches need property and religion needs delineation. Jean-Jacques Rousseau in his 1754 paper, *On The Origin of the Inequality of Mankind,* argued that "the first man who, having enclosed a piece of ground, bethought himself of saying 'This is Mine,' and found people simple enough to believe him, was the real founder of civil society." Rousseau warned, "Beware of listening to this imposter; you are undone if you once forget that the fruits of the earth belong to us all, and the earth itself to nobody."[129] Blaise Pascal, the great, seventeenth century mathematician and Enlightenment malcontent, argued in his *Pensées* that "tyranny consists in the desire to dominate everything" and there is a "funny sort of justice whose

xv It is important to consider that Dart is most notable for his discovery and following inspection of a human skull found in the north-west of South Africa that he identified as *Australopithecus africanus,* one of the earliest walking hominins ever found. Dart was disturbed by his discovery when he identified the cause of death was murder. But paleoanthropologist Lee Berger proved in 2006 that the culprit was not human-to-human aggression that progressed to murder but a bird of prey. Source: Berger, Lee R. "Brief communication: predatory bird damage to the Taung type-skull of Australopithecus africanus Dart 1925." *American journal of physical anthropology* vol. 131,2 (2006): 166-8. doi:10.1002/ajpa.20415.

xvi One author finely pins the rise of property with the rise of progress in the linear story of industry, of the mechanical mind. "The earliest ideas of property were intimately associated with the procurement of subsistence, which was the primary need. The objects of ownership would naturally increase in each successive ethnical period with the multiplication of those arts upon which the means of subsistence depended. The growth of property would thus keep pace with the progress of inventions and discoveries. Each ethnical period shows a marked advance upon its predecessor... in the variety and amount of property which resulted therefrom. The multiplicity of the farms of property would be accompanied by the growth of certain regulations with reference to its possession and inheritance. The customs upon which these rules of proprietary possession and inheritance depend, are determined and modified by the condition and progress of the social organization." Source: Morgan, Lewis. *Ancient Society,* Part IV, Chapter 1: The Three Rules of Inheritance, 1877.

limits are marked by a river" that changes its "colour as it changes climate."[130] This is civil society and its civilization, Rousseau and Pascal wrote: dependence, desire for independence, depression, then servitude.[xvii]

A period of comical soul-searching ensued, like literary critics around school papers, lost in its defense of structures inadequately built but necessarily maintained.[xviii] Together, the Enlightenment "imposters" have taken on the ineffable air of piquancy, like saffron over spoiled meat.[xix] Their discourse short of actual change, it fractures, segregates, and flamboyantly celebrates the helplessly generative, socioculturally regressive, and hegemonically contaminated offspring of industry: divergence and dependence. It has also imbued our society today, convincing us that no cultural improvements can succeed without political or institutional power behind them and that this power can only be heaped up by dollars, votes, and social prestige.

To Rousseau, progress is a paradox, corrupting as it grows. It creates wars because it first created property and it first created property in order to inoculate the roots of its inequality with potency—anything to help bust through the wild sod. In place of *amour de soi* (love of the self)—the instinct of self-preservation through self-understanding and community's expression—progress and its industry created *amour propre* (self-love)—the imposter, lifting and weighing man over man and then man over the world, creating masters and enslaving Earth's balance.[131] Civilization is the lie sold to us. The lie we consumed. The lie we turned into us, us self-loving people.

The ancient *Shrines* of Çatalhöyük and the cave art of Lascaux

xvii In one Pensée, titled *Causes and Effects*, Pascal discussed that justice and equity must flow from an "equality of possessions." While this "is no doubt right," Pascal continued, "men could not make might obey right, they have made right obey might. As they could not fortify justice, they have justified force." Are we any different today?

xviii Both Robespierre and the Jacobins admired Rousseau, but only the figure they needed him to be. Rousseau is scarcely worth reading if you want to understand the Enlightenment or the politics of the eighteenth-century, for his work seeks to understand humanity, I think, and nothing more. "The Enlightenment" is a term which stems from the German word, *Aufklärunge*, but Rousseau talked about *éclaire*, a French word meaning literally, "well lit," like an artist's studio. He is writing not on the nature of human beings but rather about who we are, here, in this place, and what our organization or community is for. He admits himself as only a citizen of Geneva, a small town, celebrating that localism and communities need proximity, equality, and similarity. Without them there is no sociocultural virtue. In his opening lines to one of his greatest essays, he claims, I am "an honest man who knows nothing." See: Rousseau's *Discourse on the Sciences and the Arts, 1750.*

xix Read, Fyodor Dostoevsky's *The Brothers Karamazov*, to experience a deep challenge of the "western idea" through story. Dostoevsky wrote the work following six years of hard labor in Siberia in the early 1850s for reading banned books and more. Captivated in the richness and potency of story, Dostoevsky puts Russia and the West itself on trial.

stand together against Rousseau's "imposter" and stalwart across epochs as a challenge to this social evolutionary thesis. The nameless unit of change rests inside the masses but the masses are indifferent to it, for they do not know it, the nameless unit. But the nameless moves in the common, freely, with potency, and the common is moved by the nameless. This is the power of ancient memory yet unnamed but not unknown arising in the modern soul, for no society, power, or institution can stand in the common's way for long.

Strangely, the same social philosophers that negate the pagan animism and place-based wisdom of ancient peoples assert a similar, social animism at play in human society. That is, culture has a biology about it but biology does not have a culture.

Necessity and Truth

The doctrine that large herds of mobbing, mowing, and moving herbivores that existed in some static state in nature comes from the early to mid-twentieth century.[xx] Not unlike its industrial and Enlightenment predecessors, its linear, imposter mythology is readily observable in that it posits biology and culture as interposed by the masters of necessity and competition—both *intraspecies* and *interspecies*.

John Acocks' vision that we learned about in the previous Section and the resulting grazing systems that imbue the grazing movements and protocols of today are built upon the idea that herbivores ranged in large herds historically, leaving a ravaged and truly "animal impacted" landscape in their wake. Herbivores mob, mow, and move, as the saying goes. *This works*, the experts tell us, *because it has already worked*. The foundation of regenerative grazing is this high-herding herbivory of history and the call for non-selective grazing both in the 1930s and today is the call to mimic the herds of old and the ancient impact their great numbers sustained since time immemorial.

---

xx This very sentence illumines the problem of this modern creation, even if the history was correct, it puts nature over there, beyond that fence, so that when we farm in its (always an IT!) image, we may feel good about ourselves and our work. We are doing what nature would do, but she is not invited—she has never *actually* been invited.

But is this *actually* true? Its proponents argue that, because of competitive nutrient pressures inevitable in large herds where hunger's pull generally outpaces the landscapes nutrient-delivering abilities, grazing animals naturally defoliate most if not all of the available vegetation, regardless of their individualized needs. This is the *mob*—a uniform harvest of dense and competitively packed livestock. This is the *mowing*—the competitive pressure of force over area that combines the many into the one is located, internally, in the minds of herbivores. If they do not eat that plant now, someone else will, leaving less for them and leaving them hungry and weak. Grazing, it is argued, is constructed from the wellspring of *intraspecies* competition.

Allan Savory, another African ecologist, colleague of Acocks, and mentor of mine, discovered that grazing pressure within the herd was only half of the story. In Savory's *Holistic Management Framework*—a holistic decision-making protocol for managing the complexity of natural environments that he co-developed in the mid to late twentieth century after examining the way armies are structured and battles are managed—he observed what is now called the "Predator-Prey Connection." It posits that predators push prey animals (grazing herbivores) naturally in nature into tight herds for protection and they do this from behind, stimulating an ever-moving and ever-forward grazing behavior. The soil and its vegetation developed for millions of years in this co-evolutionary framework between large, mobbing herds and the impact and devastation erupting in their wake—severe defoliation, manure concentration, and soil disturbance. Because of predation pressure packing them together, large and tight herds poo and wee all over their dinner plates and so forward movement is the only option. This movement formed by predators and defecation prevents the overgrazing of plants and abundant soil and vegetative communities arise in their wake. Regenerative grazing, it is argued, is constructed from the wellspring of *interspecies* competition.

This key insight, the "apple of Gold," to borrow the phrase from Abraham Lincoln, is the historical legacy of large herds and their predators that frequented the lands before colonization—both in the Western and Eastern hemispheres. It is a natural process and nature's holy processing.

But is it *really* an apple of gold? Is it *really* true? Or, just like Çatalhöyük's hunter-husbandmen and their goddesses, Lascaux's fertile cave art, and Boone's enigmatic history, is our story that depicts nature as a damsel in distress and us as her prince charming riding in to save the day with polywire in hand and grazing conferences complete with goodie bags *actually* true or does our industrial culture just need it to be true?

Mara #4

"I think you are letting your fear—"

"—I'm just questioning what needs questioned," Morgan interjected thoughtfully.

I looked out of the window that rested between Morgan's bouncing cast iron and the hearth's flame, silently. A leaf caught my eye and flicked off an ivy-veiled bough of the black walnut that grows on the eastward side of a persimmon that a family of deer—a doe, her daughter, and her daughter's daughter—often frequent this time of year and then many leaves followed forming a torrent, an autumn trickster of gilded wings, dancing and shapeshifting with the wind.

"Life is not ugliness." Morgan thought out loud, waking me, lifting me from my trance, her eyes turning to mine, letting the golden herd of leaves go, to drift, freely, out of sight. "Beauty out of darkness, don't you think?"

"They say to rotationally graze. To mob, mow, and move. To mimic natural herds of old."

"Who? Who says that?" Her eyes moved back to the onions, now bouncing in the broth.

"The experts—scientists, the speakers at conferences—" my hand drifting as its fingers twisted in the smoke above my head, "—everyone does it, says it must be done, especially these days with the climate and all—"

"—Mara has never spoken at a conference." Morgan paused. The broth bubbled. "She has never been asked."

The fire crackled. The dusking light fell behind the walnut. The skunk that lives under our porch striddled and sidled from the persimmon, a trail of marmalade dripping from his curious mouth. No deer tonight. Again, the fire. Smoke purled. A pallid gleam of gold filtered in the window, piercing the brume, dusk now here. Memory primed to erupt anew—stories holstered at the ready to break spells, to open hulls when the firelight falls.

Mara #5

Mara's fortnight in the woods was our foray into a new life. Over the years, we had progressively released control, giving up standardized harvest structures, controlled breeding, and regular mineral and feed rations.

We opened the box, allowing some natural processes in, developing roots and new shoots, and wider species flew and crawled and slithered in as well, expressing new characteristics in the new community. The landscape was a crescendo of emergent life, a great swelling over harbor walls, a stampede of brumbies. The herds had self-organized to a degree, throwing calves and kids and lambs all during the same season, on their own, without our help. Their resulting grazing instincts instilled a sacred health and alchemized a growing adaptation to the land, unforeseen to us. Their palates over the years expanded over the landscape as cattle foraged like goats and goats grazed like cattle, delicately devouring the emerging meadow and savanna's vegetative species like herbalists in their apothecary.

But it was still a box and it was still our box and we still held, firmly, onto the lid.

Mara was speaking.

The green agriculture and better grazing movements of today talk about pastures as salad bars, where grazing herbivores select what they need from a buffet of options. There are five types of salad greens (grasses) that you can mix with six types of dried fruits or nuts (trees) topped with a melody of grated cheeses (forbs) and dressings (legumes). If we are lucky, there may even be a handful of soggy pasta (shrubs and briars and ferns) at the end of the line to ladle and slap onto our already full plates. No one takes the saltines (sedges and rushes), they mold in their moist containers.

Animals are drivers of habitat creation. They migrate fertility and deliver biodiversity. Without them, the land is static, penurious, drifting toward an oxidative death.[xxi] In some larger sense, it is the reason that many commercial farms and conservation projects are failing—they lack the animals they so depend upon and spray and kill the rest.

Earth needs her offspring, all of them. But Earth also needs her offspring as them, themselves, acting in their own ways in their own time.

Controlled, non-selective grazing was the structure we had long deployed in our own management. We moved the herds in polywire and electric nets to mimic the Predator-Prey Connection of wolves and bison and managed for increased animal impact.

"We are the wolves!" I said, buffing my chest one morning after we finished moving the cows.

"You are dumb." Morgan replied.

But Mara was speaking and the night we found her in the milking parlor with her three kids piled and playing on top of her pierced the peace in our minds. We could not forget the happiness she exhibited that rudely contrasted to the unhappiness of the goats at our backs.

We began studying other grazing methodologies, searching for answers on why our nature-mimicking management was failing, so entirely, completely.

"What the hell is this called again?" Morgan asked, dropping the headphones to her lap.

"Instinctive grazing, or migratory something—I could check the podcast title—"

---

xxi What Allan Savory calls the "Brittleness Scale" in Holistic Management is simply brilliant in this respect. In more arid environments, what Savory calls "brittle regions," where precipitation occurs seasonally and is not well spaced throughout the calendar's landscape, vegetation that is not cycled through an animal's digestion or trampled back to the floor of the meadow to begin decomposition, slowly oxidizes. This is chemical decomposition, occurring from the top down, from the tips of the leaves to the base of the plant, slowly. This slow mineral cycling results in weak plants that, if not aided, wither away into desert.

"Daniel. It's a cattle handling system. Nothing more." Morgan sat, feet on the floor, unfettered by it all. "He is saying by working the cattle in a way that causes less stress makes them, somehow, to want to stay together."

"Yes, rebooted, as they say."

Morgan laughed. "Yes, like computers." She paused, collecting her thoughts, dispensing the headphones on the chair. "Handling them nicely in the corral or in a cattle drive is not letting them go—" She got up and began to walk away then paused, sighing, "—it's just humans controlling nature."

SECTION IV: LOST HERDS, WOUNDED LAND

Breaking Spells

Our near universal affection for the bison is a strange love affair. She is our national mammal, but few of us would trade our modern and industrial conveniences such as roads, property rights and their fences, and domestic animals for her free, *wild,* and roaming life. She is the largest land animal on our continent, but few of us have ever seen her. We love her coat's rust-stained anarchy alongside her gait's grandeur and, the lucky few among us stand like sandstone statues when she walks by. We love the thought of her hooves shaking and shattering the soil beneath our feet and we love the idea of her, but do we *actually* know her?

There is a deep and consuming passion in the American spirit to dream of bison. While it is clear that they occupied and called the Great Prairies home for the last few hundred thousand years and seldomly migrated in large, combined herds, our modern, regenerative mythology that posits its grazing and management systems upon the drum of a thousand hearts beating as one may be just that—a mythology of our modern mind.[xxii]

Where are the Bison?

Throughout my research of the early American "west," I poured

<hr />

xxii Organizations and communities such as *Indigenous Led* are pioneering pathways forward with Land Back and Bison Repatriation projects across the central and northern west. They work through an Indigenized approach of ecological restoration with roots firmly nestled in community and communal choice (humans and animals!). They are more than an exemplar, but also are leaders in this reawakening.

over thousands of primary sources from a multitude of library collections—letters, memoirs, untold family stories, unpublished interviews, and lost papers. I read, studied, and synthesized more than forty biographies written of Daniel Boone and his compatriots between 1787 and the turn of the twentieth century and studied the historical journals of over three dozen travelers within the early American west and indigenous cultures from the early 1500s through the later 1800s. I attempted to understand the European ethos and its history as it understood itself, for better or worse. Mostly worse.

Boone was what history calls a Long Hunter—isolated and silent people who ventured deep into the western forests for extended periods to trap and hunt, sometimes for as long as two years at a time. It is believed that, during his nearly seventy-years of Long Hunts, Boone traveled as far west as the Pacific and as far south as Orlando, Florida before the year 1800. When Lewis and Clark's 1803 expedition to locate the great Northwest Passage to the Pacific Ocean commenced, they stopped at the now aged Boone's lonely and hand-built cabin in the Missouri wilderness and asked him for directions.

But in all of my research and through all of Boone's and his era's writings, stories, and mythologies, I found only a minor trace of these large and mob-like herds of herbivores and none went in the same direction. Yes, there were a few European accounts of herds of bison a million strong, but, as we will see, they are few, historically problematic, and are ultimately romantic imaginations of the set-tler's worldview.

If regenerative grazing systems are constructed from the histori-cal legacy of large herds of mob-grazing herbivores that regenerate the soil through *intraspecies* and *interspecies* competition, why are they so hard to find? Every book on grazing and every conference speaks as if they know—that they have seen these herds. Where? We have the frame of silver, but where is the apple of gold? In order to answer this question, we have to first look at the history and cultures of these ancient mammals.

Bison, Our Earliest Records

In their 2021 defense of bison's historical presence in the east, namely West Virginia, the United States Forest Service's paper, *Primeval Paths: Bison in West Virginia*, argued that "although considered an animal of the western plains, bison were also present in the eastern United States from Pennsylvania southward to Georgia and Mississippi."[132] To substantiate this claim, the authors quote heavily from a 2006 paper written by anthropologist, Bruce McMillan who discovered bison remains in Illinois at the Lonza-Caterpillar site. If we read McMillan's and his colleagues' findings ourselves, however, we will discover, embedded in their framing and conclusions, the Forest Service's very familiar (and misguided) desire to connect our now lonely spirit to the once-ranging "great regenerators."

According to McMillan and his colleagues' *actual* findings using both geological and archeological assessments, both *Bison latifrons* and *Bison antiquus,* the ancestors of modern bison, inhabited the lands as far east as present-day Missouri during the Sangamon Interglacial and the interstadials of the subsequent Wisconsin glacial epochs. Some of the artifacts have been Uranium-Thorium (U-Th) dated to be from 147,000 to 153,000 years ago.[133] Both *latifrons* and *antiquus* bones have been discovered in small quantities (a half a skull here, one tooth there) in springs and caves throughout the region.[134] But the interval of maximum glacial ice advance, what is called the Last Glacial Maximum (LGM), between 22,000 and 17,000 years ago, saw the spruce forests of the far north raid and inhabit the south and eastern prairies and the once parklands transformed into conifer forests.[135] This reduced the bison's habitat and constricted their already small herds into thin bands.[136]

But the land was yet at work. Bison diminution in the east heightened greatly during the *Younger Dryas* from thin bands to nearly no animals at all.[137] Recent studies have correlated decreasing bison numbers with rising C_4 grasses, or warm-season grasses, following the postglacial warming of this era, around 12,000 years ago. As the C_4 grasses replaced the cool-season adapted and more nutritious C_3

grasses, bison numbers and their individual body sizes[xxiii] seem to have decreased concurrently.[138] This is the era that Bruce McMillan studied at the Lonza-Caterpillar site in 2006 that the Forest Service based their paper on. McMillan found that the site was continuously occupied by humans from around 2,000 B.C. to 1200 A.D, or about 3,200 years. McMillan's team unearthed nearly five hundred bison bones from the site, substantiating the general presence of bison in this region and providing the framework for the Forest Service's claim. But the bone fragments represented, McMillan acknowledged, only about nine individual animals in total, most of which were "deposited along the Illinois River shoreline as a result of natural deaths or accidental deaths in the river, perhaps due to falling through weak ice."

McMillan's team ultimately concluded that two of the specimens met their death at the hand of humans.[139] After 3,200 years of occupation, the site's archeological record speaks of only a handful of bison. If large herds did range these eastern lands, then why did thousands of years of hunting and gathering only witness the death of two to nine bison? The Forest Service's paper ultimately concludes by calling the bison in the east "nomadic grazers" that ultimately lacked the biome they so depended upon.

Bison: 1500-Present

William Cronon's award-winning and definitive 1983 history of the ecology and peoples of New England titled, *Changes in the Land,* does not even mention the word bison or buffalo at all, and the biggest herd of any species that his research discovered in the historical record was roughly one hundred white-tailed deer over the area of one square mile, or about six hundred and forty acres. To be clear, even today during Wildland tours, we will often see sixteen to twenty deer on the two-hundred and sixty acres that the tour encompasses,

---

xxiii Body size diminution was determined via metapodial measurements, that is the bones that link the phalanges of the digits to the more proximal bones of the limb, placing the earlier adaption periods somewhere between 9,000 and 7,500 years ago. (source: Hill, Matthew E., Jr., Matthew G. Hill, and Christopher C. Widga. 2008. Late Quaternary Bison Diminution on the Great Plains of North America: Evaluating the Role of Human Hunting Versus Climate Change. *Quaternary Science Reviews* 27 (17–18):1760.).

or half of what Cronon described.

In a seventeenth century, southern New England Indigenous village of about four hundred people, the winter meat supply was recorded at eight and a half thousand pounds of deer and seven thousand pounds of bear meat.[140] If million-head herds of bison were ranging the landscape all around them, why would four hundred indigenous hunter-gatherers live on roughly 40lbs of deer and bear meat apiece for the winter? To put this in perspective, the USDA's 2000 Factbook reports that modern humans consume one hundred and ninety-five pounds of meat a year, or about one hundred pounds over the winter. While deer may have been easier to hunt than bison, or while bison—in any concentration—may not have been present, these numbers should startle us into asking deeper questions.

When the Florentine explorer, Giovanni da Verrazzano visited the northeastern regions in 1524, he observed extensive meadows and open forests, membered by a few stags and lynx, that could be "penetrated even by a large army."[141] But where are the large herds of mobbing and mowing herbivores?[xxiv] The landscape was an open and undulating savanna, but where were the herds that supposedly created this landscape? In the *Journal of Mammalogy*, archeological curator and author Allen Glover wrote, there is "no proof that the bison ever occurred within the present limits of New England." Glover further considered that, for "periods anterior to the coming of white men," it is clear from the known archeological and social record that large herds of bison ranged no farther east or south than Lake Erie.[142] At least, never substantially.

Dan Flores, in his latest book, *Wild New World* argues instead for complexity. In place of the linear narrative of competition and that mob-grazing and marauding herds of herbivores pushed by predators ultimately transformed our ecological past into a pristine

---

xxiv According to the Nature Conservancy's Geospatial Conservation Atlas, southern New England is contained in the *Northern Piedmont* ecoregion, a landscape not entirely dissimilar to the *Piedmont* ecoregion that extends from Pennsylvania to Alabama. Ecoregions are a helpful albeit general tool for understanding particular microclimates and regionalized ecological norms. They speak to what grows best where and they speak to the geological and evolutionary development of regions over large expanses of time—glaciation to present. To make the argument that large herds of bison or other herbivores historically ranged in central Pennsylvania and south (the Piedmont) but not in central Pennsylvania and north (the Northern Piedmont) is to place a human-conceived limit and bound on the flow of ecological development and it is to stand in the way of history herself.

wonderland, Flores speaks instead of a dynamic and ever-evolving climate-animal balance.

It was an equilibrium writ in co-evolution not competition. In place of great herds, Flores argues that large collections of grazing herbivores occurred only in migration events and, while momentarily large, the aggregated mob was comprised of a multitude of smaller herds. Fred Provenza dubs these small herds as "extended families" and writes finely about them in his book, *Nourishment*.[143] The Great Plains and their eastern plateaus were a speckled landscape of smaller and autonomous herds and, while they would momentarily combine during seasonal migrations, it is clear that "small groupings led by high-ranking cows" dominated the great prairies, writes Flores.

What about in the east? While the prairies of the west became a bison belt, it was the eastern Indigenous people's anthropocentric fire that produced patches of ecotones and ecological edges that were perfect browse for whitetail deer and not homes for the large, marauding mobs of bison. Bison herds in the east were never large, never teeming, never resembling the truly vast patchwork of extended families that seldomly clapped across the central and western prairies together. Notice the word: seldomly.

Human archeology also speaks of this complexity. The oldest and most well-dated Eastern human habitation site in North America is the Cactus Hill terrace, located on a wind-deposited bank of the Nottoway River, in eastern Virginia, or *Tsenacommacah*. The site dates to between 18,000 and 20,000 years ago. What is interesting for our current study is that, in their *Nottoway River Survey*, archeological husband and wife duo, Lynn and Joseph McAvoy discovered "a hearth with small fragmentary calcined bones of deer and mud turtle" but "there is no direct indication of large game hunting on this site."[144] Undulating herds of deer and other small game occupied their diets but what has yet to be found are concentrations of large herbivores, or large herbivores at all. The land is speaking, but are we listening?

The modern belief in primordial lands infused with great herds of large herbivores is a frame to marvel at, to behold on museum walls, to found great eco-movements of agriculture, to subscript the young and eager millions, but it is only a frame, and it is only here to spark romantic imagination. The "great" American novelist, James Fenimore Cooper's first book, *Precaution*, is believed to have been influenced not by the rushing rivers of the interior but the English writings of Jane Austin. Our golden apple is the very white mythology where civilization's ascendency arrives to control and remake the supposed ancient and wise lands of yesteryear, if we just try hard enough. Ranchers and farmers encourage "natural herd instincts" of their grazing herbivores, completely unaware that an herbivore's actual instinct is to live in small, relational bands of extended families and that these small, family units were made up by deer and small, browsing ruminants in the east, and not large, grazing bison (at least for the last 100,000 years or more).

While it is true that holistic and intensive management of larger herbivores (bison or cattle) via non-selective grazing protocols and systems increases soil organic matter, vegetation of perennial grasses, and more, it is completely untrue that this legacy is writ in the veins of our actual world—it is a human-created tool like a tractor and tractors do marvelous things.

But it cannot be denied that, during the seventeenth and eighteenth centuries, European explorers reported large herds of herbivores ranging the lands around the eastern and western slopes of the Appalachian Mountains. They wrote of grasses so tall a rider could tie them in knots above their saddle. But it also cannot be denied that they greatly exaggerated the witnessed numbers—for, it is more likely that they saw a couple dozen or even, perhaps a hundred head of bison, elk, deer, or pronghorn and not a couple thousand or million. How do you even count to a million when the things being counted keep moving?

Writers of this period recorded daily harvest of their hunting parties of five men or more at ten or less bison per day. If five men, shooting for sport or for the fur trade, with even adequate shooting abilities stumbled on a herd of a million bison, taking ten animals would be a joke. Their harvest would be as easy as their ability to reload.

In 1613, sailing up the Potomac River near modern day Washington D.C., the European colonists of Jamestown came across a small herd of bison, which they took and reported tasting "very good and wholesome." During his seventeenth century exploration of the upper Mississippi River, Father Louis Hennepin observed Indigenous hunters harvest a small herd of bison, using grass fires to push them into the rivers. In 1733, James Oglethorpe, the founder of the colony of Georgia, received a buffalo skin after his treaty with Chief Tomochichi of the Yamacraw in modern-day Savannah.

From the fur hunter to the frontiersmen, it is clear that bison to some small degree occupied these eastern lands. But these examples have been stretched on European parchment and strained under European empire. We learn of buffalo licks and bison swamps but we grasp at every thin example in order to demonstrate their universal promise in healing the world we destroyed—we need them to regenerate our misdoings.

"So much of my blood memory has to do with buffaloes," writes the Kiowa poet N. Scott Momaday. "We are friends."[145] While it is true that the bison are a set piece in the American consciousness and its static view of the natural world, their uniform treatment across the undulating and unique ecotones of this great continent illustrates the Eurocentric industrialism that still dominates our world. To their indigenous cousins and our ancient ancestors, they are living beings, friends of the cross-fertile hope. To us, they are tools.

Making a Wilderness

Two historical realities must be considered in order to properly deconstruct our "regenerative myth" and place it gently into the operations of a more complex and kinship-based reality where reciprocity meets actual diversity and where health helps the actual state of things.

First, it is not often considered that European colonists arrived in their "new world" as sheltered peoples. For more than half a millennium leading up to the European expansion events of the sixteenth century, European peasants and nobles were not allowed to hunt. Hunting in the King's Forest was for kings. When the Normans invaded England in 1066, William the Conqueror instituted a Frankish legal system called, *Forest Law,* or *Game Law.* Namely, that the animals of the forest were the property of the crown and taking a deer or even owning a hunting weapon was punishable by prison or death.[146] Modern social scientists claim that it only takes three generations to forget something. While the first generation may know how to hunt, if they do not give it to the second, the second always sees the hunt as that which their parents could do but rarely did do and the act becomes a rarity amongst them and their peers. If the skill and art of the hunt is then not passed to the third generation, the third sees it as an antiquated and distant belief of their ancestors and the act of hunting becomes the mythology of the wilderness. Between William the Conqueror's *Game Law* and the initial settlement of their "new world," European settlers experienced nearly 30 generations—ten times more than is needed to forget something. The great, millennia-long sprawl of European colonization in the Eastern Hemisphere reduced wild game and wild places to the peripheries of their lives and those wild few that managed to exist were reserved for the king. When these untrained and unlearned peoples landed in *their* new land and witnessed herds of anything at all, their minds must have exploded, like children, with genetic visions of their pagan, pre-Christian, and pre-colonized pasts.

Secondly, it must be considered that, by the time the first, "stable" European colony landed on the banks of the James River in 1607, ninety to ninety-five percent of the Indigenous peoples east of the Mississippi were gone—European-induced plagues and wars had eradicated them. One Spanish friar wrote, "they died in heaps like bedbugs."[147] Historians call this period the "Great Dying" and believe that this great death put over ten percent of the world in their graves. Mothers buried sons and fathers followed. In some villages, the diseases traveled so quickly and with such precision that none were left to burry anyone at all and the ravens and maggots were burdened with the work. The Pilgrims of Massachusetts found empty homes, winter corn drying and just-harvested fields waiting for them.

William McNeill, in his 1976 book, *Plagues and Peoples,* demonstrated that the European biological and physical gun, between 1492 and 1600, created the greatest population decays in world history. Greater, in fact, than the Black Death in Europe and greater in magnitude than the summed death toll of the first and second world wars in the twentieth century. It was, in some way all too real, World War Zero. And much worse—true genocide that grew, like a desert storm, westward. Carbon uptake from vegetation's increase and carbon stability from anthropocentric fire's decrease occurred on a scale and time-table sufficient enough to bring about a Little Ice Age.[148]

The ancient Hominoids of Eurasia evolved as a great patchwork—from ages of disease, like smallpox, to ages of discovery, like bronze or iron. The intercontinental landmass allowed for pathogens and ideas to flow freely and mutate as they went from human to human and from domestic animals to human as well. More than sixty percent of human diseases are zoonotic in origin.[149] Cattle, pigs, and horses all share around thirty diseases with humans and sheep, dogs, and goats share around twenty with humans—from smallpox and tuberculosis to influenza and salmonella. Recent research has also demonstrated what is called, "reverse zoonosis," that humans pass pathogens that are "reservoired" inside our species to other vertebrates, especially mammals.[150] Domestic diseases, flowing in two directions, have long infused and impacted Eurasian genetics.[xxv]

But these pathogens were novel to the Indigenous peoples of the Western hemisphere, who had evolved in relative isolation and free from overt domestication of their wild cousins. These pathogens also wreaked an internal havoc. While plagues and diseases walked like reapers amongst them, external changes in their ancient world occurred in front of them. Wild game and their people's nutrient-rich and wild diets receded as sugar, alcohol, and processed flours replaced them. Their longstanding health-vectored life steadily became a disease-vectored demise as the landscape's great

xxv In a recent, 2011-2012 study, it was found that nearly 62% of homes in the United States today have pets, urging veterinarians to step beyond their current practice and more "fervently protect animals under their care from human disease threats." (Source: Leighton, Frederick A. "Veterinary medicine and the lifeboat test: a perspective on the social relevance of the veterinary profession in the 21st century." *The Canadian veterinary journal = La revue veterinaire canadienne* vol. 45,3 (2004): 259-63).

biological diversity was ransacked in the name of European wealth and status. This is the often untold story of colonization.

Select estimates conclude that, before contact, there could have been as many as seventy million Indigenous peoples living north of the Rio Grande. A recent analysis completed by Jan De Vries estimates that, in the entirety of Europe at that same time, there were only sixty-one million peoples—nine million less. If Indigenous peoples were actively managing the relations within their lands for many thousands and thousands of years through their mythologies, hunting, and fire, what would their world look like if ninety-five percent of them died and then you arrived over a hundred years later?

Their colossal death was the great transformation of an entire hemisphere—social and ecological. What would New York City look like if ninety-five percent of its residents died and you visited over one hundred years later? Central Park, like a slimy intestinal parasite, would have consumed the city from its inside out. Ivy and vined creepers would conceal most of the lower-story buildings and oaken roots would have long ago exploded through the concrete-paved and linear traces of the once bustling flow of millions of stressed humans. Fast-growing and sinuous trees would scrape the clouds as they replaced the decadent, metal trappings of the once awe-inspiring skyscrapers and the oak and hickory forest of tomorrow would obscure our view from the ground. You would, as either an archeologist or anthropologist, believe that New York City was built long ago within a great forest once called Central Park. You would say they worshiped the goddess in green. You would say many false things.

"Europeans did not find a wilderness," wrote Francis Jennings, an early American historian. "They made one."[151]

A Toxic Wasteland

We know this because we have already tested this hypothesis. Chernobyl, the once Ukrainian town turned modern, nuclear oopsy is a specter of nature's implicit regenerative abilities. After The #4 Reactor caught fire and exploded in 1986, sending world-ending plumes of radiation into the countryside, over one hundred thousand people lost their homes and over one hundred villages and farms were immediately abandoned for an expected twenty-four thousand years. Radiation killed and would continue to kill every life within range, the experts said.

Today, the Chernobyl Exclusion Zone, a six million acre, completely abandoned expanse of northern Ukraine, has operated without modern humanity and lived outside of our overt control for forty years. What has it become? It is now the third largest and most bountiful nature reserve in Europe! Two extinct species of eagles have reemerged from the toxic wasteland, one of which, the Greater Spotted Eagle, is a direct indicator of healthy hydrologic cycles and wetland habitat.[152] Another study found great abundances of elk, roe and red deer, and wild boar, with seven times more wolves than is typical in the ecoregion.[153] The truly comedic aspect of that study was that it was completed by helicopter, for the land is still too toxic, it seems, for us modern humans.

All things considered—from the limited vistas of the colonized, European mind and culturally myopic concepts that followed (emphasis on commodities and ecology as servants to progress) to the simple fact that the lands east of the Mississippi had long lost ninety-five percent of their nurturing, keystone cousins—produced a record inevitably incorrect and unabashedly linear. This is the settler myth and this is becoming the regenerative myth as well.

Return of the Wolves

But there is one last example challenging the settler and regenerative myth that we need to unpack. The reintroduction of wolves to Yellowstone. The video detailing their return has over forty million views on YouTube and is graced by voices such as Sir David Attenborough and George Monbiot.

The story goes like this. In 1872, Yellowstone becomes the world's first national park. Grey wolves well populate the region and dynamically influence the health and balance of the ecosystem as a whole. By 1884, the state of Montana erects a bounty on the heads of wolves and by 1915, they officially declare wolves as "a menace to the herds of elk, deer, mountain sheep, and antelope."[xxvi] The last wolf in Yellowstone was killed in 1926. To resolve the problem, the largest public-commented federal proposition was taken in 1994 concerning their reintroduction. In January of 1995, fourteen wolves were transferred to Yellowstone to acclimate to their surroundings. On March 31st, the pens opened and the wolves made their way into Yellowstone National Park. Throughout the next few years, other packs were reintroduced into different areas of the park, increasing the diversity of the project.[154]

Throughout the wolves' century-long demise, elk numbers soared and overgrazed plant life, it is argued. This produced knock-on effects throughout the ecosystem. The rising elk numbers worked to reduce biodiversity, diminishing sapling health of willows, cottonwoods, and other tree species along the riverbanks, and drying up the wetlands. Yellowstone was in ecological collapse because the of elk.

By the early 2000s, after the wolves stabilized in their old domain, they began hunting the elk. This, we are told, reduced elk numbers and pushed their marauding few into mobbing and moving herds. Berries and their bushes returned for the bears. Saplings sprouted alongside their rivers, holding old banks in place and allowing the river's flow to cut new courses. This created new wetlands. Beaver populations soared and fish reproduced in the shallow ponds. Moose and deer flourished with more vegetation. And the scavengers returned, like coyotes, to clean it all up. That is the story we are told, at least.

While the return of apex predators is surely a pivotal step in ecosystem restoration (stay tuned for Book III of *The Wildland Chronicles*), this story may not be what we think. Yes, the berries and trees and grasses returned when the elk decreased but is this an example of healthy ecosystem function? Is this an example of the Predator-Prey Connection and the foundation of mobbing, mowing, and moving herbivores in nature? Anthropologist and Pleistocene animal-to-human interaction specialist, Pat Shipman says no. Or,

[xxvi] $1 per wolf trapped and killed. Quote from Yellowstone Superintendent Annual Report 1915.

at the least, she questions this story and its supposed outcome with a hard eye.

After watching a wolf pack chase off a grizzly and then murder another wolf to protect a bison kill in Yellowstone, Shipman wrote, "We saw each pursuing wolf literally jump into the fray. Fur flew. Tails went up in the air. The lone wolf never came out. ...dancing and jumping, the pack celebrated its third triumph of the day." Shipman concluded alongside others such as Yellowstone guide and wildlife filmmaker, Brad Bulin that Yellowstone's story is not as cut and dry as we are led to believe. "Restoring an ecosystem to primitive grandeur is no simple matter in a complex world," Shipman wrote.[155]

Before they were eradicated by European settlers, it is estimated that there were over four hundred wolves in the area that Yellowstone now encompasses. But, while at a meager ninety wolves in total by the mid 2010s (less than quarter of the argued numbers), Shipman and others have concluded that "there are not enough ungulates to allow other wolves in [their] territory." Intraspecies competition is now killing the wolves.

Others have studied the wolves' reintroduction and concluded that they immediately also began killing their competitors, the coyotes, the park's former apex predator, and not the elk. Coyote populations have dropped precipitously and other scavengers like ravens and bears have returned, not for the berry bushes, but because there are more carcasses to clean up. This is never mentioned in the documentaries. This reorganization of the trophic triangle allowed the coyote's prey, both red fox and pronghorn antelopes, to rise exponentially. The elk herds continued to range loosely, as they had previously done, albeit gradually less in number.[156] With fewer elk to defoliate saplings alongside the riverbanks, the trees grew and the rivers did what rivers do, flow. With fewer elk, there are less mouths defoliating and hooves eroding the riverbanks. This makes complete sense. But the wolves are hungry, and they are eating each other.

Lastly, it is important to consider the oft hushed prey of the wolves: bison. While wolves hunting bison is a common motif across history and supplies the oft abused metaphor at regenerative grazing conferences, Yellowstone's bison are strangely never mentioned in this story. Why? If this is such a success story for modern conservationists and climate scientists alike, then why are the bison leaving the park? Shipman reported that more than three thousand bison have been culled since the wolves returned for trying to leave. In 2021, bison numbers exceeded five thousand. It was determined by the powers that be that this was too many for the park to hold. By 2023, according to The New York Times, more than one thousand were hunted and killed. The bison are trying to leave but are also overpopulating, overgrazing, and ecologically harming Yellowstone's "successful" ecosystem, like the elk. I do not blame those who leave this information out of the official story. I would hide it, too.

If wolves and apex predators push herbivores into tight herds that mob and mow and move, then why are they failing at Yellowstone? Depleting elk populations is not a regenerative success story. Antelope, fox, and bison numbers are exploding at cullable rates and elk and coyote are dwindling. Shipman, I think, said it well enough: humans attempt simple solutions in a complex world. Is modern farming any different?

Dynamic Upheaval

The Delaware chief, "King Beaver," viewing the past events and rising portents of the future, prophesied, "there is a high wind rising." Desertification and its many dustbowls and eroding mountaintops were on the horizon but it was our relationship to the land that was causing it—is causing it. Mathematically, the European biological and physical gun forever changed the landscape of this world: socially, it eradicated its many peoples and ecologically, we have so much still to learn. Cultural critic and historian, Richard Slotkin argued that the evolution of American western mythology was the evolution of the American mind's "too-slow awakening to the significance" of Indigenous peoples and I cannot help but think that the evolution of our regenerative mythology is the evolution of our soul's too-slow awakening to the actual realities of our actual world, its indigenous life, and the reciprocity required to transform what we perceive as resources into relations.

Henry David Thoreau mourned the passing of the wild and its wild places. "I should not like to think some demigod had come before me and picked out some of the best stars," he wrote. But demigods there were and the best stars have long been picked out. "I wish to know an entire heaven and an entire earth," he wrote. Yes, but it begins in wholeness. These conclusions are the same that Indigenous peoples have long put forth—and it is high time we learned to listen.

Around 8,500 years ago, a post-glacial climate emergency settled as the Northern Hemisphere wobbled slightly closer to our sun and warmed for 3,700 years. It was called the *Holocene Climatic Optimum*—or the Altithermal period—where forty centuries of intense global warming threw some parts of North America into true desserts and came close to burning the rest. Animals and their peoples migrated both eastward and westward and the bison and other species left their central homelands for climate reprieve.

It was an upheaval of biome, and life shifted accordingly. As the Altithermal cooled, millennia molding like stagnant bathwater, animals and their peoples returned home and, in some cases, even returned to the same homes they left thousands of years prior. The climate and its animals then seemingly remained happily in place for nearly 4,000 years in the cooling and cleaning bathwater.

But change was again on the horizon. It is always just over the hill. About 1,000 years ago, severe droughts cast the central prairies again into a shriveled and decadent ecotone sandwiched between the more-moist east and the west. The large herbivore numbers again plunged as they spread out and sought habitable lands. Once again, their numbers in the east rose slightly. A few hundred years later, they returned to their great homes in their great prairies and lived in their great halls of waving grasses and their ancient peoples. They then came together in a great, migrating thunder, as their ancestors did before the great drought and before the great warming and before the great cooling and life redeveloped, together, once again.

Then, as though a great, cruel joke, between the sixteenth and seventeenth centuries, the climate changed again, perhaps due to the great eradication and genocide of Indigenous peoples, sending our world into a deep wet and cooled season and the bison and large herbivores once again returned east for safe harbor under its forested cathedrals.[157]

Where are the large herds of herbivores that our regenerative grazing protocols and systems mimic? Even the highest estimates conclude that three million buffalo ranged the lands east of the Mississippi during the time of European colonization. To put that into context, however, there are nearly twenty million cattle east of the Mississippi today, but these lesser, domestic cousins occupy only fifty-three percent of the land (cities and roads and shopping malls and such occupy the rest), according to the USDA's 2018 agricultural census. This means that, at the highest point and after ninety-six percent of all Indigenous peoples passed from plagues and war that directly caused wild game to rise steeply and exponentially, there are still nearly seven times more large herbivores here than there ever have been and they occupy only half of the same land base. Mathematically, that is a fourteen-fold increase in density.

Our Shifting Baseline

While much is left undiscovered and much will continue to come to light in the coming years of increased archeological investigation and ancestral wisdom, what is clear is that the artificial human boundary on the outer ecotones of the central, great prairies is exactly that—artificial. Life is movement and she has always moved freely. That said, over the recent history of the last 20,000 years, it is decorously clear that bison and larger herbivores prefer their central and western biomes more than their eastern alternatives and, while they do migrate eastward occasionally, they seemingly have never done so in great, marauding, and sustained numbers.

This dynamic and richly complex ecological story of bison-climate co-creation must be understood in light of the European settler-colonialism and its naivety along with the Indigenous extinction and genocides. Herding herbivores live in small, extended families and only migrate in larger groups. But where those animals call home is complex and, to be honest, not the point. Life lives to freely move. But, for centuries, even in our modern literature around regenerative and sustainable agriculture, we have entirely neglected the rich complexities of a continuously changing and moving climate, its undulating ungulates, and the millions of peoples that used to live amongst them and with them. Most importantly, as them—one singular being.

Historian Richard Etulian wrote that, during the colonization of the early west, the settlers exhibited "an ambivalence that cherished the open landscape and freedom of the West on the one hand but hesitated to embrace the frontier characters and sociocultural life on the other."[158] Are we today any different? Before the reintroduction of the horse in the later seventeenth century, the Indigenous peoples of the Great Plains hunted the buffalo by donning the wolf's skin and creeping on all fours until they got so close to a buffalo that they could strike or lance at it from under the animal's stomach. A difficult and artful procedure to say the least, this technique also calls attention to a strange reality—if predators push prey animals into tight groups naturally in nature, then why did humans for thousands of years dress up as wolves in order to get within an arm's reach of them? Perhaps, *intraspecies* and *interspecies* competition has little to do with natural, ecological functioning and relationship.

David Graeber and David Wengrow argued, "Our standardized historical meta-narrative about the ambivalent progress of human civilization...was invented largely for the purpose of neutralizing the threat of indigenous critique."[159]

This is what industrial ecologists call socially shifting baseline theory: the difference between what is normal and that which we *perceive* as normal—what we *need* to be normal. Modern farmers mimic natural herd instincts through managing high stock-densities and non-selective grazing events because we are told this is natural. But what if an *actual* herd's natural instinct is to live in small, extended families and not a mob at all? What if the predators that bunch them together in fear are actually not predators but the clean-up crew—stay tuned for Book II.

Life is complex and it is near time that we allow it to be so. But we must give up control. Both the science and our forgotten history calls us to remember. It calls us to learn that large and mobbing herds of herbivores have rarely been the dominant social structure of our world and *intraspecies* and *interspecies* competition have never been the dominant decree of our Mother Earth.

Our spells are beginning to break as the old stories reawaken from the ashes.

Mara #6

From its countless green leaves a dew of golden light flowed downward. The ground beneath dappled in a passing warmth, a shadow fluttering from canopy to meadow to canopy again. Acorns splashed from her branches in clusters of copper and ochre. Songs drifted, rapt in flowers, from the deep blue horns that spilled from above, the liquor of life, the cloudless autumn sky.

I led the goats from their day's paddock on a walk to the oak tree. The saplings in the valley below that grew along the riverbank were silent—no charge tonight. The cedars on the ridge rested.

A gentle quietness ushered me deep into my head and Morgan's words drifted between my ears.

Just humans controlling nature.

I looked around. Pennsylvania everlasting flowered a pale white at the goat's knees and their muzzles drifted under the now stemless, elephant ear leaves of the lyreleaf sage, harvesting an oaken meal—tannins and proteins. Mara and her kids foraged separately, nibbling the yet red berries from the Indian currants that grew just beyond the oak's drip line.

Maybe she doesn't need the tannins? I thought.

Does are most susceptible to worms and intestinal parasites after birth. But Mara's foraging behavior said otherwise. Indian currant berries contain some of the highest saponin content in the autumn landscape. Saponins are surface-active glycosides that derive their name from their faculty to form stable foams in aqueous solutions.[160] They are members of the newly bustling class of secondary compounds called phytochemicals (like the ones covered in Section I). These foams develop post ingestion and work through the body to decrease blood lipid count.[161] In a 2012 study of postpartum women in the *Journal of Women's Health*, high blood lipid count was found to be associated with "major depression," a risk factor of cardiovascular disease.[162] High blood lipid count, high postpartum depression.

Was Mara self-medicating, bolstering her body's support against post-partum depression? By foraging these berries, in the autumn, well-watered and juicy at the edge of the mother oak's drip line, was she strategically seeking saponins? In place of dewormers and tannins, acorns and oak leaves, she sought berries.

Morgan's voice again echoed around me, through me. I could not believe my eyes. The herd was cleft in two and the void between them was increasing by the moment. In front of me, the herd foraged for whatever it could get; beside me, Mara and her kids deftly alchemized the meadow's medicine.

Just humans controlling nature.

We had witnessed the emergence of self-medication and phenotypic plasticity with Nancy and Nelly and our herd of cattle but Mara was showing us something altogether special. The goat herd's ability to forage was limited to our walks and they spent their time in this external environment solving internal imbalances. But Mara self-medicated prophylactically because she already satisfied her internal balances, she already self-selected her *wild* diet. You cannot truly self-medicate when you are starving.

Her health was not limited by fence lines and what vegetation grows within them as opposed to outside of them. Her health was not limited by our management's ability to cut down trees or harvest comfrey. Her health was not limited by anything other than her locomotion and the overall health of her greater environment. Her health, in this way, was a crescendo of interbeing. That is, the "whole and tributary to its glory," Earth known by being Earthlings and not Earth known tethered to tensile or polywire fence lines.

If one is always playing catch-up, health is always beyond reach. This simple truth—and it is simple—cannot be overlooked.

Dusk had fallen by the time we reached the barn for milking.

"Opal, Rose, Ogden, Mara—good!" As was her custom, Morgan named the goats as they entered the parlor.

This time Morgan milked and I steadily worked over their hooves, udders, and eyelids.

"Half are anemic," I admitted, entering Morgan's milking stall. "More than half, if I was an honest man and their hooves—" I paused, laughing the hate from my words, "—they need trimming and copper baths."

We finished milking in silence. Anemia is the clinical presentation of parasites and nutrient deficiencies and hooves and hoof rot also trail behind such deficits. Our stomachs welled up in our throats like sour meat and we felt uncomfortable, incapable, out of place. No matter what we did, the parasites and disease always seemed ahead of us. Pick up any book on raising goats and you will see work and humans doing the most of it.[xxvii] Fighting, combating problems, attempting to smile among it all, to believe in the romance of husbandry.

"These are not animals in our care but engines in our production." Morgan said thoughtfully as we stood in the parlor's doorway, our stomachs locked in our throats, the herd waiting in the stall in front of us. To share nourishment is to be alive. That is not the problem. To linearize nutrition into prescriptive lines of production, like cars, is altogether uncomfortable but still not the problem. To do these things in the name of nature and natural systems—that is the problem. *Just humans controlling nature.*

"What do we do?" I asked, blushing my humanity outwards.

The herd of goats shifted in the stall but one head remained fixed on us. In the confusion of the sunless mass held in the stall in front of us there was stability. Some kids tried to nurse, thrust-

---

xxvii "After kidding, give the doe a treat," one book writes. Another issues an ingredients list for kidding that contains clean cloth towels, water, and feeding tubes, suggestive of an obstetrician. What about feed? That is simple: "Buy good hay and commercially prepared grain rations." What about worms? That is simple: "levamisole (Tramisol), thiabendazole (Omnizole), cambendazole (Camvet), fenbendazole (Panacur), mebendazole (Telmin), and oxfendazole (Benzelmin)" will do the trick!

ing their little black noses deep into their mothers.[xxviii] Other goats, mostly bucks, shoved broadside with horns down for more space. Two bucks reared back and smacked down, four horns, two hollow heads, one thud. But Mara remained perfectly still. Her two, black and latitudinal eyes scythed through the unstilled stall and pierced us through. Our *anam cara,* our soul friend, her eyes remained perfectly still, fixed on us, unmoving, seeing right through our fears. I looked at Morgan. She looked at Mara. I turned to Mara. Morgan looked at me. Mara stayed on Morgan.

Mara bounced her head. *This is me. I see you. Do you see me?*

Morgan bounced her head in return. *And this is me. I see you.*

"What do we do?" I asked again, impatiently.

"We do nothing at all."

"But their fence isn't ready—" I said, confused. A mystery running about, an incant of sod and stars, of grass and gut, scudding in moonlight, falling around us.

"—That's alright." Morgan said, interrupting my words. Questions snapped, fears crackled like dim, dank air in the warm, wet light. She grabbed my hand, turned me around, and we walked away, together. We did not run, skate, or laugh. We ambled homeward, silently. Two nightwalkers stepping the cloudless night, the stars and small dreams sparked wonders that look the world like a beautiful glimpse in time, a curation of copse. Haywain yellow love bawling autumn in. Summer's bloom and boom drifting, now, among the stars, drinking from curved horns, reuniting the yarls, once more.

We walked on. The locust was above us, scythed and scrubbed for winter, silent. A junco and then a fallen tree swallow flaked from soused grasses, too winded from their songs to care about the end, already amber marked in autumn, mashed and mangled, soon, winter rains and sunless days. The scudding wales of wind propelled song in signatures at once familiar but restless.

We are restless, absolutely restless, we are the wind as we slip beyond the burr and needle hedge of overcome fence lines that hide the bracken-clutched bay and umber grasses that attempt their own

---

xxviii It was our practice never to milk to completion. While we never separated the kids from their mothers, allowing them full access to each other to nourish and co-create a relationship in their own ways, we expressed every evening whatever each doe had to share. If a doe lost a twin or triplet, which often was the case, we moderated their supply downward, slowly, to prevent mastitis but also to prevent them drying up due to a lack of demand.

song:

And I behest the beast,
Charging, I belch spent breath anew,
From old moors I betide the world,
The secret pools that heath on stone shape soft,
Let me be, you shit, you croft.

I wanted to turn around, to run back, to see if Mara was looking, to see what the other goats were doing. I wanted to cry or laugh, maybe smile. I wanted to do something. Morgan squeezed my hand, softly.

"Who will take care of them?" I asked.

"Them." She returned, pointing up, the four letters galloping a small band of wild horses across her outstretched arm. A family of squirrels in their solitary haunt, their airborne clubhouse, hurling whatever they may at whatever they hit danced in the persimmon to our right and bounced and juggled her words. Under the autumn donning and once golden leafless night of the walnut they spoke to us. *I charm you dreamers, stumbling bards, daughter of Merlin and son of Mokoš, across the leylines: run with us.*

We did.

Mara led the herd out of the stall, through the milk moist parlor, across the barn, over the moonlit meadow, and into the deep woods. Did she look back?

Years passed and every night they returned to the parlor to say hello and to share the wild harvest with us. Every few days, Morgan and I would walk the Wildland, chasing their trail, and play with them in some lost valley or ancient respite. Small, family units led by a matriarch formed and herds of ten to fifteen developed that would come together, every night, for the migration to milking. They were never fenced again.

But Mara the matriarch was not yet done and soon her spirit animated a cow named Saree, the matriarch of the cattle herd. That came next.

And so ends this branch of the *Stagtine*.

MACHINED, SOME TIME AGO

I woke in burning sweat. The salt of my body slowly maneuvering like cold, black oil back into itself, a scared and profuse continuum of death and its life.

It burned and I remember its burning well. Its lithe pathway cutting new channels through the many scrapes and blisters born during my summer of work in blackberry fields and their forests. But its coolness also chilled my place in the bed—a wet morass within which Understanding could visit me. My ancestors knew *Mokoš*, the goddess of Water and the shapeshifting mother of the Sun, but I have never met her. Generations of migrations and settlement have long infused my once-rooted genomics with rot.

Tonight, Understanding appeared and I felt her. A shadow's shadow, she clothed the dark room in comforting chaos—a place when everything is neither alive nor dead, conscious nor unconscious, and when nothing is everything and everything is just nothing filled with a bounty of itself. And she stood in the corner of the room and stared at me. I sat up uncomfortably and tucked my feet more securely in my sweat-moistened blanket. The room stood still. For how long I did not know, could not know, do not know, but its stillness shattered when she moved eastward, a sidestep toward the door of the bedroom and my eyes followed. With a gentle glance and a shadow of smile her eyes connected with mine and a strange terror infused homeliness narrowed upon me like the sight of a distant gun or the twisted pupil of the raven.

I woke up. Startled from the dream, I looked around the empty room and she was gone. What was once in shadow was now plainly lit in the moonlight that filtered through the open window. I laid my body back against the warm, dry bed and for a moment or two felt like something was missing—some hollow heart of the mother oak or some hollow core of a distant planet. Something was not where it was supposed to be. I was unsure of what came next and I felt unprepared for whatever it was. I tried to stay awake. Tried. But eventually some force pulled on the lids of my eyes and soon I was snoring and the second dream began.

I was in the basement of some house and there were many people around me. It felt like a party. There were drinks and music and dancing. There were many happy and drunk people, enough to fill a crowded arena, but space did not seem to be an issue. The mass of movement and cheer surrounded a structural anomaly in the center of the room. Like plankton in the open ocean drifting and floating endlessly in space, the dancers moved rhythmically around the anomaly but they never seemed bothered by it. Like an alter in an otherwise open courtyard, a cage lay in the middle of the dancefloor.

It was clear that some object, or some *thing*, occupied the space inside the enclosure but the space was shadowed and well concealed by the shifting darkness. The size of the cage was also unknown to me, for, although many drinking and dancing people surrounded the cage in some great circle, I could not see where it ended. Its back corners drifted deeper into the dark basement than my eyes could follow. All converged into a single vanishing point where limited light fell against complete darkness—the dream's horizon line.

The cage rattled, rhythmically but jarring, every minute or so, and a great metallic vibration echoed across the drinking and the dancing and the happiness and the unknown expanse that I thought was a basement. But it did echo and so I knew there was a limit somewhere that threw the waves back on us. But no one seemed to take notice of the rattles or its vibrations. Everyone seemed to accept that there was a cage but no one noticed its noise. All continued on, creating their own songs, dancing according to their own rhythms.

On the cage there was a plaque that read: *Machined, some time ago.* It was a metal cage with a metal plaque, like those you see on the side of the road that mark forgotten places. Its patina demonstrated its age of *some time* and so I believed it.

The party lasted for *some time* and I remember watching its decline. I stood near to the cage and watched as person by person fell into a deep sleep, their cups always splashing to the floor just before their bodies. Great heaps of happy people lay sleeping around me and the music slowly faded. I was now alone and standing in the room. The silence moved over the sleeping bodies like the morning mist moves across the valley. It was only then that I noticed that the rattles we had all grown accustomed to that echoed from the cage were precipitated by deep, shadowed snarls. I was afraid. Terror struck me. It was not the cage that was *machined, some time ago,* but the thing inside of it. A zoo of death, a Jurassic and uncommon enclosure.

The snarl and its rattle's echo then faded and an empty silence settled. Everything grew heavy in the void. I could not move. My feet were buried under the sleeping and happy many and then even the silence stopped her slithering.

After an amount of time unknown to me a *click* animated the still darkness but there was no echo, just empty waves of energy hovering in place. Breath left the room that I thought was a basement as even exhales became motionless and the lights flickered and their flash highlighted the cage's door. Too many locks to count hung from its great latch and snaked over and around and even under the now sleeping, happy people. The people for *some time* must have, between their dances and their songs, placed lock after lock on the cage's latch. Some sort of rhythmic ritual.

But another *click* and then another animated the silence. I lost all breath.

The bodies on the floor began to jolt and a hectic scarcity plagued the ensuing confusion, lifting everyone up. The slumbering ran this way and that and screamed as whatever life they had left was strangled. The door slammed open against the cage's wall. The locks exploded. Shrapnel screamed in all directions, killing many of the confused and scarring the rest. I hid behind a shadowed array of wooden liquor barrels and I covered myself in a torn bundle of cotton. I remember seeing a staircase to some upper room that I had not noticed before. Where did the bundle of cotton come from? Where did the stairway lead?

Nothing emerged that I could see from the cage but the now blood-stained and scurrying people ran like spiders from their nest and they ran as though something was chasing them. They screamed and scurried in a great frenzy. Pure hysteria animated the once-happy people and their new and sad songs squealed as a rich, black substance dripped from loose rivets above their heads and burned their skins.

I looked on behind my barrel and under my cotton.

And that is when I saw them—felt them, really. The Unknowables. Standing up from behind my oaken and cotton corner, I watched as the burning and yelling few that remained turned and faced some force, some amassing monster that I could just barely make out under the swinging and flickering lights.

Some people turned and tried to climb the stairs to escape and others just ran like lost, basement rats. But, one by one, the scurrying stomachs of the confused mass began to swell and turn an orange-blue hue, like fire inside an egg. The confusion stopped and everyone together, still and sure, looked down and placed their hands on their stomachs, like pregnant women do as they near the day of birth, and, inhaling, breath returned. As though one, great orchestra after landing the final, great note, everyone settled and every breath slowly released. But as it did it ignited the fuse and the lights flickered again and flashed. One by one, the spirits of the now swelling, confused mass exploded from inside and mixed in a great fire above our heads. All seemed to hover in the air, like smoke, and that is when I saw them. The Unknowables were hunched over and a rich, black oil fell from their eyes that reminded me very much of my own and they looked at me. For a moment I thought I saw myself in their faces but the lights flashed and my eyes blinked and I lost them in the darkness. A strange terror overtook me. Trying to get away from the pain and the plasma, I hid my head in my hands and I cried. Explosions and drifting souls and flashing and waving lights echoed all around, but I sat there and cried, my head buried in my hands.

After *some time,* everything was again still and the lights gently swung above me, creaking metallically. I was alone in the empty room. The chaos of the dream fully emptied but the dream remained. A vacuum of silence, of meaning. The room was bare, the cage was gone, and the lights were on and I saw no one else. Pulling my hands away from my face I held them up to the lights. They were covered in oil. Then, I awoke.

It is not often that I dream dreams. It is even less often that I dream dreams of dreams and it is even less often that their spirit visits with me before their great work. The public exposition of dreams and visions is dangerous, for it allows foreigners to do the intimate work of interpretation. But this dream, I believe, was given to me so that I may give it to you and I do so willingly.

We have long confused the wailing in the wind as portents of a coming disaster. Unseasonal torrents of tears struggle as they work to cool the hottest summer on record and our soil is running out, we are told. *We have a few harvests left,* beckon the experts. Pollution and pandemics plague modern life and one million species face imminent extinction. But the wrens have already gone, this much is true. Their morning song lessens year over year outside of my morning's window. Even the magnificent blue herons are seldomly seen as our wetlands run away and the dung beetles are struggling to survive in the now toxic and breathless womb of our world.

The shrill shrieks of machined monsters echo atop the brisk and dew-infused dawn as I write this. I turn the music up to drown them out. Someone is clear cutting their forest; someone is becoming rich; some land is becoming poor; and some community is already gone. *The climate is changing,* and *we have to do something to save it* are phrases that well infuse, like pokeberries in warm summer water, the narrative of our settler culture's mythology.

We have to do something. We have to. Act!

Machined, some time ago. Yes, like locks on a cage, our incessant work secures the climate. Like locks on a cage, our incessant focus on saving the world secures our place within it. Like locks on a cage, we, the latecomers, the discoverers of everything, know what to do and the landscape's productivity profits our businesses.

Like locks on a cage, our work molds the land into something more rich, something more progressive, something more secure, something that benefits us—only us, always us. But we continue dancing and we continue drinking and we continue singing and slapping just one more lock on the cage.

But the cage, it rattles. It snarls and its echoes shake our world. And so, we sing even louder and we dance even harder and the drinks become even stronger. I turn the music up louder. No avail, the machining and felling rings through the valley.

We drunkenly drift around the core of room, never noticing the cage that we are, ourselves, in. Yes, the cage in the middle of the room is the room and the snarls are just our songs echoing against its walls. We are locked in the civilized crapulence of the cage, colonizing ourselves by colonizing everyone else. The locks we place to save our world are the same locks that enclose the commons and that uncommonly close whatever abundance she has to share with us. The Unknowables will never be known until we know ourselves, the dream portends. The end is coming but that is okay.

This book that you hold now in your hands is about becoming known by first knowing that becoming whole requires nothing but acknowledgement. This is a book about being human, for that is all we need to do.

Standing Rock Sioux author and activist, Vine Deloria Jr. wrote,

> The future of humankind lies waiting for those who will come to understand their lives and take up their responsibilities to all living things. Who will listen to the trees, the animals and birds, the voices of the places of the land? As the long-forgotten peoples of the respective continents rise and begin to reclaim their ancient heritage, they will discover the meaning of the lands of their ancestors. That is when the invaders of the Northern American continent will finally discover that, for this land, God is red.

It is not work that is required, but something else entirely. *Who will listen?*

All I ask is that you read this and in its reading you learn to see, to listen, to eat—to live in respect and harmony with our many relations. Better yet, that you live as the harmony. Because you are. The harmony.

I write with a concern not for the saving of the world, for I no longer believe that balance is attainable before some ultimate collapse—before our cage explodes open. The end of the world is coming and that is okay. I write with optimism and hope for, as my friend Wahinkpe Topa, who Sun Dances with the Lakota, told me, hope is not the expectation of an outcome, but the eradication of outcomes altogether in the belief that being human will be enough. Enough for what? Wrong question.

I write so that I become human and I write so that, when the next world rises from the ashes of this chemically-infused and churned and oil-burned wasteland, the basement of history, we may work together to rebuild, to try again, and, most importantly, to love and to have better memories.

I write under the shadow of mountains. But soon these ancient crags will be fully naked, clear cut past their epidermis and their eroding hills will become rocky knolls and our grandchildren, bouncing on our calloused knees, will ask about the great Appalachians.

"What were they like, grandpa?" They will ask as they ride on giggles or maybe they will ask as they kneel before our graves.

"They were profitable," we will respond, either in tears or under them.

Our grandchildren walk our dreams. They will either smile at us or curse our graves. I pray they smile. I live for them to smile. I dream their smiles. We do not have to move mountains.

Give up, like a ship on the sea blast or a stag's tines before *Bealtaine*, in the late winter, riding the dark dusk deep down. It is time for the night, for nakedness, for letting it all go, for communing with the gods. It is time to drop our tools and rest, to dream.

A POWERFUL COMMUNITY WITH D. FIRTH GRIFFITH

JOIN US FOR THE START OF SOMETHING OLD, BORN NEW AGAIN, THROUGH A NEW ONLINE COMMUNITY, ONLINE COURSES, AND IN-PERSON EXPERIENCES.

RECOMMENDED READING

The writing of this book and every book within *The Wildland Chronicles* is a work of silent filtration through long and sustained filaments, strings, intention, and accidents. Anyone who reads anything knows that sometimes the best somethings are found through accidental stumblings at local, used bookshops or forgotten library shelves. Nearly a decade spent filling the accidental cauldron of research and chance combines to make a book and I hope that this one was impactful to you. That is my hope. My hope at the very least and also at the very most.

The many pages of citations, footnotes, and organized bibliographies provide an ordered shadow to this section. I encourage you to start there. But hundreds of papers and equally many books did not make it into this book but they, perchance, helped write the text and so I have filtered them, determined the most important or influential friends, and combined them into a hopefully helpful compendium for those readers who may want to dive as I dove. Maybe not. That is up to you.

Introduction

For a source and commentary of ancient Celtic mythology, albeit a translation from monastic documents from the early Middle Age Europe, consider: Tom Peete Cross, Clark Harris Slover, eds.,

Ancient Irish Tales. New York: Barnes & Noble Books, 1936; or Sioned Davies, trans., "The Second Branch of the Mabinogi," in ***The Mabinogion***. Oxford: Oxford University Press, 2007, 28.

For a short read on the nature of Creative and Imagining Science, consider: Thompson, William Irwin. ***Imaginary Landscape: Making Worlds of Myth and Science***. New York: St. Martin's Press, 1989.

Section I: Of Memory & Time

For overview of how the modern world of chemical stress is imperiling the future of the human race, consider: Swan, Shanna H. ***Count Down****: How Our Modern World Is Threatening Sperm Counts, Altering Male and Female Reproductive Development, and Imperiling the Future of the Human Race*. New York: Scribner, 2020; or Jay, Anthony, G. ***Estrogeneration****: How Estrogenics are Making You Fat, Sick, and Infertile*. Tallahassee: Pyrimidine Publishing, 2017.

For an accessible but deep overview on the nature of stress in the body, consider: Sapolsky, Robert M. ***Why Zebras Don't Get Ulcers****: The Acclaimed Guide to Stress, Stress-Related Diseases, and Coping*. New York: St. Martin's Press, 1994; or Cannon, Walter. **The Wisdom of the Body**: How the human body reacts to disturbance and danger and maintains the stability essential to life. New York: W. W. Norton & Company, 1963.

"Those who cultivate competence in the use of a new technology become an elite group that are granted undeserved authority and prestige by those who have no such competence...New things require new words. But new things also modify old words, words that have deep-rooted meanings." (pp. 8-9). For a brief study on the role of technology and its monopoly over modern humanity, consider: Postman, Neil. ***Technopoly****: The Surrender of Culture to Technology*. New York: Vintage Books, 1993.

Section II: In Nature's Image

For plant communication, generally understood for the lay reader, consider: Calvo, Paco. *Planta Sapiens: The New Science of Plant Intelligence.* New York: W. W. Norton & Company, 2022.

For a more-lyrical and engrossing narrative on plant communication, consider: Gagliano, Monica. *Thus Spoke the Plant: A Remarkable Journey of Groundbreaking Scientific Discoveries and Personal Encounters with Plants.* Berkeley: North Atlantic Books, 2018.

For all things fungi, carried in a truly entangled writing style, consider: Sheldrake, Merlin. *Entangled Life: How Fungi Make Our Worlds, Chane Our Minds & Shape our Futures.* New York: Random House. 2020.

For tree communication and a captivating narrative-led memoir of the wood wide web, consider: Simard, Suzanne. *Finding the Mother Tree: Discovering the Wisdom of the Forest.* New York: Alfred A Knopf, 2021.

"This is modern man: the individualist in quest of inner peace and happiness." (pp. 467). For a general discussion about the western world, reason's unfortunate mastery, and the delinquencies of nature's freedoms, centered on the destructive role of capitalism and 'experts,' consider: Saul, John Ralston. *Voltaire's Bastards: The Dictatorship of Reason in the West.* New York: Simon & Schuster Paperbacks, 1992.

For a deep and surprising analysis of what makes us human: peace or war, consider: Bregman, Rutger. *Humankind: A Hopeful History.* New York: Back Bay Books, 2019.

For general plant communication and cognitive intelligence, consider: Trewavas, Anthony. *Plant Behavior and Intelligence.* Oxford: Oxford University Press, 2015.

Section III: Phenotypic Release

"Comrade, I did not want to kill you. If you jumped in here again, I would not do it...But now, for the first time, I see you are a man like me. I thought of your hand-grenades, of your bayonet, of your rifle; now I see your wife and your face and our fellowship... Forgive me, comrade; how could you be my enemy?" (pp. 223) For a deep examination of 'warring for the chancellor' carried in lucid prose (novel), consider: Remarque, Erich Maria. ***All Quiet on the Western Front***. New York: Fawcett Books, 1928.

For a complete overview of adaptive landscape genomics, extended families, and palate feedback loops, consider: Provenza, Fred. ***Nourishment***: *What Animals Can Teach Us About Rediscovering Our Nutritional Wisdom*. White River Junction: Chelsea Green Publishing, 2018.

"A civilization that recognized no higher principle, but is in reality based only on a negation of principles, is by this very fact ruled out from all mutual understanding." (pp. 21). For a ruthless exposure of the "Western deviation," its loss of tradition, its exaltation of action over knowledge, its rampant individualism and general social chaos, consider: Guenon, Rene. **The Crisis of the Modern World**. Edited by Marco Pallis, Arthur Osborne, Richard C. Nicholson. Hillsdale: Sophia Perennis, 2001.

"We are aware of this significance through our inner nature. In that the good to which nature conduces is now a purely natural, self-contained good, and in that the proximate moral source is a self-subsistent order of interlocking beings." (pp. 315). For epic-length inspection into the self, self-identity in community, the role of Creation in understanding oneself, and more, consider: Taylor, Charles. ***Sources of the Self***: *The Making of the Modern Identity*. Cambridge: Cambridge University Press, 1989.

"Conservation must focus on protecting the ability of ecosystems to adapt and change in a changing world, rather than attempting

to stop or reverse all change." (pp. 7). For an intimate discussion on the role of conservation and the problematic ideologies behind protecting wild places with only more human industry, consider: Marris, Emma. **Wild Souls**: *Freedom and Flourishing in the Non-Human World*. New York: Bloomsbury Publishing, 2021.

For minerals in grazing animal health and café-style free-choice mineral information, consider: Holliday, Richard, Jim Helfter. **A Holistic Vet's Prescription for a Healthy Herd**: *A Guide to Livestock Nutrition, Free-Choice Minerals, and Holistic Cattle Care,* Austin: Acres U.S.A: 2015.

"No species except mankind has reached the point at which culture becomes the main driver of an evolutionary surge, outrunning environmental and physical constraints." (pp. 16). For a 30,000 foot review of the last 10,000 years of cultural evolution under the coverlet of really hard questions, consider: Wright, Ronald. **A Short History of Progress**. Anansi Press, 2004.

For soil food web: bacteria, fungi, nematodes, protozoa and more along with in-depth study on soil profiles and the biochemical nature of emerging soil science, consider: Lowenfels, Jeff, Wayne Lewis. **Teaming With Microbes**: *The Organic Guide to the Soil Food Web*. Portland: Timber Press: 2010; or, Masters, Nicole. **For the Love of Soil**: *Strategies to Regenerate Our Food Production Systems*. Integrity Soils Limited, 2019

For general unpacking of all things soil health, written in scientific style but approachable, generally. Albrecht, William. Ed Charles Walters. **Soil Fertility & Human and Animal Health**: *The Albrecht Papers, Volume VIII*. Austin: Acres U.S.A: 2013.

For an overview (history or mythology) of pre-Christian Ireland and the Celtic peoples, consider: Roberts, Alice. **The Celts: Search for a Civilization**. London: Heron Books, 2015; or Rees, Alwyn, and Brinley Rees. **Celtic Heritage**: *Ancient Tradition in Ireland and Wales*. United States: Thames and Hudson, 1961; or Koch, John, T.

ed., **The Celtic Heroic Age**: *Literary Sources for Ancient Celtic Europe & Early Ireland & Wales* Fourth Edition. Aberystwyth: Celtic Studies Publications, 2013.

For a pivotal epic on do-nothing-farming, formed in the mid-twentieth century Japan, consider: Fukuoka, Masanobu. **The One-Straw Revolution**. Edited by Larry Korn, New York: New York Review of Books, 2009.

"Better if they had been born in the open pasture and suckled by a wolf, that they might have seen with clearer eyes what field they were called to labor in." (pp. 3). For all things Henry David Thoreau, wilderness, stories that wake us up (pp. 90), reflections on simple living with Earth, and more, consider: Thoreau, Henry D. **Walden**. Edited by Jeffrey S. Cramer. New Haven: Yale University Press, 2006.

"To live within ideology, with utopian expectations, is to live in no place, to live in limbo. To live nowhere. To live in a void where the illusion of reality is usually created by highly sophisticated rational constructs." (pp. 30). For an ideological overview of humanity's great leap backward and an erudite detailing of modern man's unconsciousness and unease, consider: Saul, John Ralston. **The Unconscious Civilization.** New York: The Free Press, 1995.

"What with mothers and lovers, what with the prohibitions they were not conditioned to obey, what with the temptations and the lonely remorses, what with all the diseases and the endless isolating pain, what with the uncertainties and the poverty—they were forced to feel strongly. And feeling strongly, how could they be stable?" (pp. 47). For a penetrating portrayal of a fully industrialized future carried in lucid prose (novel), consider: Huxley, Aldous. **Brave New World**. New York: Harper Perennial, 2004.

Section IV: Lost Herds, Wounded Land

For a general overview of the geological and resulting ecological realities following the Last Glacial Maximum (ice-age), consider: Pielou, E.C. *After the Ice Age: The Return of Life to Glaciated North America*. Chicago: The University of Chicago Press, 1991.

"Our standardized historical meta-narrative about the ambivalent progress of human civilization, where freedoms are lost as societies grow bigger and more complex—was invented largely for the purpose of neutralizing the threat of indigenous critique." (pp. 32). For a monumental study on the history of the world, peering into archeology, anthropology, and sociocultural philosophes, consider: Graeber, David and David Wengrow. *The Dawn of Everything: A New History of Humanity*. New York: Farrar, Straus and Giroux, 2021.

For general early notes and a consideration on why agriculture arose from the peripheries of life into a central role, consider: Cohen, Mark. *The Food Crisis in Prehistory: Overpopulation and the Origins of Agriculture*. Yale University Press. 1979.

For study on Jean-Jacques Rousseau, consider: Garrard, Graeme, *Rousseau's Counter-Enlightenment*. New Albany: SUNY Press, 2003; or Rousseau, Jean-Jacques, *Basic Political Writings, Second Edition*. Donald A. Cress, ed., Indianapolis: Hackett Publishing, 2011. *See also endnote 24 in Section 4 for more.*

For a purely philosophical study on Blaise Pascal (no mathematics), consider: Pascal, Blaise. *Pensées*. Translated by A. J. Krailsheimer. London: Penguin Books, 1995.

For a sizeable exploration into European customs that brought different groups to these shores, including an examination of Game Law and colonial European naivety, consider: Fischer, David Hackett. *Albion's Seed: Four British Folkways in America*. New York: Oxford University Press, 1989.

"Discovering the biological diversity of America and ransacking it for wealth and status twinned into a Moebius loop that shaped a new, global destiny for the content's wild animals." (pp 159). For a natural history and philosophical inquiry into the western hemisphere, consider: Flores, Dan. *Wild New World: The Epic Story of Animals and People in America*. New York: W. W. Norton & Company, 2023.

For an examination of the attitudes and traditions that shapes early "American mythology," consider: Slotkin, Richard. *Regeneration Through Violence: The Mythology Of the American Frontier*. Norman: University of Oklahoma Press, 1973.

For general ecological and eco-social history of the Northern Piedmont pre and post European colonization, consider: Cronon, William. *Changes in the Land: Indians, Colonists, and the Ecology of New England*. New York: Hill and Wang, 1983.

For a history of the term "Long Hunters," consider: Belue, Ted Franklin. *The Long Hunt: Death of the Buffalo East of the Mississippi*. Mechanicsburg: Stackpole Books, 1996.

For a deep dive into the genocide and early extinction events of colonial America, consider: Crosby, Alfred. *The Columbian Exchange: Biological and Cultural Consequences of 1492*. Westport: Greenwood Press, 1972.

For a general history of American history writing, what is called "historiography," consider: Etulain, Richard W. **"Introduction: The Rise of Western Historiography,"** in *Writing Western History: Essays on Major Western Historians*. ed., Richard W. Etulain. Albuquerque: University of New Mexico Press, 1991.

Indigenous Voices

For a deft retelling of western history, namely, United States, from an Indigenous perspective, consider: Blackhawk, Ned. ***The Rediscovery of America***: *Native Peoples and the Unmaking of U.S. History*. New Haven: Yale University Press, 2023.

For an autobiography of Indigenous tribal life, consider: **Mourning Dove**. *A Salishan Autobiography*. Edited by Jay Miller. Lincoln: University of Nebraska Press, 1990.

For a lyrical and engagement epic on Indigenous thought, consider: Yunkaporta, Tyson. ***Sand Talk***: *How Indigenous Thinking Can Save the World*. New York: HarperOne, 2020.

For an anthology of Indigenous ecological knowledge, consider: Nelson, Melissa and Dan Shilling, ed., ***Traditional Ecological Knowledge***: *Learning from Indigenous Practices for Environmental Sustainability*. Cambridge: Cambridge University Press, 2018; and Jamail, Dahr and Stan Rushworth eds., ***We Are the Middle of Forever***: *Indigenous Voices from Turtle Island on the Changing Earth*. New York: The New Press, 2022.

For a brief but packed overview of Sitting Bull's worldview, impacting the world of late nineteenth century political relations, consider: Wahinkpe Topa. ***Sitting Bull's Worlds***: *For A World In Crisis*. New York: DIO Press Inc., 2021.

For a deep anthology of Indigenous poetry and verse, consider: Harjo, Joy., ed., ***When the Light of the World was Subdued, Our Songs Came Through***: *A Norton Anthology of Native Nations Poetry*. New York: W. W. Norton & Company, 2020.

For an intimate and personal history (written by his grandson) of the Lakota and Sitting Bull, consider: LaPointe, Ernie. ***Sitting Bull***: *His Life and Legacy*. Layton: Gibbs Smith, 2009.

For an epic and well-known ethnobotanist memoir of life, family, and history, consider: Kimmerer, Robin Wall. ***Braiding Sweetgrass****: Indigenous Wisdom, Scientific Knowledge, and the Teachings of Plants*. Minneapolis: Milkweed Editions, 2013. Also, Krawec, Patty. ***Becoming Kin****: An Indigenous Call to Unforgetting the Past and Reimagining Our Future*. Minneapolis: Broadleaf Books, 2022.
For an Indigenous view of religion and history, consider: Deloria, Vine Jr. ***God Is Red****: A Native View on Religion*. Wheat Ridge: Fulcrum Publishing, 1973.

For a groundbreaking and pivotal read on kinship and the indigenous worldview, consider: Wahinkpe Topa and Darcia Narváez. ***Restoring the Kinship Worldview****: Indigenous Voices Introduce 28 Precepts for Rebalancing Life on Planet Earth*. Berkeley: North Atlantic Books, 2022.

For a first-person telling of the Monacans, consider: Wood, Karenne and Diane Shields. ***The Monacan Indians****: Our Story*. Office of Historical Research, Monacan Indian Nation.

Migrant Voices

For a first-person account (1738 - 1768) of an Irish migrant who spent 40 years amongst the southeastern peoples—Cherokee, Catawba, Creek, Choctaw, and Chickasaw—consider: Adair, James. ***History of the American Indians***. Edited by Kathryn E. Holland Braund. Tuscaloosa: The University of Alabama Press, 2005.

For an errored first-person account (1727 - 1747) from the New York Governor and first colonial representative to the Iroquois Confederacy, consider: Colden, Cadwallader. ***The History of the Five Indian Nations****: Depending on the Province of New-York in America*. Ithica: Cornell University Press, 1958.

For a first-person account (1830 – 1839) of the Plains nations from an artist's perspective, consider: Catlin, George. ***Letters and***

Notes on the Manners, Customs, and Condition of the North American Indians. Wiley and Putnam, 1841.

For a well-researched, respected, and intimate history of the Hopi, consider: Waters, Frank **Book of Hopi**: *The First Revelation of the Hopi's Historical and Religious World-view of Life*. New York: Ballantine Books, 1963.

For a vivid memoir (1756 – 1765) of the Cherokee people from a British lieutenant, consider: Timberlake, Henry. **The Memoirs of Lt. Henry Timberlake: The Story of a Solider, Adventurer, and Emissary to the Cherokees, 1756-1765**. Edited by Duane H. King. Cherokee: Museum of the Cherokee Indian Press, 2007.

For a modern history of the Monacan (past, present, and future people of author's home), consider: Hantman, Jeffrey L. **Monacan Millennium**: *A Collaborative Archeology and History of a Virginia Indian People*. Charlottesville: University of Virginia Press, 2018.

Settler Voices

For an early memoir of Spanish explorer, consider: Lawrence C. Wroth, ed., **The Voyages of Giovanni da Verrazzano**, *1524-1528*. New Haven: Yale University Press, 1970.

For a three-hundred year history of North American French settlement, consider: Lescarbot, Marc. **The History of New France**. Translated by W. L. Grant. Toronto: The Champlain Society, 1907.

For a general socio-ecological overview of the lands that are today Kentucky, Tennessee, Virginia, and Ohio, consider: Belue, Ted Franklin. **The Hunters of Kentucky**: *A Narrative History of America's First Far West, 1750-1792*. Mechanicsburg: Stackpole Books, 2003.

For a first-person account of western settlement, ecology, and the implantation of democracy in the west, consider: Marder, Daniel ed., **A Hugh Henry Brackenridge Reader**: *1770-1815*. Pittsburgh: University of Pittsburgh Press, 1970.

For a first-person, religious account of the early ecology, consider: Dexter, Franklin, B. ed., **The Diary of David McClure**. New York: The Knickerbocker Press, 1899.

For a first-person frontiersman account of the ecology (and wars) of the eighteenth century, consider: Flint, Timothy. **Indian Wars of the West**. Phaistos Publishing.

For a second-hand account of early settlers and surrounding ecology in the Allegheny regions, consider: McClung, John Alexander. **Sketches of Western Adventure**: *Containing an Account of the Most Interesting Incidents Connected with the Settlement of the West, from 1735 to 1794*. Dayton: L. F. Claflin & Co., 1852.

STAGTINE

ENDNOTES

[1] Postman, Neil. *Technopoly: the Surrender of Culture to Technology*. New York: Knopf, 1992.

[2] Thompson, William Irwin. *Passages About Earth: An Exploration of the New Planetary Culture*. New York: Perennial Library, 1973, 11.

[3] Bateson, Gregory, *Mind and Nature: A Necessary Unity*. New York: Dutton, 1979. pp. 8.

[4] Deloria, Vine, Jr., *Custer Died For Your Sins: An Indian Manifesto*. New York Avon Books, 1969. pp. 85.

[5] These two epic poems are collected and translated from: Tom Peete Cross, Clark Harris Slover, eds., "The Book Of Invasions, " in *Ancient Irish Tales*. New York: Barnes & Noble Books, 1936, pp. 19-21; and Michael R. Burch's 2020 translation of *The Song of Amergin*.

[6] West, John B. "The strange history of atmospheric oxygen." *Physiological reports* vol. 10,6 (2022): e15214. doi:10.14814/phy2.15214.

[7] Ettwig, Katharina F et al. "Bacterial oxygen production in the dark." *Frontiers in microbiology* vol. 3 273. 7 Aug. 2012, doi:10.3389/fmicb.2012.00273

[8] Holland, Heinrich D. "The oxygenation of the atmosphere and oceans." *Philosophical transactions of the Royal Society of London. Series B, Biological sciences* vol. 361,1470 (2006): 903-15. doi:10.1098/rstb.2006.1838

[9] Uvnäs-Moberg, Kerstin et al. "Self-soothing behaviors with particular reference to oxytocin release induced by non-noxious sensory stimulation." *Frontiers in psychology* vol. 5 1529. 12 Jan. 2015, doi:10.3389/fpsyg.2014.01529.

Light, Kathleen C et al. "More frequent partner hugs and higher oxytocin levels are linked to lower blood pressure and heart rate in premenopausal women." *Biological psychology* vol. 69,1 (2005): 5-21. doi:10.1016/j.biopsycho.2004.11.002

[10] Young, Rosamund. *The Secret Life of Cows*. New York: Penguin Press:

2018.

[11] De Viney E., Dickert J., Lockwood R. The Care of Pets within Child Abusing Families. Int. J. Study Anim. Probl. 1983;4:321–329.

[12] Ascione F.R. Battered women's reports of their partners' and their children's cruelty to animals. J. Emot. Abus. 1998;1:119–133. doi: 10.1300/ J135v01n01_06.

[13] Krienert, Jessie L et al. "Examining the nexus between domestic violence and animal abuse in a national sample of service providers." *Violence and victims* vol. 27,2 (2012): 280-95. doi:10.1891/0886-6708.27.2.280.

Ascione F.R. Men in Prison Who Abused Animals and Who Abused Their Wives and Girlfriends: Voices of Perpetrators; Proceedings of the 11th International Conference on Human-Animal Interactions, People & Animals: Partnership in Harmony (IAHAIO); Tokyo, Japan. 5–8 October 2007.

Volant, Anne M et al. "The relationship between domestic violence and animal abuse: an Australian study." *Journal of interpersonal violence* vol. 23,9 (2008): 1277-95. doi:10.1177/0886260508314309.

Bright, Melissa A et al. "Animal cruelty as an indicator of family trauma: Using adverse childhood experiences to look beyond child abuse and domestic violence." *Child abuse & neglect* vol. 76 (2018): 287-296. doi:10.1016/j.chiabu.2017.11.011.

Faver C., Cavazos A. Animal abuse and domestic violence. A view from the border. J. Emot. Abus. 2007;7:59–81. doi: 10.1080/10926798.2007.10766832.

Simmons, Catherine A, and Peter Lehmann. "Exploring the link between pet abuse and controlling behaviors in violent relationships." *Journal of interpersonal violence* vol. 22,9 (2007): 1211-22. doi:10.1177/0886260507303734.

[14] Data derived from USDA, National Agricultural Statistics Service surveys (2011 and 2021) https://www.ers.usda.gov/topics/natural-resources-environment/organic-agriculture. Accessed 10 Nov. 2023.

[15] Goodwin, Renee D et al. "Trends in U.S. Depression Prevalence From 2015 to 2020: The Widening Treatment Gap." *American journal of preventive medicine* vol. 63,5 (2022): 726-733. doi:10.1016/j. amepre.2022.05.014

[16] Saeedi, Pouya et al. "Mortality attributable to diabetes in 20-79 years old adults, 2019 estimates: Results from the International Diabetes Federation Diabetes Atlas, 9th edition." *Diabetes research and clinical practice* vol. 162 (2020): 108086. doi:10.1016/j.diabres.2020.108086

[17] Bitsko RH, Claussen AH, Lichtstein J, Black LJ, Everett Jones S, Danielson MD, Hoenig JM, Davis Jack SP, Brody DJ, Gyawali S, Maenner MM, Warner M, Holland KM, Perou R, Crosby AE, Blumberg SJ, Avenevoli S, Kaminski JW, Ghandour RM. Surveillance of Children's Mental Health – United States, 2013 – 2019 MMWR, , 2022 / 71(Suppl-2);1–42.

[18] C. Mapiye, M. Chimonyo, M.C. Marufu, V. Muchenje, Stress reactivity and its relationship to beef quality in Nguni steers supplemented with Acacia karroo leaves, *Animal*, Volume 5, Issue 9, 2011, 1361-1369, ISSN 1751-7311, https://doi.org/10.1017/S1751731111000395.

[19] Foury, A et al. "Stress hormones, carcass composition and meat quality in Large White×Duroc pigs." *Meat science* vol. 69,4 (2005): 703-7. doi:10.1016/j.meatsci.2004.11.002.

[20] Carrasco-García, Apolo A et al. "Effect of stress during slaughter on carcass characteristics and meat quality in tropical beef cattle." *Asian-Australasian journal of animal sciences* vol. 33,10 (2020): 1656-1665. doi:10.5713/ajas.19.0804.

[21] Roberta Barrasso, Edmondo Ceci, Vincenzo Tufarelli, Gaia Casalino, Francesco Luposella, Fanny Fustinoni, Michela M. Dimuccio, Giancarlo Bozzo, Religious slaughtering: Implications on pH and temperature of bovine carcasses, *Saudi Journal of Biological Sciences*, Volume 29, Issue 4, 2022, Pages 2396-2401, ISSN 1319-562X, https://doi.org/10.1016/j. sjbs.2021.12.002.

[22] Hawley, John A, and Jill J Leckey. "Carbohydrate Dependence During Prolonged, Intense Endurance Exercise." *Sports medicine* (Auckland, N.Z.) vol. 45 Suppl 1,Suppl 1 (2015): S5-12. doi:10.1007/s40279-015-0400-1.

[23] Immonen, K., Ruusunen, M., Hissa, K., Puolanne, E., 2000. Bovine muscle glycogen concentration in relation to finishing diet, slaughter and ultimate pH. *Meat Sci.* 55, 25–31. https://doi.org/10.1016/S0309-1740(99)00121-7.

Newton, K G, and C O Gill. "The microbiology of DFD fresh meats: A review." *Meat science* vol. 5,3 (1981): 223-32. doi:10.1016/0309-1740(81)90005-X.

[24] Apple, J.K., Kegley, E.B., Galloway, D.L., Wistuba, T.J., Rakes, L.K., 2005. Duration of restraint and isolation stress as a model to study the dark-cutting condition in cattle. *J. Anim. Sci.* 83, 1202–1214. https://doi.org/10.2527/2005.8351202x.

[25] Gardner, G.E., McIntyre, B.L., Tudor, G.D., Pethick, D.W., 2001. The impact of nutrition on bovine muscle glycogen metabolism following exercise. Aust. *J. Agric. Res.* 52, 461–470. https://doi.org/10.1071/

AR00108.

[26] Lebret, B et al. "Influence of rearing conditions on performance, behavioral, and physiological responses of pigs to preslaughter handling, carcass traits, and meat quality." *Journal of animal science* vol. 84,9 (2006): 2436-47. doi:10.2527/jas.2005-689

[27] Hematyar, Nima et al. "Considering Two Aspects of Fish Welfare on African Catfish (Clarias gariepinus) Fillet throughout Postmortem Condition: Efficiency and Mechanisms." *Foods* (Basel, Switzerland) vol. 11,24 4090. 17 Dec. 2022, doi:10.3390/foods11244090

[28] Smith, R.F.; Dobson, H. Effect of preslaughter experience on behaviour, plasma cortisol and muscle pH in farmed red deer. *Vet. Rec.* 1990, 126, 155–158.

[29] Tomljanović, Kristijan et al. "The Impact of Premortality Stress on Some Quality Parameters of Roe Deer, Wild Boar, and Red Deer Meat." *Foods* (Basel, Switzerland) vol. 11,9 1275. 28 Apr. 2022, doi:10.3390/foods11091275.

[30] Bowers, Mallory E, and Rachel Yehuda. "Intergenerational Transmission of Stress in Humans." *Neuropsychopharmacology : official publication of the American College of Neuropsychopharmacology* vol. 41,1 (2016): 232-44. doi:10.1038/npp.2015.247.

[31] Nicolaides, Nicolas C et al. "Stress, the stress system and the role of glucocorticoids." *Neuroimmunomodulation* vol. 22,1-2 (2015): 6-19. doi:10.1159/000362736.

Graves CN, Eiler H (1979). Cortisol content of semen and the effect of exogenous cortisol on the concentration of cortisol and minerals (Ca, Mg, K and Na) in semen and blood plasma of bulls. *Biol Reprod* 21: 1225–1229.

Gitau R, Cameron A, Fisk NM, Glover V (1998). Fetal exposure to maternal cortisol. *Lancet* 352: 707–708.

[32] Stahn C, Lowenberg M, Hommes DW, Buttgereit F (2007). Molecular mechanisms of glucocorticoid action and selective glucocorticoid receptor agonists. *Mol Cell Endocrinol* 275: 71–78.

[33] Yehuda R (2002). Post-traumatic stress disorder. *N Engl J Med* 346: 108–114.

[34] Yehuda R, Bierer LM, Schmeidler J, Aferiat DH, Breslau I, Dolan S (2000). Low cortisol and risk for PTSD in adult offspring of holocaust survivors. *Am J Psychiatry* 157: 1252–1259.

[35] Bierer LM, Bader HN, Daskalakis NP, Lehrner AL, Makotkine I, Seckl JR et al (2014). Elevation of 11beta-hydroxysteroid dehydrogenase type 2 activity in Holocaust survivor offspring: evidence for an intergenerational

effect of maternal trauma exposure. *Psychoneuroendocrinology* 48: 1–10.

[36] Two excellent books include: *Toxic Legacy: How the Weedkiller Glyphosate Is Destroying Our Health and the Environment* by Stephanie Seneff and *Estrogeneration: How Estrogenics Are Making You Fat, Sick, and Infertile* by Anthony G Jay.

[37] van Vliet S, Provenza FD and Kronberg SL (2021) Health-Promoting Phytonutrients Are Higher in Grass-Fed Meat and Milk. *Front. Sustain. Food Syst.* 4:555426. doi: 10.3389/fsufs.2020.555426.

[38] β-carotene is really a provitamin A carotenoid, or a nutrient that the body readily converts into vitamin A. Kawata, Akifumi et al. "Anti-inflammatory Activity of β-Carotene, Lycopene and Tri-n-butylborane, a Scavenger of Reactive Oxygen Species." *In vivo* (Athens, Greece) vol. 32,2 (2018): 255-264. doi:10.21873/invivo.11232.

[39] Lobo, V et al. "Free radicals, antioxidants and functional foods: Impact on human health." Pharmacognosy reviews vol. 4,8 (2010): 118-26. doi:10.4103/0973-7847.70902.

[40] Das, Bhaskar C et al. "Retinoic acid signaling pathways in development and diseases." *Bioorganic & medicinal chemistry* vol. 22,2 (2014): 673-83. doi:10.1016/j.bmc.2013.11.025.

[41] Darwish, Wageh Sobhy et al. "β-carotene and retinol contents in the meat of herbivorous ungulates with a special reference to their public health importance." *The Journal of veterinary medical science* vol. 78,2 (2016): 351-4. doi:10.1292/jvms.15-0287.

[42] Parker, R S. "Absorption, metabolism, and transport of carotenoids." *FASEB journal : official publication of the Federation of American Societies for Experimental Biology* vol. 10,5 (1996): 542-51.

[43] Erdman, J W Jr et al. "Absorption and transport of carotenoids." *Annals of the New York Academy of Sciences* vol. 691 (1993): 76-85. doi:10.1111/j.1749-6632.1993.tb26159.x.

Parker, R S. "Absorption, metabolism, and transport of carotenoids." *FASEB journal*: official publication of the Federation of American Societies for Experimental Biology vol. 10,5 (1996): 542-51.

[44] This idea is represented in another of Yun's work. Yun AJ, Lee PY, Doux JD, Conley BR. A general theory of evolution based on energy efficiency: its implications for diseases. *Med Hypotheses* 2005;66(3): 664–70.

[45] Yun, Anthony J et al. "Are we eating more than we think? Illegitimate signaling and xenohormesis as participants in the pathogenesis of obesity." *Medical hypotheses* vol. 67,1 (2006): 36-40. doi:10.1016/j.mehy.2005.11.022.

[46] Lamming, Dudley W et al. "Small molecules that regulate lifespan: evidence for xenohormesis." *Molecular microbiology* vol. 53,4 (2004): 1003-9. doi:10.1111/j.1365-2958.2004.04209.x

[47] Baur, Joseph A, and David A Sinclair. "What is Xenohormesis?." *American journal of pharmacology and toxicology* vol. 3,1 (2008): 152-159. doi:10.3844/ajptsp.2008.152.159.

Langcake P, Pryce RJ. The production of resveratrol by Vitis vinifera and other members of the Vitaceae as a response to infection or injury. *Physiol Plant Pathol.* 1976; 9:77–86.

[48] Diggle, Stephen P et al. "Evolutionary theory of bacterial quorum sensing: when is a signal not a signal?." Philosophical transactions of the Royal Society of London. Series B, *Biological sciences* vol. 362,1483 (2007): 1241-9. doi:10.1098/rstb.2007.2049.

[49] Baur, Joseph A, and David A Sinclair. "What is Xenohormesis?." *American journal of pharmacology and toxicology* vol. 3,1 (2008): 152-159. doi:10.3844/ajptsp.2008.152.159.

[50] Berlinski, David. *Science After Babel.* Seattle: Discovery Institute Press, 2023. 41.

[51] Aristotle, *The Nicomachean Ethics*, Translated by David Ross, Oxford: Oxford University Press, 1998. 159.

Aristotle, *De Anima* 2.3.414a32-b19.

De l'Ame (Paris: Les Belles Lettres, 1966); On the Soul, Parva Naturalia, *On Breath*, tran. W. S. Hett (Longdon: W. Heinemann, 1936).

[52] Aristotle, *Politics*, Book I, tran C. D. C. Reeve (Indianapolis: Hackett), 1998.

[53] Simard, S., Perry, D., Jones, M. et al. Net transfer of carbon between ectomycorrhizal tree species in the field. *Nature* 388, 579–582 (1997). https://doi.org/10.1038/41557.

[54] J.D. Lewis. Mycorrhizal Fungi, Evolution and Diversification, ec. Richard M. Kliman, *Encyclopedia of Evolutionary Biology*, Academic Press, 2016, Pages 94-99, ISBN 9780128004265, https://doi.org/10.1016/B978-0-12-800049-6.00251-1.

[55] Weyrich, Laura et all. "Neanderthal behaviour, diet, and disease inferred from ancient DNA in dental calculus." *Nature.* 544. 2017. 10.1038/nature21674.

[56] Sheldrake, Merlin. *Entangled Life: How Fungi Make Our Worlds, Change Our Minds & Shape our Futures.* New York: Random House. 2020. 9.

[57] Yafetto, Levi et al. "The fastest flights in nature: high-speed spore discharge mechanisms among fungi." *PloS one* vol. 3,9 e3237. 17 Sep. 2008, doi:10.1371/journal.pone.0003237.

[58] Simard, Suzanne. *Finding the Mother Tree: Discovering the Wisdom of the Forest.* New York: Alfred A Knopf, 2021. pp. 60-62.

[59] Segundo-Ortin, M., Calvo, P. (2019), "Are plants cognitive? A reply to Adams," *Studies in History and Philosophy of Science* 73: 65.

[60] Baluska, Frantisek et al. "The 'root-brain' hypothesis of Charles and Francis Darwin: Revival after more than 125 years." *Plant signaling & behavior* vol. 4,12 (2009): 1121-7. doi:10.4161/psb.4.12.10574.

[61] Beiler, Kevin J et al. "Architecture of the wood-wide web: Rhizopogon spp. genets link multiple Douglas-fir cohorts." *The New phytologist* vol. 185,2 (2010): 543-53. doi:10.1111/j.1469-8137.2009.03069.x

[62] Simard, *Finding the Mother Tree*, 185.

[63] Morin, Alain, Famira Racy, "Dynamic self-processes" in *The Handbook of Personality Dynamics and Processes*, ed John F. Rauthmann. Academic Press: 2021, 365-386.

[64] Appel, H M, and R B Cocroft. "Plants respond to leaf vibrations caused by insect herbivore chewing." *Oecologia* vol. 175,4 (2014): 1257-66. doi:10.1007/s00442-014-2995-6.

  Chatterjee et all. 2007. A BELL1-like gene of potato is light activated and wound inducible. *Plant Physiology* 145(4): 1435-1443.

[65] Vivaldo, Gianna et al. "The network of plants volatile organic compounds." *Scientific reports* vol. 7,1 11050. 8 Sep. 2017, doi:10.1038/s41598-017-10975-x.

[66] Shiojiri, Kaori et al. "Airborne signals of communication in sagebrush: a pharmacological approach." *Plant signaling & behavior* vol. 10,12 (2015): e1095416. doi:10.1080/15592324.2015.1095416.

[67] These defensive compounds are toxic alkaloids, like nicotine and anabasine. Karban, R et al. "Communication between plants: induced resistance in wild tobacco plants following clipping of neighboring sagebrush." *Oecologia* vol. 125,1 (2000): 66-71. doi:10.1007/PL00008892.

[68] Charles A. Petersen, Juan J. Villalba, and Frederick D. Provenza "Influence of Experience on Browsing Sagebrush by Cattle and Its Impacts on Plant Community Structure," *Rangeland Ecology and Management* 67(1), 78-87, (1 January 2014). https://doi.org/10.2111/REM-D-13-00038.1.

[69] Paco Calvo. *Planta Sapiens: The New Science of Plant Intelligence.* New

York: W. W. Norton & Company, Inc. 2022, 19.

[70] Gaillochet, C., Lohmann, J. U. (2015), "The never-ending story: from pluripotency to plant developmental plasticity," *Development* 142: 22137.

[71] Calvo, P., Gagliano, M., Souza, G. M., Trewavas, A. (2020), "Plants are intelligent, here's how," *Annals of Botany* 125: 11-28.

[72] Powers, Richard. *The Overstory: A Novel.* New York: W. W. Norton & Company: 2018, 115.

[73] Read, Robin Wall Kimmerer's 2015 book, *Braiding Sweetgrass: Indigenous Wisdom, Scientific Knowledge and the Teachings of Plants* to learn more about this wording and its potent difference.

[74] McGilchrist, Iain. *The Master and His Emissary: The Divided Brain and the Making of the Western World.* New Haven: Yale University Press, 2018. Pp. 21-22.

[75] Krawec, Patty. *Becoming Kin: An Indigenous Call to Unforgetting the Past and Reimagining Our Future.* Minneapolis: Broadleaf Books, 2022. 17.

[76] Taylor, Charles. *Sources of the Self: The Making of the Modern Identity.* Cambridge: Cambridge University Press, 1989. Chapter 18.

[77] Taylor. *Sources of the Self.* Preface, pp. x.

[78] Anderson JG, Abrahamson K. "Your Health Care May Kill You: Medical Errors." *Stud Health Technol Inform.* 2017;234:13-17. PMID: 28186008.

Pilar MR, Eyler AA, Moreland-Russell S, Brownson RC. Actual causes of death in relation to media, policy, and funding attention: examining public health priorities. *Front Public Health.* 2020;8:279. PubMed PMID: 32733836.

[79] Playford, Raymond John, and Michael James Weiser. "Bovine Colostrum: Its Constituents and Uses." *Nutrients* vol. 13,1 265. 18 Jan. 2021, doi:10.3390/nu13010265.

[80] Tesseraud, Sophie et al. "Role of sulfur amino acids in controlling nutrient metabolism and cell functions: implications for nutrition." *The British journal of nutrition* vol. 101,8 (2009): 1132-9. doi:10.1017/S0007114508159025.

[81] Magan, Manchan. *Thirty-Two Words for Field: Lost Words of the Irish Landscape.* Dublin: Gill Books, 2020. 78.

[82] Sioned Davies, trans., "The Second Branch of the Mabinogi," in *The Mabinogion.* Oxford: Oxford University Press, 2007, 28.

[83] Frederick D. Provenza and David F Balph, "Applicability of Five Diet-

Selection Models to Various Foraging Challenges Ruminants Encounter," in *Behavioral Mechanisms of Food Selection*, ed. Roger N. Hughes (Berlin: Springer-Verlag, 1990), 432-460.

[84] Singh RP, Sahai BN, Jha GJ. Histopathology of the duodenum and rumen of goats during experimental infections with *Paramphistomum cervi*. Vet Parasitol. 1984;15(1):39–46.

[85] Villalba JJ, Miller J, Ungar ED, Landau SY, Glendinning J. Ruminant self-medication against gastrointestinal nematodes: evidence, mechanism, and origins. *Parasite*. 2014;21:31. doi: 10.1051/parasite/2014032. Epub 2014 Jun 30. PMID: 24971486; PMCID: PMC4073621.

[86] M. Du et al., "Fecal Programming of Skeletal Muscle Development in Ruminant Animals," *Journal of Animal Science* 88, E. Suppl. (2010): E51-60.

[87] Provenza, Nourishment, 179-180; P. D. Gluckman et al., "Predictive Adaptive Responses and Human Evolution," *Trends in Ecology and Evolution* 20 (2005): 527-33.

[88] Vinton, Anna C., et al., "Pasticity's role in adaptive evolution depends on environemtnal change components," *Trends in Ecology & Evolution*, December 2022, Vol. 37, No. 12.

[89] Provenza, Fred. *Nourishment: What Animals Can Teach Us About Rediscovering Our Nutritional Wisdom*. White River Junction: Chelsea Green Publishing, 2018, 65.

Sarwat N. Mirza and Frederick D Provenza, "Preference of the Mother Affects Selection and Avoidance of Foods by Lambs Differing in Age," *Applied Animal Behavior Science* 28 (1990): 255-265.

[90] Gerber, P.J., Steinfeld, H., Henderson, B., Mottet, A., Opio, C., Dijkman, J., Falcucci, A. & Tempio, G. 2013. Tackling climate change through livestock – A global assessment of emissions and mitigation opportunities. *Food and Agriculture Organization of the United Nations* (FAO), Rome.

[91] Provenza, *Nourishment*, 183.

[92] Whitewoods, Christopher D. "Riddled with holes: Understanding air space formation in plant leaves." *PLoS biology* vol. 19,12 e3001475. 6 Dec. 2021, doi:10.1371/journal.pbio.3001475.

Earles, J Mason et al. "Beyond Porosity: 3D Leaf Intercellular Airspace Traits That Impact Mesophyll Conductance." *Plant physiology* vol. 178,1 (2018): 148-162. doi:10.1104/pp.18.00550.

[93] Kell, Douglas B. "Large-scale sequestration of atmospheric carbon via plant roots in natural and agricultural ecosystems: why and how." *Philosophical transactions of the Royal Society of London*. Series

B, *Biological sciences* vol. 367,1595 (2012): 1589-97. doi:10.1098/rstb.2011.0244

[94] Lowenfels, Jeff, Wayne Lewis. *Teaming with Microbes: The Organic gardener's Guide to the Soil Food Web.* Portland: Timber Press. 2010. 84

[95] Rebecca Therby-Vale, Benoit Lacombe, Seung Y. Rhee, Laurent Nussaume, Hatem Rouached. "Mineral nutrient signaling controls photosynthesis: focus on iron deficiency-induced chlorosis," *Trends in Plant Science,* vol 27, Issue 5, (2022) 502-509.

[96] Leann Beanland, P. Larry Phelan, Seppo Salminen, Micronutrient Interactions on Soybean Growth and the Developmental Performance of Three Insect Herbivores, *Environmental Entomology*, Volume 32, Issue 3, 1 June 2003, Pages 641–651.

[97] Jeandet, Philippe et al. "The Role of Sugars in Plant Responses to Stress and Their Regulatory Function during Development." *International journal of molecular sciences* vol. 23,9 5161. 5 May. 2022, doi:10.3390/ijms23095161

[98] Geiger, Dietmar. "Plant glucose transporter structure and function." *Pflugers Archiv : European journal of physiology* vol. 472,9 (2020): 1111-1128.

[99] Ishfaq, Muhammad et al. "Physiological Essence of Magnesium in Plants and Its Widespread Deficiency in the Farming System of China." *Frontiers in plant science* vol. 13 802274. 25 Apr. 2022, doi:10.3389/fpls.2022.802274.

[100] Albrecht, William. ed Charles Walters. *Soil Fertility & Human and Animal Health: The Albrecht Papers,* Volume VIII. Austin: Acres U.S.A, 2013. xxv.

[101] Lowenfels, Jeff, Wayne Lewis. *Teaming with Microbes: The Organic gardener's Guide to the Soil Food Web.* Portland: Timber Press. 2010. 19.

Anthony, Mark A et al. "Enumerating soil biodiversity." *Proceedings of the National Academy of Sciences of the United States of America* vol. 120,33 (2023): e2304663120. doi:10.1073/pnas.2304663120.

[102] Singh, B. & Schulze, D. G. (2015) Soil Minerals and Plant Nutrition. *Nature Education Knowledge* 6(1):1

[103] Guil-Guerrero, José. (2010). Nutritional composition of Plantago species (P-major L., P-lanceolata, L., and P-media L.). *Ecology of Food and Nutrition.* 40. 481-495. 10.1080/03670244.2001.9991663.

Pinotti, Luciano et al. "The Contribution of Dietary Magnesium in Farm Animals and Human Nutrition." *Nutrients* vol. 13,2 509. 4 Feb. 2021, doi:10.3390/nu13020509.

Maguire, Michael E, and James A Cowan. "Magnesium chemistry and biochemistry." *Biometals : an international journal on the role of metal ions in biology, biochemistry, and medicine* vol. 15,3 (2002): 203-10. doi:10.1023/a:1016058229972.

[104] Shoeibi, Sara, and Mohammad Mashreghi. "Biosynthesis of selenium nanoparticles using Enterococcus faecalis and evaluation of their antibacterial activities." *Journal of trace elements in medicine and biology : organ of the Society for Minerals and Trace Elements (GMS)* vol. 39 (2017): 135-139. doi:10.1016/j.jtemb.2016.09.003.

Túlio Silva Lara et all. "Selenium biofortification of wheat grain via foliar application and its effect on plant metabolism." *Journal of Food Composition and Analysis* vol 81. 2019. 10-18, doi:10.1016/j.jfca.2019.05.002.

[105] Sordillo, L M. "Nutritional strategies to optimize dairy cattle immunity." *Journal of dairy science* vol. 99,6 (2016): 4967-4982. doi:10.3168/jds.2015-10354.

Brigelius-Flohé, Regina, and Matilde Maiorino. "Glutathione peroxidases." *Biochimica et biophysica acta* vol. 1830,5 (2013): 3289-303. doi:10.1016/j.bbagen.2012.11.020.

[106] Shang, Xiaofei et al. "Lonicera japonica Thunb.: ethnopharmacology, phytochemistry and pharmacology of an important traditional Chinese medicine." *Journal of ethnopharmacology* vol. 138,1 (2011): 1-21. doi:10.1016/j.jep.2011.08.016.

[107] Dashtdar, Mehrab et al. "The Concept of Wind in Traditional Chinese Medicine." *Journal of pharmacopuncture* vol. 19,4 (2016): 293-302. doi:10.3831/KPI.2016.19.030

[108] Veljkovic, Emilija, et al. "Chapter 10 - Other Compounds From Tobacco With Potential Impact on Neurodegenerative Diseases" in *Nicotine and Other Tobacco Compounds in Neurodegenerative and Psychiatric Diseases*, ed. Emilija Veljkovic, Wenhao Xia, Blaine Phillips, Ee Tsin Wong, Jenny Ho, Alberto Oviedo, Julia Hoeng, Manuel Peitsch. Academic Press: 2018, 83-97. Doi:10.1016/B978-0-12-812922-7.00010-X.

[109] Sachin L., Kishorkumar A., Bhavbhuti M., Suresh V. Goat milk in human nutrition and health—A review. *Int. J. Curr. Microbiol. Appl. Sci.* 2017;6:1781–1792.

[110] Pietrzak-Fiećko, Renata, and Anna M Kamelska-Sadowska. "The Comparison of Nutritional Value of Human Milk with Other Mammals' Milk." *Nutrients* vol. 12,5 1404. 14 May. 2020, doi:10.3390/nu12051404.

Yuan, Tinglan et al. "Role Medium-Chain Fatty Acids in the Lipid

Metabolism of Infants." *Frontiers in nutrition* vol. 9 804880. 9 Jun. 2022, doi:10.3389/fnut.2022.804880.

[111] A.C. Ayers, R.P. Barrett, P.R. Cheeke, Feeding value of tree leaves (hybrid poplar and black locust) evaluated with sheep, goats and rabbits, *Animal Feed Science and Technology*, vol. 57, Issues 1–2, 1996. doi:10.1016/0377-8401(95)00845-4.

[112] Renssen, Hans. 2020. "Comparison of Climate Model Simulations of the Younger Dryas Cold Event" *Quaternary* 3, no. 4: 29. https://doi.org/10.3390/quat3040029

[113] As we will see in Book II, the term, "Clovis Culture" is problematic, archeologically debunked, and stems from a colonial terminology that destroys whatever truth the soil yet clothes.

Anderson, David G. Climate and Culture Change in Prehistoric and Early Historic Eastern North America. *Archeology of eastern North America*, Vol 29, 2001. Pp. 143-186.

[114] Angel J. L., "Health as a crucial factor in the changes from hunting to developed farming in the eastern Mediterranean" in *Paleopathology at the Origins of Agriculture*, Armelagos G. J., Cohen M. N., Eds. (Academic Press, 1984), pp. 51–74.

[115] Raichle, Marcus E, and Debra A Gusnard. "Appraising the brain's energy budget." *Proceedings of the National Academy of Sciences of the United States of America* vol. 99,16 (2002): 10237-9. doi:10.1073/pnas.172399499.

[116] Herrmann, Esther et al. "Humans have evolved specialized skills of social cognition: the cultural intelligence hypothesis." *Science* (New York, N.Y.) vol. 317,5843 (2007): 1360-6. doi:10.1126/science.1146282.

[117] Thoreau, Henry D. *Walden*. Edited by Jeffrey S. Cramer. New Haven: Yale University Press, 2006. 3.

[118] Snir A, Nadel D, Groman-Yaroslavski I, Melamed Y, Sternberg M, Bar-Yosef O, Weiss E. The Origin of Cultivation and Proto-Weeds, Long Before Neolithic Farming. *PLoS One*. 2015 Jul 22;10(7):e0131422. doi: 10.1371/journal.pone.0131422. PMID: 26200895; PMCID: PMC4511808.

[119] Ko KH. Hominin interbreeding and the evolution of human variation. *J Biol Res* (Thessalon). 2016 Jul 16;23:17. doi: 10.1186/s40709-016-0054-7. PMID: 27429943; PMCID: PMC4947341.

[120] Wells, Spencer, *Pandora's Seed: Why The Hunter-Gatherer Holds the Key to Our Survival,* New York: Random House Trade Paperbacks, 2011. 53.

[121] Thoreau, *Walden*. 90.

[122] Read, *Courting The Wild Twin* by Martin Shaw to unpack the nature of good storytelling, spells, and their powers to awakening.

[123] Dykeman, W.. "Appalachian Mountains." *Encyclopedia Britannica,* June 14, 2023. https://www.britannica.com/place/Appalachian-Mountains.

[124] Mellaart J. Excavations at Çatal Hüyük: First Preliminary Report, 1961. Anatolian Studies. 1962;12:41-65. doi:10.2307/3642517. Mellaart J. Excavations at Çatal Hüyük, 1963: Third Preliminary Report. *Anatolian Studies.* 1964;14:39-119. doi:10.2307/3642466.

Mellaart J. Excavations at Çatal Hüyük, 1965, Fourth Preliminary Report. *Anatolian Studies.* 1966;16:165-191. doi:10.2307/3642483.

[125] Jens Notroff, Oliver Dietrich and Klaus Schmidt, "Building Monuments, Creating Communities. Early Monumental Architecture at Pre-Pottery Neolithic Göbekli Tepe" in James F. Osborne (ed.), *Approaching Monumentality in Archeology* (New York, 2014), pp. 83-105.

[126] Sussman, Robert W., 'Why the Legend of the Killer Ape Never Dies: The Enduring Power of Cultural Beliefs to Distort Our View of Human Nature', in Douglas P. Fry (ed.), *War, Peace, and Human Nature: The Convergence of Evolutionary and Cultural Views* (New York) 2013.

Dart, Raymond, "The Predatory Transition from Ape to Man," *International Anthropological and Linguistic Review* (No. 4, 1953).

[127] David Hume, "Of National Characters," 1777.

Voltaire, "The Negro," 1733.

[128] Chesterton, G. K., *The Collected Works of G. K. Chesterton*, vol. 1. David Dooley, ed. San Francisco: Ignatius Press, 1986. 115-121.

[129] Quote from Jean-Jacques Rousseau's, *On The Origin of the Inequality of Mankind*, 1754.

Further reading to consider: Hulliung, Mark. *The Autocritique of Enlightenment: Rousseau and the Philosophes.* Cambridge: Harvard University Press, 1998.

Roosevelt, Grace G. *Reading Rousseau in the Nuclear Age.* Philadelphia: Temple University Press, 1990.

Damrosch, Leo. *Jean-Jacques Rousseau: Restless Genius.* Boston: Houghton Mifflin, 2005.

Shklar, Judith, N. *Men and Citizens: A Study of Rousseau's Social Theory.* Cambridge: Cambridge University Press, 1969.

Garrard, Graeme, *Rousseau's Counter-Enlightenment.* New Albany:

SUNY Press, 2003.

[130] Pascal, Blaise. *Pensées*. Translated by A. J. Krailsheimer. London: Penguin Books, 1995. pp. 15-21.

[131] Dent, N. J. H. "Rousseau on Amour Propre," in P*roceedings of the Aristotelian Society:* Supplementary Volumes 72 (1998), pp 57-74;

Neuhouser, Frederick, *Rousseau's Theodicy of Self-Love*. Oxford: Oxford University Press, 2008.

[132] Thomas-Van Gundy, Melissa A.; Perkins, Jessica D.; Smith, Linda S. 2021. Primeval paths: Bison in West Virginia. Fort Collins, CO: *Forest Service Research Data Archive*. https://doi.org/10.2737/RDS-2021-0055.

[133] McKinney, Curtis R., Jr. 1991 The Determination of the Reliability of Uranium Series Dating of Enamel, Dentine, and Bone. Unpublished Ph.D. dissertation, Southern Methodist University, Dallas. 1991, 116.

[134] Saunders, Jeffrey J. 1988. Fossiliferous Spring Sites in Southwestern Missouri. In Late Pleistocene and Early Holocene Paleoecology and Archeology of the Eastern Great Lakes Region, edited by Richard S. Laub, Norton G. Miller, and David W. Steadman, pp. 138–141. Bulletin No. 33. *Buffalo Society of Natural Sciences,* Buffalo, New York.

Harlan, Richard. 1843. Description of the Bones of a New Fossil Animal of the Order Edentata. *American Journal of Science and Arts* (1ˢᵗ series) 44:70.

Hay, Oliver P. The Pleistocene of the Middle Region of North America and its Vertebrated Animals. Washington D.C: *Carnegie Institution of Washington, D.C.*, 1924. 191-192, 203.

Mehl, Maurice G. Missouri's Ice Age Animals. *Missouri Geological Survey and Water Resources*, Rolla. 1962. 93, 100.

Parmalee, Paul W., and Ronald D. Oesch. 1972. Pleistocene and Recent Faunas from the Brynjulfson Caves, Missouri. *Reports of Investigations* No. 25. Illinois State Museum, Springfield.

[135] Dyke, Arthur S., John T. Andrews, Peter U. Clark, John H. England, Gifford H. Miller, John Shaw and Jean J. Veillette. 2002. The Laurentide and Innuitian Ice Sheets during the Last Glacial Maximum. *Quaternary Science Reviews* 21(1–3):10.

[136] King, James E. 1973. Late Pleistocene Palynology and Biogeography of the Western Missouri Ozarks. *Ecological Monographs* 43(4):539–565.

[137] Hill, Matthew E., Jr., Matthew G. Hill, and Christopher C. Widga. 2008. Late Quaternary Bison Diminution on the Great Plains of North America: Evaluating the Role of Human Hunting Versus Climate Change.

Quaternary Science Reviews 27 (17–18):1752–1771.

Hofman, Jack L., and Lawrence C. Todd. 2001. Tyranny in the Archaeological Record of Specialized Hunters. In People and Wildlife in Northern North America: Essays in Honor of R. Dale Guthrie, edited by S. Craig Gerlach and Maribeth S. Murray, pp. 200–215. *BAR International Series* 944. Archaeopress, Oxford, England.

[138] Lewis, Patrick J., Eileen Johnson, Briggs Buchanan, and Steven E. Churchill. 2010. The Impact of Changing Grasslands on Late Quaternary Bison of the Southern Plains. *Quaternary International* 217 (1–2):117–13.

[139] McMillan, R. Bruce. "Records of Early Bison in Illinois," *Illinois State Museum Scientific Papers,* Volume 31. Springfield: 2006. 59.

[140] Cronon, William. *Changes in the Land: Indians, Colonists, and the Ecology of New England.* New York: Hill and Wang, 1983, 47.

[141] Lawrence C. Wroth, ed., *The Voyages of Giovanni da Verrazzano*, 1524-1528 (Yale, 1970), pp. 133-143.

[142] Allen, Glover M. "Bison Remains from New England." Journal of *Mammalogy* 1, no. 4 (1920): 161–64. https://doi.org/10.2307/1373305.

[143] Provenza, *Nourishment*. 181-182.

[144] Johnson, Michael. "Cactus Hill Archaeological Site" *Encyclopedia Virginia*. Virginia Humanities, (07 Dec. 2020). Web. 05 Sep. 2023 *Last updated: 2020, December 07.*

[145] Duncan, Dayton. *Blood Memory: The Tragic Decline and Improbable Resurrection of the American Buffalo.* New York: Alfred A. Knopf, 2023. 4.

[146] Manning, Roger B. "Unlawful Hunting in England, 1500-1640." *Forest & Conservation History 38*, no. 1 (1994): 16–23. https://doi.org/10.2307/3983583.

[147] Crosby, Alfred. *The Columbian Exchange: Biological and Cultural Consequences of 1492.* Westport: Greenwood Press, 1972, 52.

[148] Koch, Alexander et al. "Earth system impacts of the European arrival and Great Dying in the Americas after 1492." *Quaternary Science Reviews* vol. 207. 2019, pp. 13-36, doi.org/10.1016/j.quascirev.2018.12.004.

[149] Rahman, Md Tanvir et al. "Zoonotic Diseases: Etiology, Impact, and Control." *Microorganisms* vol. 8,9 1405. 12 Sep. 2020, doi:10.3390/microorganisms8091405.

[150] Hubálek, Zdenek. "Emerging human infectious diseases: anthroponoses, zoonoses, and sapronoses." *Emerging infectious diseases* vol. 9,3 (2003): 403-4. doi:10.3201/eid0903.020208.

Messenger, Ali M et al. "Reverse zoonotic disease transmission (zooanthroponosis): a systematic review of seldom-documented human biological threats to animals." *PloS one* vol. 9,2 e89055. 28 Feb. 2014, doi:10.1371/journal.pone.0089055.

[151] Jennings, Francis. *The Invasion of America: Indians, Colonialism, and the Cant of Conquest.* New York: Norton, 1976, 30.

[152] Dombrovski, V.C., Zhurauliou, D.V. and Ashton-Butt, A. (2022), Long-term effects of rewilding on species composition: 22 years of raptor monitoring in the Chernobyl Exclusion Zone. *Restor Ecol*, 30: e13633. doi.org/10.1111/rec.13633

[153] T.G. Deryabina, S.V. Kuchmel, L.L. Nagorskaya, T.G. Hinton, J.C. Beasley, A. Lerebours, J.T. Smith, Long-term census data reveal abundant wildlife populations at Chernobyl, *Current Biology*, Volume 25, Issue 19, 2015, Pages R824-R826, ISSN 0960-9822, doi.org/10.1016/j.cub.2015.08.017.

[154] Dates and data from The Greater Yellowstone Coalition.

[155] Shipman, Pat. (2012). The Cost of the Wild. *American Scientist*. 100. 454. 10.1511/2012.99.454.

[156] Pettitt, Paul. *Homo Sapiens Rediscovered: The Scientific Revolution Rewriting Our Origins.* London: Thames & Hudson, 2022. Pp 72-73.

[157] Thomas-Van Gundy, Melissa A., Jessica D. Perkins, Crystal Krause, Cynthia D. Huebner, Lorenzo Ferrari, Linda S. Smith. "Primeval Paths: Bison in West Virginia," *Natural Areas Journal*, vol. 41, 2021. 315.

[158] Etulain, Richard W. "Introduction: The Rise of Western Historiography," in *Writing Western History: Essays on Major Western Historians.* ed., Richard W. Etulain. Albuquerque: University of New Mexico Press, 1991. 3.

[159] Graeber, David and David Wengrow. *The Dawn of Everything: A New History of Humanity.* New York: Farrar, Straus and Giroux, 2021. 32.

[160] Marrelli, Mariangela et al. "Effects of Saponins on Lipid Metabolism: A Review of Potential Health Benefits in the Treatment of Obesity." *Molecules* (Basel, Switzerland) vol. 21,10 1404. 20 Oct. 2016, doi:10.3390/molecules21101404.

[161] Shi, John et al. "Saponins from edible legumes: chemistry, processing, and health benefits." *Journal of medicinal food* vol. 7,1 (2004): 67-78. doi:10.1089/109662004322984734.

[162] Prairie, Beth A et al. "Postpartum lipid levels in women with major depression." *Journal of women's health* (2002) vol. 21,5 (2012): 534-8. doi:10.1089/jwh.2011.3256.

Wulsin, Lawson R et al. "Depressive symptoms, coronary heart disease, and overall mortality in the Framingham Heart Study." Psychosomatic medicine vol. 67,5 (2005): 697-702. doi:10.1097/01. psy.0000181274.56785.28.

Why, hello there! We made it.

If you enjoyed the book, visit www.danielfirthgriffith.com and let us know your favorite part and we will send you a free copy to give to a friend! Stay tuned for Book II (*Cliffhawk*) and Book III (*Spearhead*). We have yet a fine journey ahead of us!

Let's be friends and relearn, together, how to be, simply, human.

Your friend,

D. Firth Griffith

Printed in the USA
CPSIA information can be obtained
at www.ICGtesting.com
CBHW031000050524
7983CB00002B/6